# MEANINGFUL
# CONFLICTS

# Also by Off Campus Writers' Workshop

*Overcoming (2013)*

*A Reason to Be Here (2019)*

*Turning Points (2021)*

# MEANINGFUL CONFLICTS

## THE ART OF FRICTION

from the members of

## Off Campus Writers' Workshop

WINDY CITY PUBLISHERS

# MEANINGFUL CONFLICTS
## THE ART OF FRICTION

Windy City Publishers
info@windycitypublishers.com

Printed in the United States of America

ISBN:
978-1-953294-33-3

Library of Congress Control Number:
2022921982

WINDY CITY PUBLISHERS
CHICAGO

WWW.WINDYCITYPUBLISHERS.COM

To Fred Fitzsimmons

He saved the dream

# Contents

## FICTION

### Short Fiction with a Wallop

### Heroines in Crisis

# Life-Changing Challenges

# POETRY

# CREATIVE NONFICTION

## Overcoming

## Coming of Age

# What's in a Life?

# Foreword

## The Developmental Anthology

You wrote 3,000 words of prose, a first draft worthy of any of the giants of contemporary publishing. Then you re-wrote it, and revised it, and edited it to achieve absolute purity. You had your best friend read it and anoint it with a thousand blessings. Now what?

In the conventional world of publishing, you would begin submitting the work to magazines or anthologies, where editors would accept or reject it.

In the world of the developmental anthology, your best draft is just the beginning. The 49 prose authors whose stories appear in this volume composed the best stories they could, then entered a six-month peer-review process in which colleagues representing a full range of creative writing experiences exchanged thoughts and ideas on how to improve every piece. The process for prose authors began with ad hoc critique groups in which each author gave and received impressions of their fellow writers' works, and submitted revisions for further review.

Our critique groups met for two months, after which our authors worked with developmental editors for two months, and final editors for another two months. All of the authors, critique group leaders, and editors were Off Campus Writers' Workshop members and volunteers. The final prose drafts were then copy edited by an industry professional, in preparation for production.

Our 24 poets submitted directly to a poetry editor, who offered critiques and editing suggestions.

*Meaningful Conflicts* is OCWW's second developmental anthology, having been preceded by the 2021 collection, *Turning Points.* Both anthologies evolved from a collaborative novel project, *A Reason to be Here,* led by Jay Rehak, a Chicago Public School teacher and lecturer on creative writing. Rehak introduced the critique-group/editing process that has been employed in both anthologies.

There are several benefits to authors and poets in the developmental model. Most obvious, perhaps, is the benefit new authors and poets get from the mentoring of more experienced authors and poets. But experienced writers also benefit from learning how their work is viewed by others. One of the great truths all writers face in developing their work is that they can never read their story or poem for the first time, and yet, in the publishing process, the judgments of everyone from agents to editors to readers will be overwhelmingly influenced by their first readings. And OCWW members, regardless of their publishing experience, are well read and able to clearly articulate their impressions of another writer's work.

The other benefit of the developmental process is the opportunity it allows writers to emerge from our often-isolated writing cocoons to network and bond with others who share this passion and pain. In the Covid years, this was an especially important benefit for many.

There are benefits for the reader of this volume, too. While some traditional anthologies may offer more cover-to-cover literary excellence than *Meaningful Conflicts*, the many different voices and life experiences that are the foundation of this collection create a uniquely diverse expression of life in our times. We hope you enjoy it.

—The Editors

# FICTION

SHORT FICTION WITH A WALLOP

# Thoughts Before the Group Session

by Peter Hoppock

On a bench outside the meeting room, he pictures his daughter Jenny lying with her back pressed against the cold linoleum floor, the black, wrought-iron legs of the kitchen table encasing her like a cage. She had used a black Sharpie to fill the underside of the unpainted, natural-pine table with hundreds of phrases, sentences, whole paragraphs—some stretched the length of the table, some in spirals, others elaborately designed. Some scribbled, as if by her left hand; others in elegant script. It appeared no open space remained; more recent writings overlapped earlier ones. He searched for dates—some sign of a progression, the way he had measured Jenny's growth spurts on the vertical frame of her closet door—but found none.

To read this cache of confessions, he had lain in the position he assumed she must have taken: coffin-cramped, arms stretched up, clenching the pen. He could not sustain the reaching, and his hands dropped heavily, weighted by grief. Or was it guilt, for having made this discovery only after her transfer to the Arizona residential facility? Only after she had made an enemy of the body she inhabited?

Everything you needed to know about her anxieties, her doubts, her gender confusion, was in those little stories. She must have felt safe there, for as he read that first time, he felt a curtain draw open, revealing expressions of an inner life so finely wrought, so acutely described in all its tortured realism, that he knew immediately: this was the only way she felt she could release her demons. He imagined her sneaking downstairs in the middle of the night, for when else could she have scrawled out such a masterpiece of dysmorphia? She might have been wearing the pajamas with the yellow flowers on them, a gift for her eleventh birthday. Is that when the struggle began? Or had it started later, when she would have been wearing the extra-large Nirvana T-shirt she'd lived in her entire sixteenth year? She had cut her hair short that year, and he had reacted

3

with a look she must have interpreted as disapproval, when it had, in his mind, never gone beyond mild annoyance.

How difficult it must have been, each night, to remount the stairs and return to her bed—where so many mornings he or his wife would find the light cotton sheets pooled around her feet. Had she thrashed them off as part of the struggle to unburden herself? The sheets, like her thoughts, must have felt heavy, as heavy as the stones that his friend Shelly's wife had used to weigh down her pantsuit when she walked into the cold waters of Lake Dillon, and stepped off the edge of an underwater precipice, thus announcing—to everyone's stunned surprise—how deep and dark her sadness had become, as deep and dark as the place the divers found her body.

The soundtrack that accompanied the discovery of his daughter's revelations began with the slow welling up of helplessness—an untethering from the firm grip he once had of himself as a father. The sound had substance, it had weight, and to lessen that weight, the mass that overwhelmed him had pulled itself apart, and without him willing it, the one note had become five. Even as he felt helpless to stop it, he had accepted it, and the five notes formed into five syllables, and the five syllables formed four words—like a chorus—whispered at first, as he lay underneath the table.

Since that night he has learned that the chorus is as omnipresent as air. Each singing of it has its own unique melody, sung sometimes by one voice, sometimes many. The chorus could be heard on the shoreline of Lake Dillon as Shelly's wife's body broke the surface of the water, and afterwards, into the next day, and the day after that. It can be heard wherever two or more people gather to reflect on someone unexpectedly lost: in cafes and restaurants, over coffee and during elaborate meals served by strangers and friends alike; on the way to work, or at home, or in the gym, or in the check-out line at a big box store. Everywhere. Literally, there is no place on earth these notes have not been heard.

Now, outside the room with the comforting pastel blue walls and the floor-to-ceiling windows that bring the desert close, where his daughter and the other families are waiting, the notes form in his consciousness and become the words he has repeated so many times and will repeat again and again and into the future. Heads will nod. New voices will be added to the chorus. *Ostinato*, the musicians call it.

It is the soundtrack of loss. Five notes, five syllables, four words.

Once in the room, when it is his turn to share, he hears himself repeating the chorus:

"I had no idea."

He takes a deep breath. Pictures his daughter lying alone on the kitchen floor. The vision blends with the image of Shelly's family wailing in their front yard a few doors down from his own. The words come from him, and engulf him at the same time. Helpless, he cries out again: "I had no idea."

# Faith

by Allison Baxter

This is the first Saturday morning in June, days after my tenth birthday. I'm lying on my belly watching cartoons with my sister. My mom passes me the phone. My gran is on the other end. I'm nervous because adults don't call kids in the world of seen-not-heard Louisiana. She asks me about my back. My spine is twisted like an alligator's tail, is what Mama says. And it hurts like his bite, too.

"It's hurtful, but it don't keep me from riding my bike. I can't go nowhere barefooted because the tar road is hot, and I don't have shoes that fit."

I give the phone back to my mom and she narrows her eyes like a cat. My mom is a non-believer, and I know that my gran has told her something about the Lord, our savior, Jesus.

She hangs up the phone. "Your grandmother is gonna come pick y'all up at three. Pack up all your shorts and T-shirts so you can be there a month. Your grandmother will buy you a new pair of shoes."

I'm gonna get some shoes and junk food and a lot of TV.

At three, she pulls up her new Ford, all shiny clean. Mama comes out for just a second and puts me and my little sister, Rae Ann, in the car. The air conditioner is running full blast and smells cold. I look back to see my mom's face. She looks older since my daddy left, her face pulled down like a wet towel.

The first thing my gran tells me is that I'm gonna get my back fixed tonight at her church—by Jesus. I need to pray on it until we reach the Kmart, show God my faith. I squeeze my eyes tight and pray.

I peek out of my eyelids every once in a while. We are driving fast, and it starts to rain. The smell of the rain coolness comes through the air conditioner. The clouds are only a few feet from the interstate, and there's steam coming off the scorching hot tar. Gran never slows for rain. She rides with Jesus. Mama is the one who worries about tickets and accidents because she doesn't have faith.

At Kmart, Gran buys us dresses, shoes, and Moon Pies. I eat three of the banana Moon Pies for lunch. The marshmallow is soft with the heat and melts in my mouth.

We get to Gran's big two-story and drag our paper bags of stuff inside. My sister plops in front of the TV with Papa. His eyelids are nearly closed and a little snore is coming out of him.

Gran and I leave right away and head down winding roads with high weeds and trees. I crank the window down to smell the green, the wet dirt, the river. Bugs and raindrops crash into the windshield, plop–plop–plop, and the wipers smear the yellow. We pull into a gravel lot in front of a big double-wide trailer. There's pretty white lattice over the wheels so you can't see the space under it.

The trailer has wooden walls and red carpet, new and thick. We weave around a bunch of people looking for seats, and Gran nearly runs to Pastor Joe. He's the only one in a suit: a beige one with pockets the size of the paperback western novels my grandfather reads. She talks and hands him an envelope. He sticks it right in that pocket with the white tail poking out.

"We are gonna see miracles this evening. Thank you, Jesus," he announces to everyone.

Soon I'm in a line with a family of kids, their hair tangled, their faces dirty. I'm the oldest and the only one with shoes. I stand straighter, but not because I'm vain. Gran says it isn't the kids' fault that their mama and daddy keep having kids and their dad drinks.

Miracles happen here. Blind people see. Deaf people hear. My gran goes back to her fold-up metal chair. I close my eyes again and mumble a prayer. I am still and serious. I know God sees it. Pastor has the littles kneel on the carpeted floor and lays a hand on their heads.

Everyone in the congregation is standing up. They shout, speak different languages as the Holy Spirit enters them. Their hands sway like trees in a hurricane. Gran faints with the love of God and two ladies in flowered dresses catch her.

I am next. I am next.

Pastor Joe gets on the stage and announces that this will be an amazing day. He says I am afflicted with a very painful spine and can hardly walk. I open my mouth to tell him that it's not that bad, I can run as fast as the other kids, but he talks louder. He tells the story about Jesus healing the crippled man by the pool of Bethesda and explains how one day I will be crippled too. I want to tell him he's wrong but interrupting an adult, especially a pastor, would mean a good whippin' later.

He tells me to kneel. I look up at Jesus on the cross, his hands and feet nailed, his crown cutting his head. It hurts my stomach. The pastor lays his bear-sized hands on my back and runs them down my spine again and again.

My gran runs up to the stage. "I see the spine moving to a straight line. Oh, Jesus. You performed a miracle." And my head is buzzing like the fluorescent lights in this tabernacle. I twist my arm backwards and run my hand down my spine as far as I can reach. I rub my face on my sleeve because I'm crying like a baby. But I ain't embarrassed by it because everyone knows I am right with God.

Later, we say goodbye and drive back to my gran's. She parks and her headlights flash on two alligators. When they hear us crunching the gravel, they drop into the river like fishing bateaus.

Inside, Gran tells Papa how strong my faith is, about how Pastor Joe is God's vehicle. My grandpa nods, his cigarette dangling from his lip, the smoke wrapping around me like a hug.

For the month of June, I have so much faith and my gran is filled with pride and the holy spirit. I am running up and down the street in front of Gran's in my new shoes. My back still hurts but I know it's getting better.

In July, when I go home, Mama will hold the living room wall mirror to reflect the bathroom mirror and point to the S on my back. I will sink to the cold tile floor and cry.

"I didn't have enough faith, Mama."

"No, honey. Only thing Pastor Joe's healing is his wallet. He's a con man," Mama will say, stroking my hair.

When I'm done crying, I'll hide in my closet and read my picture Bible. I'll read it hard, study those pictures of Jesus healing the crippled man, try to pray serious as the people in white robes, the men with long hair. Then, I'll ride my bike in my new shoes for hours. And my back will hurt but not as bad. Not half as bad. Then I'll go back to my Bible and think about my back again.

# Apples

by Elizabeth DeSchryver

Alice picked up the first apple. She began to peel it with practiced flicks of her knife, finger-lengths of green peel falling into the kitchen sink. Granny Smith apples were best for cooking. They stood up well to heat, kept their firm texture. But when she made applesauce, Alice always mixed in two or three other kinds of apples, carefully selected at the grocery store. It made the apple-sauce richer, more complex somehow.

She felt her mother's ghostly disapproval. Too nice for cooking. Her mother had always bought dollar bags of bruised Jonathan or Macintosh, her thrift never counting the cost of her time. Alice was in college before she discovered how many varieties of apples there were, right in her local supermarket. Or that you could buy a single apple.

The half-inch of water was simmering in the pot. Good. Alice quartered and cored the apple, chopping it into rough chunks. "Always chunk apples for applesauce," her mother had instructed. "Not like for pies. For pies, you slice the apples thin, so that they cook down in layers." Not that her mother had ever made pies. At least not that Alice could remember. Alice rested the battered cutting board on the edge of the pot and slid the apple chunks into the water.

She picked up the next apple. Braeburn. Slightly tart, very juicy. She slid her knife under the skin. Stubby red peels joined the green ones, carpeting the sink.

Her father had always peeled apples in long, slow curls, curving the knife around the swelling breast of the apple, making a game of it. Not her mother. Her mother had used brisk, efficient strokes, rapid slashes up its side while her other hand rotated the fruit in precise, quarter-inch increments. Then she'd cut through the core, gouge out the ovary, and trim the little triangle of peel from the divots at each end.

Alice slid the second apple into the water. The fragrance was starting to swirl upwards, sweet and a little sharp. She leaned over the stove and let her face bathe in the steam for a moment, her short curls wilting a bit in the heat.

She picked up the next apple. Another Granny Smith. Firm and tart.

Her mother had claimed that her father's way of peeling was wasteful. That more of the flesh was lost. It made no sense to Alice's child self. But growing up, she'd never dared to question it. She had simply peeled the apples her mother's way, with quick flicks of the knife.

Why did their arguments replay in her head, intrude on the simplest tasks? They were long dead. Both her parents, nearly thirty years. Maybe because their battles were so frequent. Anything could trigger them. Eating too fast. Or too loudly. Laughing at the wrong thing. They saturated the atmosphere of the house, like the smell of gunpowder from a recently fired gun.

Next apple. Roma. Soft, pink flesh. Almost dissolves when you cook it.

They stayed together "for the sake of the children," her mother had said, laying her less-than-stoic suffering on their young shoulders. Even back then, Alice used to daydream about which parent she would choose to live with if they divorced, naively thinking she would have a choice. On one side, there was her unpredictable, alcoholic father, frequently out of work, but who, during his better moments, would play endless games of Monopoly with her. On the other side, her acid-tongued mother was reliable, but determined to gouge out of Alice anything that took after her father. Her mother's judgment still lingered, a smear of failure over every choice Alice had ever made. Never marrying. Never having children. Buying nice apples for applesauce.

Alice stretched, her back starting to ache. Why did she bother making applesauce when you could buy so many different kinds nowadays? Chunky. No sugar added. Cinnamon. Because her mother did? Or because she enjoyed making it—the lovely, slow, sensual order of it, science becoming art, the alchemy of flavors?

Or maybe it just tasted good.

Next apple. Her last Granny Smith. Flick, flick, flick.

Alice had rejected her father. She had to, to win her mother's love. Or at least, her mother's acceptance. Maybe acceptance was the best her mother could give her, this small creature who tethered her to a man she hated. It wasn't until years later, digging into the past, that Alice realized how much her mother had been twisted by the burden of that marriage, how a woman who had seemed so strong, so rigid, had been crippled in spirit, becoming a ghost of her younger self. Or how Alice's father struggled to meet her mother's expectations until the burden of constant failure and resentment drove him back to his comforting drunken stupor.

Alice stared at the paring knife in her hand, glistening with juice. It wasn't just the way he peeled apples. Her father never did anything right in the kitchen, according to her mother. It was her domain. He was the intruder. But he kept trying. Alice still wasn't sure why. Did he enjoy cooking? Was he trying to do something nice for her mother? Or was it some subtle way to get back at her? No. He meant well. He always meant well. That could have been his epitaph.

Alice picked up the last apple. Gala. Sweet, but firm. It was the smallest of the six, but perfect in its own way. Carefully, she peeled the apple in one long, slow, defiant curl.

# Summer Recess

by Michelle Dybal

The playful screams and giggles of my second graders outdoors on the last day of school always cheers me. Today is no different. The giddiness and frivolity are intoxicating. Like tiny adults, friends embrace, swap contact data and secure plans for their summer outings.

But no matter how gleeful it is on the sun-drenched playground, my mind drifts elsewhere. Our baby was due on June 15, two weeks from now. And teaching, with those little faces looking at me, has been a constant reminder of other women's pregnancies gone well.

The miscarriage itself was mostly painless, just some cramping afterwards, twinging reminders. But the emotional pain starting on that day six months ago ached like no other. And now my summer plans—feeling the softest of infant flesh on mine, listening to baby coos, even getting no sleep—had vanished.

The bell rings signaling the end of recess. A group of girls from my class rush to me at full force in a combined hug, nearly tipping me. "Ms. Sweetwater, we're going to miss you so much," they say in rehearsed unison.

"I'll miss you, too," I reply automatically, wishing I was more in the moment, but instead I start counting the little bodies lining up to go back inside. I lead the class into the building; 26 students follow obediently behind me. The last hour is used for desk cleaning. The children stuff scuffed pencil cases. Half-used, clogged glue bottles and crinkled papers that never made it home rapidly fill reused shopping bags sitting on the floor. Antibacterial wipes swish over and inside desks. I work on clearing bulletin boards of items that just yesterday seemed relevant.

A tug on my shirttail takes me out of my staple-remover rhythm, a welcome relief from the hand-cramping mundane. It's Anthony, one of the smaller of my students, tears magnified behind the lenses of his black-rimmed glasses.

"Ms. Sweetwater, do I really have to leave your class?"

I kneel, cargo pants taut against my knees, and look directly into Anthony's eyes. He and I have often had conversations on a different philosophical level. I

12

sense this would be another. He would ask incredibly thoughtful questions that needed careful, thorough responses to help him understand and cope.

"You've completed second grade, Anthony, and you've done a great job at it," I smile at him. "You are ready to move on to third grade. I am a second-grade teacher, so I can't teach you what you need to learn in third grade."

"But I like you to be my teacher," he sniffles, but his tears are dried up.

"That is the highest compliment, Anthony. Thank you." I beam a bit inside. "But we're all going to have a few months off, and I think you'll be ready for a new teacher in the fall. What are you going to do this summer, Anthony?"

The little boy's posture straightens. "We're going to the Grand Canyon! I can't wait."

"Well, that's exciting."

"Are you going to the Grand Canyon?"

"I don't have big plans like that," I say looking down. Now *I* feel like crying.

"What's wrong, Ms. Sweetwater?" Anthony is that way—he can be very in tune with others' emotions, or sometimes not read them at all, like with his classmates on the playground some days.

I meet his eyes again and compose myself, not wanting to upset him. "The plans I had are not going to happen now, but I'll be okay."

"When I get upset about second grade ending, my mom tells me third grade is a fresh start. Do you need a fresh start?"

"I believe I do, Anthony." The admission is hard and, at first, I feel a tightening in my throat. But then I feel better to have said it.

The bell rings and the class scrambles to the door with their shopping bags. We walk out together to a courtyard of expectant caretakers—parents, nannies, older siblings—waiting to greet the children they've come to gather. Big bulging bags swing from little arms as the rising third graders rush in all directions to kick off their summers. A few go in the other direction to line up for the bus. Several parents approach me to voice their gratitude; many wave their goodbyes.

Somehow seeing their little faces reunited with those who love them is less difficult than past pickups this semester. While some days tugged, other days pulled at my equilibrium, like when I tucked away the sun-covered newborn outfit—the one, too-soon indulgence I allowed myself—now behind the bedsheets in the heavy oak armoire at home. When spring arrived, I began feeling a slow drift toward center, the dark cloud breaking apart. Having a great class this year helped, but now I am itching for this last ritual to end.

Finally, the blacktop clears. The teachers head back into the building for their final room cleanups. I linger a bit, then reach into my thigh pocket and pull out my phone.

I text my husband: "Want to take a trip?"

I head back to my staple puller. In complete silence, I clear the bulletin boards, saving what little is reusable and recycling the rest. Organizing my desk will wait for another day, but it will be good to come into a room with naked walls.

Before heading out of my classroom, I check my phone. There is one text message, a reply from my husband. Not at all typical for a response from him, there are no words, only emojis: a palm tree, a tropical drink, a pineapple, and an airplane. A laugh escapes my throat.

My phone goes back into my pocket and I flip off the lights. As I walk through the building then into the parking lot, I sense a lightness I haven't felt in a very long time. It's good to have plans for the summer.

# What We're Here For

## by Marcia Pradzinski

The noonday sun showcases purple salvia, pink coneflowers, black-eyed Susans; it shimmers mud puddles to life. Stargazer lilies catch my eye—some petals closed tight and pointing, others open like fingers reaching out and down. I imagine embryonic cells budding inside me. I'm here at the Chicago Botanic Gardens to visit with my sister Izzy to tell her I'm pregnant. I worry the news will rekindle the pain of her miscarriages. She's seven years older, and the last one drove her into a deep depression. Once when we were out together, she broke into tears when a pregnant woman walking a toddler passed us. Izzy is now 40 years old and childless. I wait at the doorway of the Botanic Gardens cafe for her, where she went to buy a Coke—or *Coca*, as she now calls it after her recent trip to Spain.

"Vamanos," Izzy says. She pops open her Coke and eyes me, "Reveille-toi, Heather! We're out here to spend time together." Not sure she could hold a real conversation with the language fragments she's picked up.

Izzy's trips have kept her busy. I don't want to cause her distress. She cared for me as my big sister: she took me for walks; bought me comic books with her allowance; read to me; rubbed my back; sang to calm me when nighttime darkness frightened me.

I'd like to see her more often, but every time I call, she's busy with a sewing project, travel plans, or something else that keeps her busy and unavailable. We swat at flies as we walk along a path. The intense aroma of marigolds tickles my nose as we pass by. Their heady fragrance and the Gardens' atmosphere send me back to our backyard on Cortez Street in Chicago, where Izzy and I grew up, where our dad puttered around his tiger lilies and seven-sister roses, and Mom's marigolds.

"You remember," Izzy says, gazing at the marigolds, "the story about when I tore out the marigolds?"

A small boy runs in front of her, cutting her words short and almost tripping her. His lush black curls frame his face and accent his green eyes—eyes and hair like mine. Izzy glares at the boy as the woman with him yanks him out of the way. My heart goes out to him.

"Kids run wild everywhere," Izzy says. "At a restaurant yesterday, two kids ran like a couple of rabbits, chasing each other, circling the tables."

"So," I say, "the marigolds?" I don't want to hear Izzy's harangue about children misbehaving and also don't want to hear the much-repeated story. But I will listen; it'll give me time to think about how to break my news to her.

Izzy purses her lips. "I'm just saying: parenting nowadays…" As I wait for her to finish, I imagine my baby, yet to be born, sprouting limbs like petals on a blossom.

"Marigolds?" Izzy cocks her head.

"You started to talk about when you tore out marigolds."

"Oh, right! Mom pissed me off. She told me to weed the backyard as punishment for doing, I don't know what." Izzy sips her Coke. "So, I ripped out her marigolds." *I love those flowers.* My stomach churns as I picture their golden heads limp on the grass.

"It was the summer you were born and everyone was paying you so much attention. It was as if I'd become a ghost. Can you guess what Mom did?" *She gave you the silent treatment.* "I got the silent treatment; she didn't speak to me for a week! Over her stinky flowers! And said she didn't have time for my nonsense; she had my baby sister to take care of." Izzy crumples the Coke can and tosses it into a recycle bin alongside the path.

Mom's typical response to our misbehaving: she wouldn't talk to us unless we made a sincere apology. Her words echo from the past: *I can tell you don't mean it. Come back when you're really sorry about what you've done.*

"After I apologized again, we went to Frank's Nursery where she bought two flats of marigolds, and you know what…?" *She made you plant the damn things.* "She made me plant the damn things."

"I have news," I say. I watch a finch, its yellow body perched and pecking for seeds on purple salvia until a blue jay flies in and ousts it from the spot.

"Oh, good, me too! That's what we're here for, to do some catching up. David got a promotion and we're moving to France for a year! I've been so busy the last two months getting ready; we leave in two weeks." *How annoying to find out at the last minute! No time to visit, chat, and wish her safe travels.* "What's your news, Heather? Good, I hope."

"Uh, well, I—"

Izzy's phone chimes. She's going to make me wait again. "Sorry! Gotta run now, Heather. David's waiting for me. He needs me."

So do I.

I'll send her an announcement when the baby arrives.

# Blackfoot or Bust

by Joyce Burns Zeiss

"Detour, detour, there's a muddy road ahead," sang my father as he veered off the paved two-lane highway and steered our blue '51 Chevy by the wooden barricades and the flashing yellow signals to the gravel road. My brother Lawrence and I rolled up our windows as the dust billowed before us.

"Slow down, Howard." My mother turned to my father, clutching the crumpled road map.

Dad gave her his "be quiet, woman, I'm driving" look and floored the accelerator. "Blackfoot or bust" was his motto. He had two weeks' vacation. Every summer we piled into the family car and followed the Lincoln Highway from the banks of the Maumee River in Toledo, Ohio, past the cornfields of Iowa to the plains of Nebraska, and to the hairpin mountain turns of Wyoming to my grandparents' home in Blackfoot, Idaho.

The air in the car was blast-furnace hot. My brother, his shirt streaked with sweat, slid across the seat as we rounded a sharp curve.

"Get off my side," I growled and shoved him into his corner. He was 15 months younger than me, a skinny 4th grader with curly brown hair he hated and, although he fought back, I was still the big sister and the boss. We had established rules about life in the back seat, with a dividing line identified with a tape down the middle. Anyone who crossed it got pummeled.

"She hit me," yelled Lawrence.

Dad's right arm cut a wide swath across our air space as we both ducked. "If you don't quit fighting, I'm going to stop this car."

"I want a hamburger." I folded my arms and frowned.

"Two hours." Dad pulled back on the main highway. He sped up and around the slow-moving car in front of us as we headed straight for an oncoming diesel truck puffing a black tower of smoke. I froze. Lawrence squeezed his eyes shut. My mother's slender fingers clawed at the dashboard; her shoulders tensed. As the truck drew near enough for me to see the bright red of the driver's cap, Dad swerved back into our lane. Lawrence opened his eyes, I sat up,

18

and we continued to taunt each other. Four Burma-Shave signs appeared on the right. *Don't pass cars/On curve or hill/If the cops don't get you/The mortician will.* I bit my lip.

A giant billboard advertising Conoco Gas came into view. "I've got to pee," said Lawrence. Several minutes later the red and green gas pumps popped up like an oasis in the desert.

"Okay, we'll stop." Beads of sweat trickled down the back of Dad's bald head. While the uniformed attendant filled our gas tank and washed the splattered bugs off our windshield, Lawrence and I took the coins Dad gave us and each bought a cold Coke from the vending machine.

"Want to win some money?" Lawrence tilted his Coke bottle to his mouth. He opened his hand and showed me three dimes. I nodded and we sauntered into the station. A giant silver slot machine covered the counter. Lawrence put in one dime and pulled down on the handle. A red cherry and two yellow lemons popped up.

"Try again," I said.

He dropped the second dime in and pulled on the handle. Two cherries and a lemon this time.

"Let's go." Dad stood by the gas pump and lit up a Camel.

"Coming!" I called. "Play the last dime. C'mon. Hurry."

"I still have to pee." Lawrence put the dime in the slot and pulled down hard on the handle again. Three cherries popped up, bells chimed, and an avalanche of dimes poured out of the machine and filled his ten-year-old hands. He screamed in surprise and stuffed the coins in his pockets.

"Aren't you going to share?"

"My dimes. Not yours."

I stuck out my tongue and glared at him.

The coins jingled in his pocket as he trotted around the corner to the bathroom. After ducking in the girls' room, I stomped to the car and slid into the back seat. Anxious to make up for lost time, Dad barreled out of the gas station and down the street, leaving Lawrence behind. I stared at the spacious back seat that would be all mine and savored being an only child. I could read my book in peace and nap anytime I wanted. The car came to a stop as the light at the intersection blinked from yellow to red. I chewed my thumbnail and wondered who Dad would be the angrier with, me for not telling him Lawrence was missing or Lawrence for playing the slots and not coming when he was called. The light turned green. The car lunged forward.

I cleared my throat. "You left Lawrence."

"What?" Mother's head jerked around, then turned to Dad. Her hazel eyes flashed.

Dad swore, made a U-turn, and shot back down the street to the station. Lawrence was nowhere to be seen. Dad jumped from the car and stormed inside. A few minutes later they both appeared. Instead of Dad's hand grabbing Lawrence's neck, it gently encircled his shoulder. The little brat was smiling.

"Lawrence won ten dollars!" Dad beamed.

I couldn't believe Dad wasn't mad. Mom sighed, just relieved her little boy was safe.

Lawrence crawled in the backseat and gave me a superior smirk. I stared at my little brother, the laughing blue eyes, the long eyelashes. I couldn't wait to get even with him. He must have read my mind. He dug a handful of dimes out of his bulging pocket.

"Here!"

I held out my sweaty palm and grabbed them. A truck rumbled past in the opposite direction. In another day, we'd be running in the fields, riding horses, and chasing cackling chickens. I curled back into the corner.

I pointed to my side of the seat. "Why don't you stretch out?"

"Okay."

He grinned and slid his feet over the taped dividing line.

# Conversations With Condiments

## by Kelly Q. Anderson

Government was tolerable because of Bingo. He was red-haired, overly freckled, and twice let me copy his homework after I got caught up in watching *Sportscenter*. It was amusing to learn about the Executive branch because Bingo would ask, "When do we get to the part about oral sex in the Oval Office?" To which our teacher, Mr. Curtis, would reply, "Keep reading, Mr. Bingham, and perhaps this chapter will answer your insightful question."

Bingo's crappy Jeep never struggled to find parking. His parents were always the easy parents. Bingo knew how to hold a girl's waist; how to slam into a guy in a way that was funny. He wore a white tuxedo for fun and counted his little sister as one of his best friends. His confidence floated down the halls.

Bingo shrugged off college, claiming it was pedestrian. He had other plans.

"If I do seven days a week at my folks' jewelry shop, I can retire by thirty."

"What are you going to do then?" I said.

"Live," he replied, as if I had asked the dumbest question he had ever heard. "I dunno, maybe go camping without a swimsuit. Get a hound dog. Could be fun."

"And you're gonna do that how? By selling little gold bracelets?"

He winked. "I'll also repair watches."

"So I guess I'll meet you on the golf course at age thirty. To celebrate your retirement."

He found an easy grin. "Golf is for people who hate themselves."

Three years later, I would roll into my fraternity house at two a.m., thoroughly drunk and planning to microwave a quesadilla. I would pass out with grease on my shirt and wake with a pair of balls drawn on my face in Sharpie.

Bingo would complete store inventory, gather the mail, and go to sleep in an apartment without a carbon monoxide detector.

The next morning, my mom would leave me three darkly whispered voicemails while I struggled through a history exam, my face raw from scrubbing at the Sharpie with paper towels.

21

I drove five hours home for the service and wore a borrowed sport coat that bagged. His sister gave the eulogy, but I didn't hear the words. Bingo's great grandmother attended, hunched in a wheelchair, clear tubes threaded under her nose. I stared at her bulky green oxygen tank, fixated on how she somehow got the better deal. I couldn't cry. I couldn't get beyond the chairs in the room.

When I turned 28, I ventured to our ten-year high school reunion, held at Chunky's, a bar known for its supersized mozzarella sticks. I gripped a watery gin-and-tonic and paced on a sticky floor while talking to McKenzie, a blonde classmate who had created an organic BBQ sauce (she set up a table and droned on about how she made a deal with Whole Foods).

No one mentioned Bingo by name, but a bit of him lingered in the room. His clever red head would have weeded through the shrieking hugs, the quiet desperation. Probably would've checked in on who had twins or who liked the Bears' chances. He would have rolled his eyes at the BBQ sauce and flicked its gaudy silver label. But he would've dipped a mozza stick in it, congratulated McKenzie, and acted like he had never tasted satisfaction until that moment.

I don't have an easy smile. I don't have a quip for people I went to Homecoming with (I never went to Homecoming). But I have a navy blazer that made me feel decent for the night.

The hours ticked by and the BBQ sauce got doled into eager hands. I chatted with Marly and Jen, who channeled Track & Field into marathons (I tried to flex while they explained tapering). I shook hands with Krueger from BioChem, who did not deserve any handshakes, but it gave me a moment to relish that his hair had thinned into soft wisps and his waist had thickened considerably. Sometimes these things just worked themselves out.

When the beers had done their job and the din of the room kicked up, I slid my empty glass onto the bar and executed my ideal goodbye—the one where I tell everyone I need to hit the restroom, lower my head, grab a bottle of sauce, and stalk toward the door. My tired Volvo beep-beeped, its headlights making yellow eyes in the parking lot.

I tried putting the BBQ sauce in the cup holder but the big, dumb organic bottle was too wide. I swatted away empty vape cartridges and set the bottle on the passenger seat but it flopped over. With a huff, I reached for the passenger seatbelt and pulled it slowly across the bottle. I had to wrap it awkwardly but eventually it secured the bottle into place. I glanced up at the bar, then back at the buckled sauce.

"Like the Bears chances this year?"

I didn't wait for a response as I turned onto the street. "Paid a helluva lot for a running back with a garbage knee."

I exhaled, filling the car with the noise of breath.

"Dustin Brooks still wears the same damn cargo pants. Same gold chain!"

I slowed, coming to a red light.

"McKenzie's face seemed softer. Nicer than I remember. Blonder too." I looked at the buckled-up sauce. "Maybe everyone's nicer after high school."

The light turned green.

I drove past the old Bingham jewelry store. It had long been sold off, becoming an insurance office, then a religious gift shop, then something else entirely, until nothing familiar remained. I hadn't thought about the store in years. But suddenly I was remembering how it looked in its prime, specifically around Christmas. The brick facade held strands of twinkle lights, the windows glowed with candlesticks. Red velvet boxes were tied with white ribbon. I imagined Bingo in a button-down, winking behind the counter.

Selling little gold bracelets.

I could almost hear his correction. *I'll also repair watches.*

"A retirement plan," I gestured to the passenger seat. The bottle sat silent as the buildings flew by.

I made a right turn and I laughed a weird, hushed laugh, the kind that choked my throat. Then I laughed louder, the sound bouncing off the windows.

The drive home took longer than expected. Streets wove into sidewalks and the stoplights seemed to linger on red. By the time I pulled into my place, I realized my face was wet, long lines streaking down my cheeks.

The next morning, I shuffled into the kitchen and pawed at the coffee maker. My eyes felt thick and the sides of my face ached. *Sportscenter* buzzed in the background.

I slurped my coffee, thinking about marathon training and nicer blondes. I scanned the countertop, piled with Coke cans and stained Comcast bills. No BBQ sauce with a silver label.

I straightened upright, careening my head toward the door.

Nothing.

I grabbed my keys and jogged out to the car.

Two empty cupholders and the stale smell of McDonald's greeted me.

I walked back into the apartment, suddenly very awake. A flash of navy caught my eye: a square piece of paper hung neatly on the fridge.

*10th High School Reunion—Be Our Guest!*

The paper was thick, the text was silver.

It wasn't from last night. It wasn't even hosted at Chunky's.

It was dated for January, several years back. At a brewery I had never been to. At a ticket price I would have never paid.

The beige walls of the apartment yellowed, drooping low at the corners. The coffee in the pot turned cold. My hair thinned to delicate wisps, my waist thickened over sagging, stained cargo pants. Same gold chain. The kitchen shrunk smaller as my cheeks puffed out, sallow and quiet. My body became vivid. The hangover boomed between my ears.

When I received the invite I remembered thinking, *I should go.*

I also remembered thinking: *no fucking way.*

I grew frantic. I raced around, opening sticky wooden drawers and shoving aside crusty oven mitts. Where the hell was that damned bottle? I bumped into the stove, a busted chair, a cardboard box. A lone golf ball bounced loudly on the floor. Dust kicked up on the linoleum and I made a mental note to mop. Mop everything, fuck, just coat this dump in bleach. I thought the fridge held a receipt from my tab at Chunky's. I looked closer, the numbers appearing in neat, tiny rows.

It was a pay stub.

In the living room, *Sportscenter* kicked up louder: "I don't know if the Bears can sustain this; time remains to see what kind of pain is tolerable."

I yanked open the fridge. Everything rattled and everything smelled. There were containers of gray rice, piles of ketchup packets, and a hodgepodge of mottled jars. Alone on a shelf sat a BBQ bottle, plastic and nearly empty. The wrinkled label was a knock-off brand. Long past its expiration date.

I stared at the BBQ sauce, demanding an answer. Demanding its mouth open up and show its teeth.

# Go in Peace

by Paco Aramburu

As I sit here, even though I see and account for the fingers of this hand, I don't know to whom they belong. The chair that faces me wrinkles its tacked-on red leather to tell me in a wooden accent: "Lives are made of instants following each other like rosary beads. But, after one of those moments, you'll find that it was the last one." Outside the window, beyond the dead neon sign, the rain, thick, noisy, makes me glad of my brew as I dawdle over a poem. Behind a marble and oak counter, a mustachioed waiter outfitted with a well-worn, almost clean white jacket, reads his paper.

The oak and beveled glass door opens and, along with the wet wind, a woman stumbles in a flutter of red umbrella, drenched raincoat, and a burst of cinnamon hair. After recovering her poise, she walks to a table near the back of the café. You can tell a lot about people by their gait. The way her feet elevate then touch the floor as if being placed on a spot calculated in advance, tells me that this is not a girl, a chick, or a dame, but a capable woman.

She drops her raincoat on the chair, bag next to it, and folded umbrella under the table. After a brief reconnaissance in the mirror, she fixes her mane and sits with a sigh. The waiter bows with a deferential smile. While rummaging in her bag, with a break of her wrist, slender fingers moving with acquisitive jerks to fish out a small, red, battered book, she places her order with a couple of short smiles. My brain suggests a memory about that red book. Kierkegaard. The scent of old, yellowed pages, the ramblings of a deeply insecure man and a mind disposed to capture life the way we do caged birds.

"Do you know her?" asks the chair with an impertinent, leathery smile.

After she welcomes her café au lait, as if impelled by an elemental force, I walk to her table and stand behind her. The waiter, abaft the enormous coffee machine, raises an eyebrow, a gesture that I catch from a sliver of a mirror between bottles of Fernet Branca. The words form themselves as I say them. "I'm sorry to disturb you, but I'm having a bit of déjà vu, I…well, I think I met you before, that I…know you."

25

She sighs. Turns to me. Her eyes, honeyed with sparks of green, open wide. Her skin turns a strange gray. Behind her clutching fingers, her mouth emits a hoarse, "Oh my God! How can you be…No! I saw you'd…" She leaps from her chair and runs to the door. From there she turns to look at me and yells: "Who are you?"

"Santiago Legorburu." I am proud to remember my name. "My friends call me Santi."

At the mention of my name her knees give way but, by grabbing the bronze door handle with her trembling hands, she maintains some form of verticality. "You, you cannot be Santi…My Santi is dead. Dead." She pushes the door and runs into the rain.

"Alma!" Like a supernova, my mind explodes with the recognition of my insatiable need for her spirit and body. I remember. Our first touch of hands, her breath, her opening to my learning and teaching of our own skin language. How could I have forgotten Alma and my own death? I remember the precise moment my present was cut, and my past became a memory in charge of others. We had been us, a two-headed synthesis of man and woman. I remember the us. The death, the rush of pain preceding dark oblivion and the sudden cut of that chord that bound us.

I recoil at all those questions. I look at the waiter, who turns on the gigantic coffee machine. From the steam come the words: "Where there is no life, there is no time. You can talk until the stars dim forever, and she would still be standing outside, in the rain, prisoner of both your desires."

I run after her.

She is shaking a few paces away, getting drenched. "Alma, I don't remember not loving you." I grab her arm.

She looks at me, eyes roll back, she utters "Santi–," and faints. I hold on to her shoulders before she hits the sidewalk. I feel a mixture of physical pleasure holding her body in my arms, and my knowledge of her anguish. The waiter, standing under the canopy, holds the door open. I carry my love inside and lay her on a chair against the wall, her auburn hair heavy with water darkening the mahogany and making a small puddle on the granite floor. That puddle has been intimate with her hair. I cover my lover with the raincoat to keep her body warm and to avoid her shapes showing through the soaked fabric.

I cannot smell her usual jasmine scent, or the musk that emanated when she was aroused. Like the previews to a movie, scenes of our life scroll through my mind: a kiss in our truck under another rain, chasing her around the apartment to grab the last piece of chocolate she had stolen like a capuchin monkey…a voice from afar…the last whisper evanescing in the steam from the coffee machine.

I look at Alma, head resting on the mahogany wall. She is being clouded by steam.

The waiter turns to me. "You met the living, but nobody gets to exist metaphysically. Go in peace."

# FICTION

HEROINES IN CRISIS

# Pilgrim's Crossing

by Anna da Silva

*American Pie* is such a Sammy song, but for once I don't change the station. Instead, I crank the volume, lower the car window and sing along like he used to, even though I hadn't thought of Sammy in ages. Maybe it's because I am on my own for the day.

I glance in the rearview mirror, so used to the girls' bucket seats in the back of my Subaru, sticky with grape juice and strewn with Cheerios. But the back seat of my in-laws' Volvo is immaculate and empty. The car swap is Jonathan's idea, as is taking the girls to the zoo with his parents. Today I am free; the world is my oyster!

The wind swoops in, smelling of hot tar and seaweed and I try to whistle along, like Sammy taught me on our road trip just after he and I got hitched in Baton Rouge a million years ago. I stick my elbow out, the way he used to when we were still married, before he had gone hard-faced and stopped listening to music on car rides. Before we couldn't as much as look at each other anymore.

I read somewhere once—only 20 percent of marriages survive the death of a child.

Exit 4 is coming up, but for a moment I want to keep driving past it. Keep going, drive all the way to the Cape, spend the day on some windswept beach, toes in the sand. Or go shopping for a summer dress, light and flowery or strappy and sleek. It's a rare and much appreciated day off for a mother of twin toddlers on a family vacation, after all, why shouldn't I spend it the way I want?

But Jonathan's mother's voice drones on in my head. *Oh, you must, dear! Plimoth Plantation is such a treat. It's history come alive!*

Like we don't have history down south.

It's as though I am free for the day, except not really. I hate that I keep trying to please her.

I take the exit.

I park near the visitor's center with a "Welcome to Plimoth Plantation" sign up front. A family of tourists mills about—Red Sox caps, five dollars off coupons in hand. A burly middle-aged guy rules the roost, giving his wife silent commands, lifting his chin up and pointing with it. Their two boys look resigned to their fate. The guy's face, hands and forearms are deeply tanned, but his meaty legs are pale, sticking out of his shorts like they have not seen the sun in ages. I wonder what he does every day—too bossy for a landscaper, too fussy for construction. I decide he is a traffic cop, walking the beat all day, slapping tickets on parked cars. I must be staring, because he glares at me and I hurry to hit the trail before they do.

The path forks, and my map says it's either Settlers' Village or Wampanoag Homesite. I remember the stupid joke Sammy would always tell, *when you come to a fork in the path—take it.* And I would roll my eyes every time and say, *you call that funny?* And laugh anyway. He always made me laugh, ever since the first time we met and Sammy, leaning close, squinting against the smoke of my Virginia Slims, had asked my name. Priscilla, I said, and he gave me this lopsided smile and crooned to me in a lush Elvis baritone. I rolled my eyes at him, but was smitten, right away.

I wonder where he is sometimes. I hope he is well.

Funny how I am the one who took the fork, after all.

I walk down a sloping path winding through the tangles of juniper bushes, tall grasses, and beach-rose until another switchback reveals a view of the bay. Icy blue water. Pale, wispy cotton-candy shreds of the clouds hang in the sky. Now, that's beautiful. Maybe not the Gulf coast, but not bad at all.

A pebble grinds between my toes and I stop to shake it out of my sandal. When I look up, a boy is standing a few yards in front of me, perfectly still. He is maybe eight, compact and lean, olive skin and dark eyes. He is dressed in full costume of tan deer hides, beaded tassels and feathered headgear. He looks like a boy from the brochure, put in my path straight from the freaking 17th century.

"You okay, Ma'am?" He watches me, dark head tilted to the side.

The child is beautiful. My chest is suddenly so tight, my knees weak.

"Yeah. I'm fine, just some sand in my shoe."

He nods, smiles, and takes a sip of his electric-blue Gatorade.

"Okay. Bye."

He takes off, but I can't move.

This is what my Timmy would look like now, same chocolate-dipped-cherry eyes that he got from Sammy, same year-round tan. This summer he would have been eight—Timmy from the future of my past that never came to be.

Maybe I should go back to Jonathan and the girls—find them at the zoo, surprise them, visit the monkeys or something, eat some strawberry ice cream together.

Get a grip, it's just some boy.

I stand still until the murmur of voices draws nearer and I am about to be overtaken by the traffic cop and his clan. I start walking again.

I can smell the Settlers' Village before I can see it. Freshly cut grass and manure, briny ocean breeze. The sight is lovely, too. Stubby saltbox structures of weathered wood sit clustered together, framed by lush greenery and stark ocean blue. There is a vegetable patch and a chicken coop, a little schoolhouse, a big barn.

I wonder how it was, in Pilgrim times. How did it feel to brave the swells of that ocean, trying to make a better life? Were they forever glancing back across the waters looking for their past? Did they ache for what could have been, or cherish what they gained?

I follow the gravel paths and saunter around the village, peeking into the buildings, meandering, eavesdropping. In a boxy house that peers at the world through one blind window, a young woman dressed in a severe gray dress and bonnet is fielding questions from a rowdy trio of girls. She is what the brochure calls *in character*, pretending she is actually a Pilgrim. I can glimpse a roped-off oven inside, pottery, bulky wooden furniture. Standing outside, I can hear only her answers, delivered earnestly, the girls' questions inaudible. A pause, then the fake settler woman pipes up with some tidbit about the Pilgrims' life, in the phoniest of accents, as far as I can tell.

"Aye, we sleep eight people on these feather beds upon the floor here."

A pause.

"Yes, pilgrim means traveler. Someone who has come from afar."

I wonder if I am a pilgrim then, too.

"We have an outhouse yonder and a chamber pot for that."

Girls snicker.

I need to pee.

33

Wisps of smoke drift upward from the chimney. Goats bleat. Girls giggle again. Did children laugh all those hundreds of years ago? Or were they earnest and grim, their hearts heavy with worry?

Above it all, photobombing this 17th century idyll, far beyond the hatched rooftops of the Pilgrim's Village, airplane vapor trails crisscross the blue skies.

I move along the path towards the Native American Homestead, wondering if the little boy I saw is there.

I smell weeping pine logs smoldering in the fire and walk faster, taunted by the aroma of cornbread and hush puppies. My pocket map shows a tangle of paths but I follow my nose instead, suddenly hungry for something real, not that muesli bird-seed crap my mother-in-law feeds everyone in the morning, with fat-free milk from a glass pitcher.

I think Jonathan also misses real food, but he is too nice to say anything to his mother. Not on this short visit. Not ever, I am guessing. He'd rather eat bird seed.

When we met, I wondered if it was a façade, him being nice. My town was overrun with strangers overnight—first the news crews showed up, then the environmentalists, then the volunteers. The diner was hopping day and night, electric with energy. But he was so even-tempered, so polite. He would order his coffee at the diner—cream, two sugars. Sometimes he asked about me, sometimes about the town, but mostly he wanted to know things about tide patterns, and the marshes, and bird migration. For weeks, he would leave after breakfast and go out on one of those skimming ships that they brought from all over, trying to contain the oil spill. And next morning he would be at the diner again, at my station, polite as ever. Until a few weeks into it, when he came in, sat down heavy at the corner booth, and sobbed quietly, bitterly, covering his face with oil-streaked hands. I brought him his coffee and sat with him, not quite knowing what to say. But as his heart broke for the birds and the marshes, my own heart thawed a little bit.

I catch the first glimpse of the site in the clearing amidst the scrawny pines and juniper bushes. Oblong huts, made of willow tree trunks and shingled with bark, circle the main campsite fire. What are these called, teepees? I still can't see the boy anywhere, but a couple of women sit by the fire, pretend-cooking something; one is holding a toddler, all are in full Wampanoag costume.

Behind the main house, a man is hacking at a giant log that looks like a half-finished canoe. He wears shockingly little: a suede tasseled vest with beads and feathers and a little man-skirt. It's just long enough to barely cover him, but when he heaves his ax, it's all I can do is not to stare. His chest is glistening, his dark hair cascades down muscular shoulders. There is a small circle of spectators around him, including the traffic cop's family, but he carries on axing like there's nobody there. The scene feels vaguely pornographic; I can't quite put my finger on it, but I feel uneasy watching them, so I move on.

There is no sign of a bathroom anywhere.

Smoke is coming out of the neat round hole in the roof of the main structure. I have to duck on my way in; deerskins brush the side of my face and my eyes sting with smoke right away. I only wanted to peek, but the traffic cop's brood is crowding in behind me so, like a fool, I step in. The house is roomy, with earthen swept floors and low wide benches piled with something furry and cozy-looking. The boy is not here either. *Oh, Timmy.*

Instead, a young girl—a teenager really, bolts up from the bench and lunges into what could only be described as a presentation. Something about the Wampanoag *wetu* and the fire pits. She is not pretending to be from the 17th century, like those crackpots in the Settlers' Village, but she is on a mission to educate. I wish I could leave, but the girl is addressing me directly, speaking earnestly, her two scrawny braids bouncing on her shoulders. Something about matriarchy and the family structure. Well, hell's bells, I should be taking notes.

I really want to leave now. The smoke is too much. But the girl has locked eyes with me and I stay, nodding and pretending to listen. It couldn't have been like this, really, Pilgrims and the Native Peoples living side by side, peacefully. We gave them smallpox, booze, and guns, and then we took their land and put what was left of them in reservations. *Reservations.* What a charade this place is!

I feel trapped. The traffic cop is arguing with the wife in a hushed whisper about lunch, something about Pizzeria Uno and the problem with their tap beer. The older boy is shoving the younger one mutely, his face flushed and savage. The younger one is trying, stubbornly, to ignore him. The girl raises her voice; it sounds urgent. She is asking me something about the Wampanoag women and controlling property, but the ringing in my ears is growing louder and the question doesn't register. I need to get out now, but the two boys are blocking my exit.

Then, to no one's surprise really, the older one shoves his brother a touch too hard, and he flies into the firepit. His sneaker kicks up sparks and smoke. I gasp and inhale smoke and then sneeze—violently, forcefully.

As air is expelled from my lungs and my body shudders, my bladder betrays me. I stand still, mortified, unable to stop the powerful flow, the crotch of my jeans instantly soaked with my own hot piss. Weakened pelvic floor after carrying twins, they said, would do that to you. Well, now I know. In the commotion, no one pays any mind to my shame, but I turn and run.

I sit slumped in the driver's seat of the idling Volvo, my own sweater tucked under my wet butt. I am waiting for my hands to stop shaking before I hightail it out of the parking lot. A small hand taps the glass and I look up to see the boy. I lower the window and smile at him, ruefully.

"You dropped your map." He hands it to me through the window.

"I don't need it anymore." I take the map.

The boy looks away, squinting. "Did you like it?"

"What, the plantation?" I shrug. "It's okay."

He nods.

I want to grab him, scoop him up, claim him as my own. His hand is still in the car window, and so is mine. I inch my fingers a little closer and touch his—lightly, briefly. Oh, boy.

"I have to go." He tilts his head like a little bird, eyeing me. "You gonna be okay?"

I nod, unable to speak.

He takes off and runs across the parking lot to catch up to the group of Pilgrims and the Wampanoag, all headed for a picnic table in full costume, Subway sandwiches in hand. Pilgrims crossing.

I get back on the highway, looking for the exit for the humorlessly named Independence Mall. I find Target and with a sweater tied around my hips, I slink to the women's clothing section and pick up the first pair of jeans my eyes settle on.

At the restroom entrance, a Hooters waitress accordingly dressed flashes me a high-voltage smile and holds the door for me. We both head for the stalls and reemerge, the waitress having changed out of her owly tank and orange shorts into some perfectly pedestrian Capris and a white T. I am wearing my new jeans and holding the old ones wadded up into a damp ball. We nod knowingly at each other—waitresses of the world unite!—and the Hooters girl walks out.

I shove my wet jeans into the giant stainless-steel trash can and stand staring at myself in the bathroom mirror. Motherhood changes a woman's body, they say. Not to mention her soul.

I run the tap and put my hot forehead on the cold marble and let the tears come. I cry until there is nothing left in me but a whimper.

I keep the radio off on my drive back to Cambridge.

I am back at my in-laws while everybody is still out, and I raid the kitchen. Against all odds, I find flour, dry yeast and milk, butter, eggs, oil, even powdered sugar. I hope I still remember how to make these—I haven't tried since Timmy. But it all comes together and by the time my Subaru is in the driveway, I have a whole platter of perfect treats ready and a fresh pot of coffee on.

Jonathan's mother is first through the door. "What are you doing, dear?" her voice is just a touch incredulous.

I grip the platter and lift it high as an offering.

"Beignets. I fixed us some beignets. It's a New Orleans thing, I wanted y'all to try." My voice trails off.

The girls trot in after her, run to me at full tilt chirping about giraffes and sloths, and I manage to give each a squeeze before they escape to the patio, their little hands filled with warm pastries.

I know what Jonathan's mother is thinking, but I reach deep inside—bottom of my heart, corners of my soul and give her a straight up, honest smile. For real.

First nothing happens, and then, like an ice floe, her impeccable mask cracks and her lips twitch and curve upwards and she produces a smile of her own, almost tender.

"What a marvelous idea, dear!"

In my mind's eye, I can almost see her pick up a beignet, gingerly lift it to her mouth, sink her perfect teeth in and take a generous, lusty bite. And then close her eyes, tilt her head back and go, "Mmm, that's so good!"

Instead, it's Jonathan who reaches for a beignet. He pulls me into a hug, playfully, his hand rests on my hip and his thumb hooks into the belt loop of my jeans.

"Are these new? We missed you all day! You had fun?"

I can't speak yet again. I nod and shake my head, somehow both yes and no, and I weld myself to him, my curves to his concaves, our separate pasts to our common future. He smiles at me and plants a light kiss on my mouth, sticky with powdered sugar and so sweet. It sends a current through me that feels like pure, undiluted love. I stand, smiling like a fool, in my husband's mother's kitchen, my children's giggles drifting from outside, and I am flooded with relief.

# One Afternoon

by Sheila Elliott

## CHICAGO, 1939

Balancing on one foot, Ida Pouelin pushed back with the heel of the other to close the apartment door. Standing firm now, she parted the edges of the cotton panels that served as a closet door and set her cloche hat on the shelf. One hand brushed a coarse patch of wool on the arm of her mother's winter coat. The blood spatters were dry as day-old bread. Same as when the police returned the coat after the accident. Two years already. She'd tried to sponge the blood away more than once, but knew now that blood was almost impossible to clean.

The curtains fluttered like bird wings as they fell in place and she stepped into the largest space in the two-room flat. Sunlight pooled on the floor of the dimly lit room. It was Saturday and she was tired. Ida slipped off her pumps and went to the sink. Maybe it was time to just get rid of the coat, she thought, filling a wash pan. But Daniel would want a say in that. Running a hand over her dress, she unsnapped one garter, then another, and unrolled her stockings. Words and phrases from the sidewalk two floors below filtered through a window. An afternoon rain had splattered the hose as she ran to catch a streetcar for home.

She submerged the hose in the wash pan. She wanted to hear from Daniel, but understood. He kept to himself even before he went off to join the Civilian Conservation Corps.

She scrubbed vigorously, but turned when she heard the soft-landing of a Christmas card blown from its place atop a bureau. It was the first thing Danny mailed her after arriving at the tree camp last winter. Two postcards, both blank, followed sometime in February, and the CCC checks, of course, that went straight to their savings account. The last one arrived in May, but there hadn't been anything since and somehow that didn't seem right. It wasn't just about the money, though that sure mattered. She just wanted to know what was happening with her brother. Soon as she finished with this washing, she'd get that Christmas card back up like it should be, she thought.

39

The stockings fell limp under jets of rinse water and she squeezed them tightly before setting them on a towel rack. She smiled, her mind wandering to the past, as it often did. Looks like old-fashioned toffee, she thought. She stepped away and slid into their only cushioned chair, weary. She needed to hear from her brother, because they needed to talk. About Mama's coat—that was one thing—and about finding another place here in Chicago, maybe, when he was finished with CCC, or maybe heading back home. They still had family in Beltram, didn't they? She wasn't so sure now. When they first came to the city—Ida, Daniel and Mama—she'd wanted more than anything to return, but that was twelve years ago. Now, well, they needed to talk.

She opened her eyes, then closed them, then opened them again, her gaze falling on their dish rack and one dinner plate, its damaged rim. A chip, small as a baby tooth, seemed to leap from the porcelain like a whisper in an empty room. It still conjured memories, how it had slipped from her hand, rolled near the chair she'd been standing on, and fallen against one chair leg. She'd been six, learning to wash dishes, but she'd never forgotten that clattering sound, the warmth of her mother's voice afterward. She'd never give up that plate.

But Mama was gone now. The driver of the Packard that ran her down never was caught. Ida was fourteen then. She and Danny had lived on their own for nearly two years after that. It wasn't great, but they were getting on okay. Why he just up and quit his job at the golf range still confused her. Maybe the CCC did pay better, she didn't know. But he was gone now and she was starting to worry about those checks. Her pay envelope was all she could count on, at least until they figured things out.

Ida heard the second-floor hallway door being pushed open. Mrs. McLaren, she thought. Once Mama had found her slumped, gray hair splayed against the hallway's chipped paint, and had to coax her back to her flat. They'd laughed about that, though it didn't seem funny now. Just memories, she thought. Memories and more memories. Sometimes the whole place seemed like nothing but memories. Or ghosts. Or maybe ghosts and memories were the same, like some folks said.

Ida folded her legs up beneath her and began reading a book on the armrest. *Man and the Nature of His Biological World* had taught her a lot about photosynthesis, which seemed like a sort of magic, but something in the hall made her turn with cat-like alertness. Old buildings, she thought. It's like the walls were always gossiping with the floors, so she returned to reading. She missed school. Missed Charlotte, missed Maxine, missed that neat little groove where her pens rested and the comforting feeling of an ink well, filled. Mama didn't want her to quit and neither did she, but when she found out about the department store job, Ida couldn't say no. Her job helped. No use thinking about that now.

She'd been reading for several minutes when she felt a quiver through the floor then heard a knock. A tradesman? Maybe, though the janitor usually met them outside. The quiet returned, and she returned to her book.

After several minutes another knock sounded, this one as careful as a metronome, and she peered forward and saw that the rim of light outlining the door jamb was gray and blurred. Ears peaked, she listened, and then, hearing nothing, rose. More taps, these more rhythmic. By the time she reached the door, her heart was racing.

"Ida."

It was a voice deep as a choir baritone and she struggled with its familiarity and strangeness. After several moments her name was called again, this time in a gentle, melodic tone, and she gripped the door's wood frame. Not until the third appellation did she understand.

"Idée," the man said. Images rose in her mind of a schoolyard near a pasture and the rushing sound of a merry-go-round too high for small children. "It's me," he said. Ida remained motionless. "I've been here a while." A slight laugh followed. "It's good to be careful." There was a pause. "But, it's me. It's Dad."

Plumbing clanged and a door opened somewhere in the building. Ida steadied herself.

They'd talked about this, she and Daniel, what they'd say when he returned. They had parsed together again and again overheard conversations and fragmented explanations for his absence. Those talks had been riddled with forgiveness or condemnation and sometimes both and ended usually with long spells of silence. Now Ida felt overpowered by everything she'd thought she'd forgotten. Cars, strangers, arguments in another room. Gone for a week, then away for a month. It all engulfed her now and she was frightened for a moment to unlatch the door and face the person on the other side. She wanted someone to tell her what to do but understood. Looking around, she felt the shadow of the apartment's emptiness.

41

"Please."

After a moment she said. "Why are you here?"

"We should talk, 'Idée," he said. "The two of us. I want to help, and—"

An uneven pacing of shoes sounded, and then she heard indiscernible voices. She wanted to retreat to her chair and book but a powerful countervailing force kept her where she stood. Ida gripped the knob and turned. Two faces, one narrow and slackened by age, the other pink with the glow of a recent shave, greeted her. Her eyes went immediately to the flushed face of the stranger. Florien Poulein answered by lowering his gaze in deference. Mr. Leonie, her landlord, stood beside him. "Uh, Miss. You got a problem here?" he asked.

Florien shifted from one foot to another, his shoe-soles sounding like waves meeting a beach.

"No, no problem," she said. "It's just—"

"You sure?" Mr. Leonie had never lost the accent of the Minnesota hometown he left decades earlier. Age had left him stooped and he stood about four inches shorter than Florien. His eyes moved slowly from Ida to the stranger. Ida looked too. A pale gray fedora's rim obscured eyes which were turned downward and he wore a dark suit. The knot of his tie had been loosened so one shirt button peeked above rows of stripes.

Sensing their gazes, Florien looked up and she saw an expression somewhere between a smile and a plea. It's him, she thought. It's him. Slowly she stepped aside and stayed quiet until she heard chair legs scraping linoleum as he sat. Mr. Leonie watched over her shoulder. "You ain't ever been a problem, Miss," he said, looking back to her, "but we gotta—"

She felt an odd sensation as her face broke into a smile. "Thank you, but he's a visitor. He won't stay long."

Her landlord seemed unconvinced. "See," Ida interjected. "I'll leave the door open." Gently, she pushed until the knob tapped the wall. "Like this."

Mr. Leonie looked skeptical, and then called to Florien. "I seen you 'round here," he said.

Ida turned, but he stared, expressionless.

"Don't say no," he said. "I know what I seen. On the street, couple of days past."

Ida looked from one man to the other, anxious. After a moment, she said, "He'll be gone in ten minutes."

Mr. Leonie's eyes remained fixed on the stranger. "Hear that? *Dix minutes. D'accord?*" he said, his voice rising before he turned and left. The uneven stomp of his prosthetic leg tapped the hallway floor.

With the door open, Ida walked to the table. "Well, you nearly got me evicted," she said. Florien's hat rested in the center.

"He watches out for things?" he said. Ida wasn't sure if it was a question.

"He was in the Ardennes," she said, sitting. "You want something? Water. Milk?"

Her father sighed. "Good man," he said. "A good man."

Ida's eyes scanned him quickly, but she was mainly surprised by herself. They—she and Daniel—had imagined this so many times. Embraces were always part of those fantasies, but she didn't feel like that now. Her throat seemed to be thickening and her voice riddled with an unfamiliar harshness. Where he'd been or why or even if the overheard whispers were true—none of that seemed to matter now. There was only one question she could muster. "Why are you here?" she asked again.

Florien nodded his head as if it carried an unseen weight, but avoided her eyes. He scanned the room, noticing the chair with the book. "You read?" he asked. Chatter from children outside sounded through the window. No answer today, Ida thought. Not this afternoon, maybe he'd never explain why he was away so long.

She replied in a solemn disappointed voice. "When I can," she said.

There was a table beneath the windows, near the day bed where she slept. Two other books were stacked there. "Got enough money for things like that?"

She shook her head. "From the lost and found. At work," she answered. "If no one claims them—" Florien met her eyes, nodded as if he understood, but she felt compelled to say more. "I'll give them back," she said, her gaze slipping towards the linoleum. She knew that was unlikely and maybe he did too. For a moment, she felt bashful.

"Well, you were smart," he said. "Both of you got brains."

"Daniel's smarter."

Florien stared, surprised by the challenging tone, then tried to amend what he'd said. "He was. A bright kid, and—" He stopped and looked at her. "You're eighteen now, almost?" he said.

"In December." The answer had a sharp edge that let him know she did not want to discuss birthdays or any other type of celebration.

43

Florien turned and surveyed the room again. The cushioned chair, a table and a bureau. One limp curtain. The nighttime partition that made it a two-bedroom space when Daniel was around, now knotted and pushed against the wall. Her bed was beneath the windows; a cot (Danny's) was folded upright and pushed to a corner. Florien's eyes went to the room's other door.

"Mama's room," Ida said. "Empty."

He stared, then said. "That was a terrible thing, being run down like that."

Ida didn't respond to the comment. Instead, she said, "Anyhow, you're the artist."

He began tapping the edge of his hat with one finger.

"You still paint?" she asked, but he answered by swaying his head side-to-side very slowly, a gesture she couldn't recall seeing before.

"People liked what you did," she said. "If you've got the talent, don't just stop." Streetcar bells from the turn-around down the street gave off a tinny sound, their chimes filling the silence that followed.

Then Ida stood suddenly, went to the bureau and returned with an envelope and set it on the table. She sat down. Her father looked up, befuddled.

"From the insurance company," she answered.

His expression didn't change.

"Mama's claim."

Florien's lower lip rose and his eyebrows clinched in a frown.

"Daniel and me, we didn't know about it either," she said. "Her company signed her up when she started working. That's our guess." Ida nodded to the documents. Slowly, Florien opened them and scanned their contents. "There was money for me and Danny." Ida paused. "And you. That's how she wanted it."

For a long moment Florien read, then he set the documents down. "No one knew where you were," she said.

Florien looked up and Ida understood she'd ventured into a forbidden area. "Or we didn't," she said. "You've been gone…" She stopped.

"Your mother—" he said.

Ida shook her head, understanding. "Uh—huh," she said, but their shared moment was broken by the sound of the hallway door. Slowly, an image formed in Ida's mind and she understood. Mrs. McLaren was returning now, and Ida realized it must have been her father who she'd heard outside her door earlier. She remembered Mr. Leonie's comments. How many times he had been here before, she thought, but she didn't ask that question. Instead, she said, "Why are you here?"

Florien looked over her shoulder. He'd heard the jangling of apartment keys too, then a door closing. He looked back at her.

"I had to see you 'Idée," he said. "You're my daughter and I need to know how things are with you. Now that Daniel's gone and...."

"You heard from Danny?" she asked. "Because there hasn't been a letter for me since—"

His face softened and for a moment Ida saw the ghost of the man who'd worn paint-splattered shirts and boots stained from the engines he repaired.

"Where is he?" she asked. The words sounded loud too loud now and Florien stood. "There hasn't been a check in three months."

"Danny won't be back," he said, his voice a whisper. He looked downward and Ida felt an urge to recoil, suspicious of gentleness and what it could mean.

"What," she said. "Why?" But her father was already headed to the door.

"Wait," she said," I need to know, because..." He was standing in the open doorway now, his face turned so she could see him in profile. "Danny and I, we've got things to decide and..." She saw the papers on the table. She grasped them.

"Here. This is yours," she said, thrusting the documents towards him.

"I can help, Idée," he said, voice still hushed. "I can. I know someone's got a business downtown. I can get you a good job so you can take care of yourself."

She felt a thousand angry cinders glowing inside.

"There are things you got to know, 'Idée," he said.

"Like what? Like disappearing? For years?"

He stood motionless as a fawn at twilight and Ida realized that nothing that mattered would be said that day. He paused, then turned, his suit jacket brushing the doorway's frame. "I'll come again."

She heard the words melding with the slow cadence of his shoes. She heard the hall-door groan as it opened, then a slam of certainty as it closed. Ida waited, closed her door, and tossed the documents on the table

She went to the window where she could watch him. A roadster was parked half a block away. From the sidewalk he stepped inside and she watched the car leave, passing the buildings that dotted the street so far from downtown. After a few blocks, the street's pavement faded into a dusty road rimmed with wide gardens and onion fields. This time of the year, if things were growing well, there was a haze over the fields that, when the sun angled just right, looked ghostly. She'd seen the same sort of thing when she was a child, in Beltram. Long time ago, she thought.

Ida returned to the chair. He'd be back, she thought, that much was true. Maybe she'd get an answer to her questions then. Or maybe not. Her book was laying where she left it and she picked it up. She was pretty sure he'd return, though, and that was about all she could expect from anyone now. That much was certain.

# Sand Daggers

by Mary Hickey

T*his too shall pass.* Miranda had repeated this mantra to herself for the
past hour as she dragged her tired body over one infernal sand dune after
another. Why had her sister Gena wanted to celebrate her fiftieth birthday with
this hike? A spa day would have been so much nicer.

While Gena raced forward as if the climb were nothing, Miranda stopped,
propping hands on her knees to catch her breath. Twenty feet till she'd crested
the Dune Climb, the three-hundred-foot sand dune that drew tourists to
western Michigan. The view Gena had promised better be worth it.

Wind blew sand in Miranda's mouth as she pushed forward once more. Up
and up the Sleeping Bear Dunes she went. Finally, she reached the top, and with
her thighs aching, she squinted at shimmering Lake Michigan. The blue lake
spanned the length of the horizon. She had to admit it was pretty amazing—
that is, if you liked miles of natural beauty and no human development. She
did not.

Miranda's deflated ego demanded more than incredible views. She patted
her vest pocket. Yes, the bottle was there. Knowing that brought her a smidge
of comfort and a heap of panic. Her perfect younger sister wouldn't approve of
her decision to self-medicate, but Miranda believed it was the most effective
way to handle her situation. Gena didn't need to know.

"This place is sacred." Gena held out her arms and raised sand clouds as she
twirled. "The dunes, the sky, the lakes. I love coming here. Best place to clear
your mind."

Clear her mind? Miranda would be happy if she could stop obsessing over
being newly unemployed. Of course, she hadn't told Gena that jerk of a boss
had recently let her go—over email, no less. She hadn't had the energy to leave
her apartment, but she couldn't turn down an invitation from her only sister.
When had Gena become an eco-nut?

Gena, outdoorsy and fit, wrapped an arm around Miranda's shoulder and
snapped a selfie. In contrast to Miranda's sweat-drenched body, Gena sported

47

a fresh, dry jersey and smelled of lavender. Miranda longed to bury her face in her sister's shoulder and sob. Butterflies erupted in her stomach. She ached to tell everything, but couldn't risk the look of disappointment on Gena's face.

Miranda tried to share in her sister's joy, but all she could focus on was her own need for a job. "Gena, is your friend still at the Illinois Tourism Board?"

Gena led the way along the sandy path. "She does social media—definitely not your thing. How's the new boss?"

Gena's casual comment crushed her. "We had an extremely short honeymoon period." Miranda's arms felt hot. She should've put on more sunscreen. Everything about the hike irritated her. Every nerve pricked. To change the subject, Miranda asked about the family.

"The kids love summer camp in the U.P.," Gena said, employing the vernacular everyone in Michigan uses for the state's upper peninsula. After further updates on her children, Gena launched into her current work quandary. "I'm breaking my own rule banning work talk, but I have a mess to unravel. It'll require sensitive handling."

"I see." She didn't, but Miranda didn't have breath enough to say more. Gena obsessed about work but never seemed to like it. Miranda had thoroughly enjoyed her dream job. She couldn't recall when she last visited her sister since she was too focused on trying to keep up.

Boy, she needed a drink. "Why are there no outdoor cafes serving classy cocktails up here? How do people revive for the walk back?"

"And ruin the beauty of unspoiled nature?" Gena asked. "The pain's worth the gain. Endorphins kicking in yet?"

Miranda huffed. "Endorphins are kicking my butt. My super power is taming troublesome tourists." *Was*. Damn. She should be spending the weekend searching job sites.

Traversing three more hills left Miranda's thighs quivering with exhaustion. So many unknowns out in nature. She tried to quiet her mind to the lurking dangers—quicksand and scratched corneas—but strayed instead to a hopeless job search and serious pay cut. Gripping the medicine bottle in her jacket pocket, she told herself to hold out just a little longer. Gena lived in suburban bliss, still happily married to Todd after twenty years, and subscribed to the conservative values of traditional everything. She definitely wouldn't approve of recreational cannabis.

Gena pointed towards the water. "You can just make out North Manitou Island. No running water or electricity. One of my children's favorite camping spots," she said, her voice cracking with emotion. "I'd love to take you."

"Camping, as in tents and backpacks?" Miranda ignored her sister's emotion. Parents got sensitive about the weirdest things.

"Spending time in nature is good for your brain." Gena shook her head. "You don't know what you're missing."

Miranda said, "Chiggers, ticks, and sand in my food." She gave the island another look. Travel brochures presented island destinations as havens of peace and relaxation. But the terrain couldn't be much different from what surrounded her. Blowing wind shaped clumps of dune grasses. Miranda imagined them as writhing bayonets poised to slice exposed flesh. Few trees dotted the landscape. Piles of sand didn't seem like anything special. She fanned her shirt tail to cool her body. "The shore looks undeveloped. My kingdom for a rooftop bar."

"Bite your tongue. All of this is National Lakeshore." Gena waved her arms in a Vanna White impression. "Thirty-five miles of pristine coastline."

Miranda peered out across Lake Michigan. Hues of innocent Caribbean-like blue hugged the shoreline. She scanned the sinister dark blue water further out for threats. Strangely, Gena seemed almost schmaltzy about the outdoors.

When they arrived at the shoreline, Gena removed her shoes. "We'll cool off in the water, then head back. You used to like days at the lake."

The icy water made Miranda flinch but she followed her sister's lead. After she scanned for broken glass and dead fish bits, she sidestepped a curved line of debris she feared would cut her tender feet. The breeze carried a faint scent of earthy algae, wet straw, and rotting driftwood.

The sisters walked on the beach and approached a lone woman who was crying. A large beach bag sat on the dry sand beside her.

Miranda asked, "Are you okay?"

Gena pulled on Miranda's arm. Miranda refused to notice her sister's quiet pleas. Gena had always disliked Miranda's outgoing nature with strangers, but she couldn't ignore the woman's obvious distress.

The woman stopped. She focused on the pair as if just noticing them. She must have thought she was alone on the beach. She answered, "This is what my sister wanted."

Miranda smiled. "*My* sister bought a cottage she loves the area so much."

"Miranda," Gena urged. "We have to go."

The woman stared out at the lake. "She loved this beach. We both loved this beach." She reached for her bag and hugged it to her chest. She seemed to be waiting for the sisters to leave.

After they walked on and glanced back, they saw the woman turn away from them. She stepped out into the lake.

Miranda glanced over her shoulder. "Do you think she's okay? Should we alert a ranger?"

Gena quickened her pace with her hand on Miranda's elbow. "She has an urn in her beach bag. Crying in public doesn't mean a person has to share their sorrow."

Miranda felt chastised. "No one wants to face hard times alone—"

"Holy crap," Gena interrupted. "I think she's dumping her sister's ashes into the lake."

"How sad." Miranda paused in thought, then smiled at Gena. "Just so I'm on record, being dumped in the lake will not be my final wish." Miranda's attempt to lighten the mood didn't work. Gena didn't laugh.

Standing in the shallows, Miranda saw the sandy bottom through the lake's clear water. Clumps of algae that looked like prehistoric deep-sea creatures floated out of reach. Her throbbing feet recoiled at the frigid waves, so she scooted out of the water. "Sorry, I've been such a city slicker. You're right. I used to love coming to the beach."

Gena rolled up her pant legs. "Remember our camping trips to Starved Rock? Back then, staying in cabins was roughing it." She strolled in ankle-deep water.

"We hiked all day and swam in the river. We played hours of beach volleyball and sang Beatles songs around a bonfire. That was over thirty years ago. Why'd we stop those trips?" Miranda asked.

"You're afraid of seaweed." Gena scoffed. "And bugs. And strange night sounds."

"Okay, okay," Miranda said. "But I like your cottage. Maybe I just prefer a real bed and indoor plumbing. I do admit, fresh air is nice."

A couple walked by, hand in hand, carrying their shoes and splashing in the shallow surf and Miranda's heart squeezed for a moment.

Unlike her sister who married her high school sweetheart, Miranda had had a string of partners on and off over the years. Lately, she'd been off the dating scene. Though she enjoyed her independence, she sometimes wondered what she had missed. "What a happy couple," she said.

The couple laughed as the woman reached down, cupped water from the lake, and sprayed the man. He tried to dodge the spritz, and then splashed her back.

Gena turned her gaze away from the couple and wiped her eyes, her shoulders sagging, then sat as she dried her feet with her bandana and put her sneakers back on. "That used to be me." She lowered her chin.

Uh, oh. This didn't sound good. Miranda tilted her head, silently encouraging Gena to continue, but not sure she was ready to hear an explanation.

Gena stared at the couple continuing their stroll along the lake. "I think Todd's cheating on me."

Miranda's eyebrows shot up. "Todd's having an affair?"

"I'm too afraid to confront him." She pressed her hands against her thighs and stood. "What if I'm right?"

Miranda reconsidered her sister's odd behavior in light of her revelation. The pain in Gena's voice brought tears to her eyes. "I had no idea." When had her job become more important than her sister?

"My worst nightmare. I haven't been sleeping." She rubbed her forehead. "I sent the kids to camp to give me and Todd time to work this out. But I've been too scared to confirm my suspicions." After shaking sand out of the bandana, she held it out.

Miranda accepted the red paisley scarf, but stuffed it in her pocket without thinking. "Todd doesn't seem the type."

"Are you blaming me?" Gena huffed and headed for the trailhead.

"No. Wait." Miranda called after Gena. Ignoring her sand-covered toes, Miranda yanked on her socks and shoes. When she took a step, grains of sand stabbed the bottoms of her feet. "Wait for me." Plopping down on the sand, she removed her shoes, shook out her socks, brushed her feet and between her toes. Damn. She wanted to hug her sister. Gena had been her anchor—married, two kids, stable job. Those choices were Gena's definition of having it all figured out. Todd was in for a world of hurt. She jogged to join Gena. "Talk to me."

51

"I'll need wine if you want the sordid details." Gena ran a hand through her hair.

"There's a bottle of Pinot Grigio chilling in the fridge."

Gena choked on a laugh. "I can't focus at work." She sniffled. "He told me he was courting new donors, but I caught him out in a lie—with the new board member."

"Maybe it's just a misunderstanding."

"I watched him go into a hotel with his arm around her." Gena snapped. "I opposed adding her to the board—we have a history."

"Who is this evil woman?" Miranda cackled and rubbed her hands together. "I can get her fitted for concrete shoes."

Gena smirked. "I don't care about her. Well I do hate her, but she's not my concern. I made my vows with Todd. But his cheating isn't the whole story. The situation is a trainwreck. The other woman's son, Kyle, is likely to be approved for our biggest grant. I'm afraid to say anything, but his grant application is bogus—smoke and mirrors. Fake, like his mom."

"Aren't you on the board?" Miranda asked. "Can't you vote no?"

"Are you really interested?"

"Yes. Of course." But more, she was worried. She wanted to keep Gena talking.

"Todd invited Kyle to apply for a start-up grant. Twenty-five thousand dollars. As foundation president, Todd can approve Kyle's application himself. I have to find a valid reason to stop the process. I've never opposed Todd—not once since I joined his family's foundation."

"That seems like a lot of money," Miranda said. "Can you delay any action until you think of a way out?"

"I need to address it, but I don't have the bandwidth to worry about it. Right now, I have to face facts. My husband's having an affair." Her raised voice drew stares from a group passing on the beach.

Blowing grit pricked her arms. Miranda turned her back to the wind, but she couldn't tame her thoughts. Her only brother-in-law was a cheater. Miranda hadn't ever trusted a man enough to commit to a relationship, but her sister had. "Is there some way I can help?"

"You already have. I knew you'd try to make me laugh. I wasn't sure I'd survive in my own head. I needed a weekend away from the mess my two-timing husband has made. I couldn't keep pretending that I didn't know. Telling you has lifted a huge weight off my shoulders." Gena squeezed Miranda's arm. "Let's enjoy the park." She pointed to a parking lot at the bottom of the hill. "Racing down the dune is the best part. Ready?"

While hot air whipped at her face, Miranda trotted a safe distance behind her sister. Sand flew as she raised each foot. Handfuls of sand collected in her shoes and acted as weights. Her arms flailed as she gained speed. Adrenaline pumped as she kept her attention on Gena who floated down the dune. Miranda mentally chided herself for missing all the signs. No wonder Gena insisted only the two of them celebrate her milestone birthday.

Without warning, Miranda tripped over her feet. She face-planted with her arms spread-eagle and her vest bunched around her shoulders. She spat out small grains of sand.

Gena picked up the bottle that fell from Miranda's pocket, then offered a hand. "Are you okay?" She brushed dust from Miranda's shoulders and guided her to the base of the hill.

Miranda stopped on level ground to catch her breath. She shook her shirt and removed her cap. "Yes, but I've forgotten how to do somersaults."

Gena held up a clear plastic bottle. "Why do you have gummy bears?"

Miranda let out a cry. "I've been so stressed. The uncertainty over the last few weeks was starting to make my hair fall out."

"Let's sit down." Gena indicated a bench at the edge of the parking lot. "Wait, these are cannabis edibles?" She laughed. "When did you become a hippie?"

Miranda tucked the bottle back in her pocket. "According to my barista, gummies knock you out without destroying your kidneys or giving you a hangover."

"You're taking drugs to zone out? Does your therapist approve? I understand taking cannabis for physical pain, but—" Gena said.

"I haven't actually tried a gummy yet." Miranda faced her sister. "I no longer have a job. My position was eliminated last week."

"Oh, no. That stupid jerk." Gena's eyebrows shot up. "Of course. Now, your weird question about the Illinois job makes sense." She ran a hand through her hair.

"They called it 'reorganization,'" Miranda said.

"Doggone it," Gena said. "After they passed you over for director."

Miranda choked. "I feel so rejected. It's my fault," she said. "I should have left after they hired someone else."

"Maybe the universe is telling you it's time for a change."

"Oh, good gravy, you know I don't believe in crystals and chakras," Miranda said. "I'm looking for wise words from my award-winning business guru."

Gena raised her chin. "What did Grandma always say? 'This too shall pass.'"

"Did she?" Miranda asked. "I thought my therapist was brilliant for suggesting that mantra, but you're right. Grandma Pat was a walking proverb machine."

As they talked, Miranda realized she and Gena could help each other. It could be a chance to rebuild their relationship.

"The park is a great place to heal," Gena said. "And you are more than a job title."

Miranda looped her arm with Gena's and smiled at her. "This morning, I thought the most important thing in my life was getting another job, but you know what? It's you. Todd's an idiot. During my break from work, I'd like to spend more time with you."

"Ditto," Gena said. "I know a lot of tourism people in Michigan. We'll update your resume. Have you working in no time. All for the small price of listening to me curse my cheating husband."

The anxiety that had clenched Miranda's body ever since the office shake-up began to dissipate. She felt a wave of calm come over her body and soul. She pulled the gummies out of her pocket. Tossing the medicine bottle into a nearby trash can, she said, "What's next?"

# Brining

by Michelle L. Thoma-Culver

What Estelle found in her mother's serviceable yellow-brick bungalow was more alarming than what she had anticipated. She expected to find her mother dead or near death. For the past two days, her mother hadn't called or answered the phone when Estelle called her. Her mother rarely went four hours without calling. Despite her eighty years, she still seemed to have several life-times' more of grievances stowed in her ever-shrinking frame, folded in some oragamic fashion, ready to be unfurled whenever Estelle answered her call. Estelle knew she should have come sooner, or called the police for a wellness check, but a break from the griping was more welcome than she cared to admit.

Her mother was alive, though. Different, but alive. She had been inexplicably transformed into a dill pickle—a garlicky, cucumber-green, hefty specimen that looked homemade, not the flaccid, unnaturally radioactive green of the store-bought pickles of Estelle's youth. Her mother was propped up against her pillow, unable to move much except to squirm a bit. This wasn't a cartoon; she hadn't magically sprouted little pickle arms and legs with which she could ambulate, and shake a little white-gloved pickle-fist at the injustice of it all. Her breath was quicker than it should have been, given her immobility. The garlic-tinged staccato wisps of air in and out of her mother's lungs sounded like over-tightened harp strings. Estelle felt queasy at the sound of her mother's breathing, the unreality of it all.

"H-how did this happen, Mom?" she coughed out, as if the words were a small swarm of flies fighting to fly down her throat, away from their certain death in her mother's ears.

"How da hell do I know? You know waht?! Sometimes you so stupit!" For once her mother's Polish-accented voice—blunt like a roughly-hewn club made to beat middling animals to death—fit her face. Her wide eyes, crisp nose and full lips were the same as they had always been, but her seemingly eternal allure was now tempered by the bodeful green of her bumpy cucumber peel skin.

"It's just…you have to admit that this is…odd. I don't understand. I…I'm just trying to figure out what happened."

"Oh yeah! You going to figure it out! You going to figure out shit! You know det? You tink you so smart. You stupit!"

Estelle had soldiered the battlefield of her mother's insults her entire life. When she was younger she fired back with the nerve that youth imbues, but she now sees that her mother's early, ceaseless blitzes were a bootcamp for what her life would become. Her mother started the process of wearing her down, and the world took it from there. The last twenty years had been a further slow burn of unfulfilled promise—undiscovered love, a dwindling congregation of friends she didn't particularly like (and who, she suspected, felt equally unenthusiastic about her), and a job that would soon be better done by a computer. And through it all, her mother's onslaughts continued, like a discordant soundtrack for the slow-motion horror movie her life had become. Estelle no longer had the mental or emotional ammunition to go forward boldly.

*If this could happen, what else is possible?*

An iciness runs through her at this thought. She shivers uncontrollably.

"So…so you just woke up this way?"

"Waht do you tink?! Why you esk such goddem dumb questions?"

"Because I don't understand, mom. I mean…this is…is a real—" She wants to say "pickle" but does not. She begins to laugh but stops too late. Her mother glares at her.

"Maybe we should go to the hospital."

"Waht da hell are dey going to do?! Nutting! Except take my money! You tink money grows on trees!"

"I'm worried about you, Mom. I don't know how to help you."

"I don't want you help! I don't want anyone's help."

Estelle looks at her mother for several minutes. Her mother won't look back at her, instead fixating angrily on a spot on the wall just beyond Estelle's left shoulder. Estelle wonders how many hours of her life she has spent gazing at her mother, aching for her to look back.

"Are you hungry, Mom?"

"No."

"Thirsty?"

"Noo-o!" She sounds like she is trying not to cry now. Her voice twinges upward on the "o," ending in an almost imperceptible crack that, like a crack in a dam, signals the flow is about to begin.

"Are you cold?"

"I'm not cold!"

"What do you want me to do? How can I help you?"

"Why don't you listen to me?! You cen't!"

As much as Estelle hates to admit it, she knows her mother is right.

"Well, I'd like to. I wish there was something I could do to help you." Estelle is surprised by how deeply she means this. *It's true. It's always been true.*

"You wish! You wish! You wish, my ass!"

Tears are flowing down her tiny but elongated, green face. Or is it brine?

"When was the last time you ate? I think you will feel better if you eat something. Let me make you something to eat. Do you have a taste for anything?"

"Yeah! I have a taste for someting!"

"What do you want?"

"Bullshit! Det's waht!" The mother's voice cuts like a machete through the canvas of the scene she and her daughter make together, what would be a low-lit still life in the softening sunlight of the fading day, except for Estelle's humanness.

Estelle thinks of picking her mother up and cradling her tiny new body like a baby, the baby she isn't sure she wants but knows she has to have soon if there is any chance of having that baby at all. But she knows that touching her never-affectionate mother at this moment, especially tenderly as—for once— Estelle desires to do, would be the worst thing she *could* do. Her mother is most combative when she is most vulnerable. But it is all she can think of to do.

Then, suddenly Estelle wants to wail like a starving baby. She wants to further brine her mother in her tears, wondering if it might not create some osmotic understanding between them, a liquid bridge to each other, the connection that they have never had.

But she doesn't touch her mother tenderly, or cry over her. She thinks, *I want my mother*, a thought that is not unknown to her, but a thought that has always been more like something impossible she wishes for, like the power to fly.

57

"Stop looking at me like det!"

"How am I looking at you, Mom?"

"Like det! Like det!" She tries to scrunch up her new little pickle brow as if it is a dark cloud trying to kill a sunny day, but she doesn't have the facial musculature that she had as a human woman.

"I'm sorry, Mom." And she is sorry that her mother is now a pickle. But she is most sorry for herself. She wonders how this will impact her:

Is this a hereditary condition? How much time will I have to take off of work to deal with this? How will I explain this to people? Will I have to move back in here?

The thought of living with her mother again, even if she is forevermore a pickle that can be picked up and put in the refrigerator at-will (*It's for your own good, Mom. You don't want to rot, do you?*) reminds her of the recurring nightmares she has been having over the last several years, since the end of her last serious relationship. In the dream, her mother is her mother (not a pickled cucumber), but Estelle still lives in that bungalow, and is older than she is now. There is a gravity from which she can't break free, that acts on her heart more powerfully than the rest of her body. It causes her to feel gloopy. It's the only way she can describe how she feels in, and just outside of, those nightmares, like her soul is partially melted, overly viscous and spilling from within her in heavy tides she is caught in, and being dragged under.

"Waht are you going to do?"

"What do you mean, Mom?"

"Waht do you mean waht do I mean? Waht are you going to do now, goddemit!"

It was a good question, a question for which Estelle had no answer, and no idea how to begin to find the answer.

*What do you do when your mother turns into a pickle?*

"Do you remember piccalilli, Mom?"

"Yeah."

"I don't see it in stores anymore. I wonder what happened to it."

"Waht? You going to make me into pickle lilly? Det's you bright idea?"

Estelle laughs.

"No, Mom."

"Why you talk about it, den?"

"I don't know. I don't know what to say. Or do."

"Maybe don't say anyting, den."

"Maybe I shouldn't."

Estelle thinks of picking her mother up and biting her head off.

*Maybe she would be better off...maybe it's the humane thing to do. This is no life for her, is it? It would be done in a moment, before she would know it. Over. Or would it? Maybe she would live on, in my stomach. Screaming from inside me.*

Estelle laughs again.

"Waht's so funny?"

"I don't know, Mom. Everything...nothing."

"You tink dis is funny?"

"I told you I don't know. I don't know what to make of any of this. I mean... what do you think it is?"

"It's just life."

The bald elegance of her mother's statement hits Estelle like a sudden spring shower on a sunny day. And in her oft-screaming, little, helpless, green mother, Estelle sees herself—scared, sad, wondering what has happened to her, how it all went wrong despite her best intentions.

*How long until my bitterness turns me into a vegetable, too?*

Estelle begins to cry, realizing that she isn't going to have that baby.

"Waht you crying about? I da one who's stuck like dis. You don't see me crying, do you?"

"No, Mom. I don't see you crying. You are one tough cookie. You always have been. Certainly tougher than me."

"Det's right. I da tough cookie. You da baby."

Estelle sees a prideful smile momentarily arise upon, and then subside from, her mother's tiny face. Despite it all, her mother has not given up. This tickles Estelle, in her heart, and she laughs gratefully. She sees that she already has that baby, not how other women have babies but how goddesses have monster-babies that in myths are unleashed upon the world as new things with which all humanity must forevermore contend. Though her mother didn't yet have arms with which to throw lightning bolts, the ability to turn anyone to stone with a glance, or a box of ills to unleash, who could say how she would evolve?

Her mother, in her monstrousness, has given Estelle a gift. Estelle could be such a goddess, and her mother could be her monster-baby for whom she would be forever responsible, because the world doesn't need another monster. And in this way, the world would need Estelle.

"Are you hungry, Mom?"

"Yeh."

"What do you want?"

"A hamburger."

"Yeah?"

"Yeh."

"Okay. Then a hamburger you shall have."

Estelle makes her mother a very small hamburger with extra onions, so small that she has to cut the onions up into tiny bits using a razor blade. She puts a half of a drop of mustard on the hamburger and lovingly feeds it to her mother on the end of a pointed knife, marveling that she is watching a pickle eat a hamburger, excited about what will come after the deep, deep sleep she is sure they will both relish tonight.

# Permanent Choice

## by Roberta Albom Liebler

Arnold was already perched on a creaking folding chair in the windowless basement of the East Village storefront Ever Lasting Hope Church when Rebecca arrived with her customary banana bread. Each year more loaves for the constant increase of mourners. Each year more difficult to leave her son, Jacob, with yet another sitter.

Every month, Arnold and Rebecca welcomed a different faith community leader to speak to the bereaved supporters of the Lower Manhattan Gay Support Group. Years ago, they had organized the services to find volunteers for their studies on the impact of AIDS deaths on families. Even after their research had expanded, they continued to attend to remind themselves their work impacted real people, not faceless subjects.

The rituals were predictable and comforting and brief. A loved one (often a lover, sometimes a mother) said the deceased's name while tears stained an embraced photo, followed by a heartfelt nondenominational prayer, and concluding with a song of hope.

After they offered solace to the families of the fallen, Rebecca followed Arnold across the street to the dissolute pocket park where three empty children's swings squeaked and swayed in the autumn chill. He could barely contain himself, as he waited until Rebecca, his associate director, gloved, hatted, scarfed, and fully buttoned, finally sat down beside him.

He spoke even more slowly than his usual thoughtful pace, as if he was analyzing each word, phrase, and nuance before it left his lips. With a broadening grin, he announced, "Kandros Foundation is offering us a wonderful professional opportunity." He paused until she responded with a quick smile. "Multi-year full funding for an entirely new project—easily renewable."

Just like Arnold to begin with a vague big picture. But having worked with him for years, Rebecca knew that interrupting him was a bad idea, even though her future hung in the balance. His well-organized explanation would scrabble into fragments that could only be recovered with well-sequenced questions.

She would have liked to join spontaneously in the happiness of her loyal boss, but experience had taught her to wait for the key points to emerge.

She leaned back on the one remaining wooden slat of the lone bench.

As she anticipated, Arnold proceeded at his predetermined pace. "The Foundation is interested in supporting community-generated solutions to public health problems. They mentioned how your research on adolescent runaways newly diagnosed with HIV/AIDS has influenced their priorities. They're interested in you developing cross-cultural protocols to help adolescents devastated by HIV/AIDS."

"Great!" Rebecca was beaming. After years of fragmented studies based on funders' fickle priorities, this was an opportunity to develop a cogent strategy.

The energy of their excitement bounced back and forth through their smiles. Rebecca thought of how her research would benefit many. With dependable funding, she could confidently make plans for her son's future.

Then she allowed herself the rare indulgence of imagining how her life could become better for herself. Maybe presenting at conferences. Long discussions with the six other people in the world who shared the same interests. Even now, in towering hotels, international conferences were being held. Relationships can happen at conferences. Having drinks in the hotel bar with people interested in discussing conference presentations. A long conversation with an unattached man about the finer points of an obscure topic that only they found fascinating. Until the dimly lit restaurant closed and they astonished themselves by spending the night together.

"Jay and his board chair selected communities that have a cultural coherency in health-problem decision making," Arnold added.

Rebecca's thoughts wandered: no cultural coherency in New York City. Maybe they're looking for us to move to Great Neck or Poughkeepsie, so I don't have to totally disrupt Jacob's life. It had taken years for him to get comfortable at his school, but maybe an excellent suburban public school offering before- and after-school activities would be better for him. How wonderful it would be to totally focus during work hours when his needs were watched over by committed educators.

"Rebecca, just think of the opportunities."

She wasn't convinced she'd ever loosen up enough for a man, a man she desired, to take a chance with her. Would Jacob ever have a good friend? Would she be willing to step out of the lukewarm bath of obligation into the unpredictable weather of self-reliance? Had clinging to each other prevented each of them from facing their solo challenges?

Arnold's increasing volume drew her back to the abandoned park. "The Foundation decided to pull out of local funding—too many advocacy groups fighting among themselves."

"The end of funding for our current work?"

"They did a worldwide search for communities with high HIV/AIDS rates and finally made a decision." He offered a congratulatory smile.

Washington, DC? Baltimore? Maybe even Miami? Jacob was finally doing well in school, she thought. He won't want to move, but she might finagle a change to a similar city with top-notch services for him and the ability for her to reach him quickly when trouble arose. Because trouble would arise.

Arnold rapidly tapped Rebecca's knee. "I'll be executive director. You lead researcher." He stopped abruptly.

Both of their emotions were climbing. Was he building up to a crashing cymbals climax?

"Career advancement for both of us," Arnold said, almost breathless. "Opportunity to be on the forefront of internationally significant research."

"International? I'd love to travel." She tried to hide her joy clashing with panic. From the increasing concern on Arnold's face, she hadn't hidden it well. Rebecca forced her lips into a smile, while her internal voice tensed: international? Please let it be Canada. No stupid, never Canada. Research is needed in countries with high AIDS rates—unstable countries. Success will receive acclaim, satisfaction. A true contribution to public health. But at what cost to a struggling boy?

Unable to contain his excitement any further, Arnold approached the crescendo: "South Africa."

"South Africa!" Of course, South Africa, with its high AIDS rate, self-contained isolated cultures, and world-class health facilities near health-deprived areas. The perfect setting for ethnographic studies and supervised clinical investigations. Suddenly an Arctic blast smacked her. She wrapped her tweed coat around her polyester pants. Were winters in South Africa less severe?

"We will investigate how homogeneous traditional African, English, and Afrikaner communities respond to the AIDS epidemic." His freezing cheeks turned rosy in his excitement. "In subsequent years, we'll research adjacent countries. This is a fantastic opportunity."

She could reconnect with the South African AIDS orphans she'd studied years ago, who were now adults, probably still caring for younger siblings. She could transform numbered participants into real people. Develop strategies for AIDS-orphaned girls to sustain themselves and their families other than with sex work, so they wouldn't threaten themselves with the disease that killed their parents. Establish herself as a respected scientist. Socialize among esteemed scientists.

"Arnold, would I be able to focus on AIDS orphans?" she caught his perplexed face. The interruption flustered him. He must have practiced this presentation.

"Ah, well, it depends…I'll send you the grant…maybe you can find a way."

Rebecca felt guilty having knowingly placed a roadblock in front of his volcanic joy. He was so pleased with his vision of their future. She admonished herself. Don't disrupt his supportive, generous flow. She suppressed a gasp, or at least she hoped her shock wasn't audible, but having worked closely together for years, she knew his next words would be an encouragement.

"Yeah, probably."

While she waited for Arnold to realign, the wind crashed the abandoned swings together, snapping her deeper into the conundrum: How could a child still uncomfortable in the school that had harbored him since pre-K survive in a new country? How could a good mother prefer focusing on anonymous orphans instead of her own son? There must be a way to bring Jacob into this picture.

Recovering from the interruption, Arnold returned to his agenda. "When we're not doing field studies, we'll work in fully-equipped facilities. Live in comfortable apartments in Johannesburg. The initial funding is for two years with almost automatic renewal." He glowed, "After a few years, you'll be in a strong position to write your career ticket."

Arnold's trying too hard. He's trying to make the offer so attractive that Jacob would be only a secondary consideration. A blossoming career for the mother; a terminal fade for the son?

"Together we can achieve so much." He puffed out his chest further. "At a new location, Jacob would make new friends. A happy son, an active mom."

If only.

"You tell me what you need to accept the position," Arnold proceeded in his problem-solving voice, "nanny, a driver, housecleaning, full tuition for one of the best schools for your son."

Jacob wouldn't last long in one of the best schools, even if he were accepted. If the kids didn't tease him for talking funny or not being competent in South African boy activities, they'd soon catch on that he's weird—smart one day, raging with uncontrollable outbursts the next, snitching on anyone who he perceives as threatening him. He'd panic when his mom couldn't drop every-thing when the school couldn't manage him. She'd be called in from a distant field base to peel him off a clinic wall followed by weeks of handheld recovery. She'd be faced with the impossible choice: either support her son, thereby fatally disrupting essential research, or continue with career-accelerating research to benefit AIDS-threatened orphans, thereby causing lifelong damage to her child. Trauma to son or trauma to research? Work/mothering balance? Impossible.

Arnold continued as if his speech was prerecorded. "We will have the resources and access to conduct one of the major public health programs of our generation. We can discover the answer to the problem that has stymied medicine forever: how to stop the spread of diseases when the vectors are pleasurable?"

Perfect, two abstinent scientists seeking a solution to: How the drive to avoid death is subsumed by raging libido? Vegans studying butchering. The blind studying color theory. No one could accuse them of experiential bias. She suppressed an ironic chuckle by focusing on his intensely committed voice.

Arnold added, "Really good schools in Johannesburg."

Maybe he thinks I've convinced myself that I'm Jacob's only savior, while in reality, in a new school, he could create a confident and affable persona. Would an independent Jacob flourish or fail? Is my success totally dependent on his flourishing or failing?

Arnold was waving his arms so rapidly that he momentarily shielded her from the quickening wind. "Rebecca, believe me, you will never get another offer this good. Plus, I know this is what you want. The potential depth of our joint achievements—momentous."

Arnold put a fatherly arm around her quivering shoulders. "Come with me to where the HIV pandemic is most severe. Our scholarly papers will be accepted in the most prestigious journals. Rebecca, your research will improve the lives of people with AIDS and their children. You'll finally be able to transform your brilliant dissertation research into action."

Rebecca felt her dear friend's embrace tighten as he exhaled deeply.

Arnold's voice became a plea. "On holiday, you'll take Jacob on wildlife safaris and anthropological digs."

Focusing on the swaying swings, Rebecca recalled how Jacob always hated swings, and slides, and monkey bars. She wondered how he was doing with the new sitter?

Just then, two coatless boys, slightly younger than Jacob, leaped off their rusty bikes, jabbed at each other, and jumped on the cold, wet swings. The metallic wheezing intensified as they pumped higher and higher. When the groaning chains catapulted them to the zenith, the boys launched themselves, landed on the cinder and broken glass pavement, punched each other in triumph, and left.

"If I had a son like that, I would be jumping on your offer of a lifetime."

Arnold cringed. "Rebecca, I should have chosen a better place for us to talk."

Rebecca shivered, "No, this is the right place." Pulling her hood up over her knit hat, she began: "Last Tuesday, we had an afternoon strategy meeting with Thomas House."

"A very successful meeting," Arnold responded. "Your facilitation skills are extraordinary. Another reason I need you in South Africa."

Rebecca leaned her head on Arnold's narrow shoulder. "What you didn't know was that was also the day Jacob's poster of protozoa mitosis was due."

A frigid wind blew over the frozen East River. She wrapped her scarf tighter, providing time to recall the evening before the incident. The contents of Jacob's backpack were placed in the correct order, zipped, and clipped. In preparation for his presentation, his poster board masterpiece was rolled into a fresh black garbage bag with an emergency finder card taped on the outside. The midpoint of the poster and the base of his backpack were aligned so the poster would lie equidistant, thereby avoiding stress bending when attached to straps. Finally, all the objects he required for the morning were placed in the hallway.

"In the morning we left on time. He headed north and me south," she told Arnold.

Rebecca paused. Arnold scooted closer. She shared what she couldn't tell anyone else, "Do you remember the phone call I received that caused me to leave Tuesday morning?"

Arnold nodded. His eyes followed a wind-blown *Village Voice*, reminding her that under the new situation, she needed to withdraw the community notice inviting teenagers recently diagnosed with AIDS to participate in experiential interviews. Monday she would cancel all future studies. Better to write up the completed research before funding ended.

With eye contact resumed, she continued, "At 9:05 a.m., two New York City police officers responded to a call that a child—my child—was lying across the sidewalk screaming. They blocked the sidewalk when they couldn't get Jacob to calm down. The same police who are trained to placate drug dealers, psychotics, and victims of violent crimes." She watched as Arnold attempted to transform his face from shock to concern. "An officer found Jacob's backpack in the muddy gutter under a truck wheel. Luckily when the FedEx truck left a few minutes later, the emergency card was found. The card that I included so he wouldn't worry that the poster would be stolen—not to identify my frenzied child." She hesitated, but now that the sealed vacuum bag of sequestered thoughts was pierced, the explosive need for disclosure was overwhelming.

"The police called his school—a university lab therapeutic school—which sent out the head psychiatrist. When after 20 minutes the child psychiatrist was unable to get Jacob to cooperate, the District Police Chief called me. He apologized about not being able to keep the sidewalk closed as the lunch hour approached." Despite the cold, Arnold was listening intently. "You remember I ran out of the office to catch a cab."

Arnold cupped her hands in his. She closed her eyes and envisioned herself encased in Arnold's sheltered wings as they flew to South Africa. Days later, a smiling Jacob, dressed in a uniform of knee pants and striped tie, would wave goodbye to his mother, and pop onto a school bus where he would be greeted by friendly boys. She would be off to spend an intense day in a shiny new lab.

A mangy dog approached. Arnold fingered his ever-present briefcase. Rebecca balanced her backpack on her shoulder. The dog tried to catch the eye of the only people in the park, failed, and left. They both knew abandoned Avenue A at nightfall was not a safe place to have a long conversation, but neither moved. Too much more needed to be said.

"Only after the psychiatrist and I promised to help redo the creased poster did Jacob finally walk to school with a dedicated adult on each side." Rebecca straightened her back.

Arnold listened patiently, but his face was losing the last flush of exhilaration.

"That afternoon, as scheduled, during sixth period, with the psychiatrist and me in attendance, Jacob eloquently delivered a 10-minute presentation on the difference between mitosis and meiosis in one-cell organisms and implications for humans. He earned an A." For a moment, she felt the warm smile of triumph she had shared with Jacob across the classroom. "Remember when I returned to the office with Jacob? He helped us collate papers."

"We had a good meeting with Thomas House at 4:00," Arnold's said with forced eagerness. "Rebecca, opportunities like this come once in a lifetime."

She watched a heavily bundled old woman shuffling slowly as she leaned on her cane. The traffic light changed to red before she completed crossing the street. Horns honked impatiently, but the man driving the car closest to the pleading face put on the brakes and offered his smile. Like a kindergartener confused by the role of a crossing guard, the old woman stopped, stared with bewilderment at her benefactor, then hesitantly completed her trek to the sidewalk.

Rebecca wondered how it was when the old woman sat alone at her kitchen table. Will she be yearning for a call from a distant son or feeling pride for a long-ago professional achievement? Does she regret the choice she made years ago? Will I?

"Rebecca, imagine Jacob at the best boarding school in Johannesburg while you're doing intense field studies in the African bush. The work you proposed in your dissertation. You and Jacob would be giving each other the gift of room to grow."

She looked deeply into Arnold's sweet face. In South Africa, the two of them, and even Jacob, could each come into their own. Maybe. Could she risk the misery of her son for the near certainty of alleviating the suffering of so many desperate children?

A gale force wind ripped the last branch off the solitary tree. The branch missed them by inches as it crashed into a swing, breaking the splintered seat into two.

In the distance, church bells chimed out of tune.

# Abbéat's Touch

by Llewella Forgie

I was standing on an uninhabited island where a duel would soon take place. Greenery, damp earth and wildflowers created a lush bouquet. It was early, so the sky above was light, but the ground was still in shadow. So far, only four of us had arrived.

My father was conversing with another man, but neither paid attention to me. I took a step away from Father and closer to Mister Dávun Jonjess, a young physician. As our fathers continued talking to each other, my favorite man also inched away from them.

Physicians helped people overcome their illnesses—my love was as valuable as a chestnut tree. Those trees not only provided food, but their wood was beautiful and rot-resistant. Perfect for bridges, boats, dams and anything else that needed to be solid and reliable.

Our fathers kept talking, so we each moved away from them. My chestnut tree—I wanted so badly to call him "Dávun," but if I spoke that name aloud it would damage my reputation—wore his unadorned blue coat, the color of a gentian flower, and a waistcoat embroidered with birds. He always looked so captivating. I suppressed the blush and grin which always sprouted whenever the young physician was near me. We had spoken to each other at dinner parties, card parties and such, many times. Danced together often. Private conversations when not dancing had, of course, been rare. Still, every time someone said something that would annoy or amuse him, I would glance his way. He would be looking at me, his expression just as I expected.

"I am leaving tomorrow," he said, for my ears only. I wanted to touch his light brown hair, but it was hidden by his tricorn hat.

"Leaving!" I whispered, "Where are you going?"

He patted my glove. I looked down, blushing even as another warmth spread through me. Unconsciously, I had clutched one of his hands with both of mine, as if I could stop him from leaving. I opened my mind. Dávun's energies spun—surely because he was leaving. I caressed them, similarly to stroking a dog—except with my mind.

Back when I first became old enough for lessons, I was inducted into the secret Sixth Sense Society. I was tested. They determined that I was an *Alfr*—someone who could help others become calm and focused. They trained me. As I caressed Dávun's energies, they settled until they moved like the water of a placid lake. His strong hand in mine was reassuring, but I forced myself to release it. I clasped my hands demurely.

"General Bernjoss has hired me to be the physician at Fort Wenjess in Sathá."

"Fort physician? But forts only have surgeons." Sathá was a faraway port city.

"The general wants an officer to supervise the surgeons and to treat any diseases. You know I have studied surgery, too. To have enough authority so others will not interfere with my work, I will be a colonel—a reliable, well-re-munerated position." He leaned close. His bellflower blue eyes were beautiful. "Elope with me."

My mouth dropped open.

"Elope?" Eloping was a scandalous act, usually involving scoundrels. While our elopement would be soon forgotten, my objection to it was that we should not have to do it. My chestnut tree was the opposite of a scoundrel. Mother had praised her parents' choice because Father was handsome, generous and prudent. My love was all those things, too. If Mother were alive, she would agree. Father was reasonable about most things—he should give his consent. But I was only seventeen—quite young to marry. I had not even tried to discuss my choice with Father.

Had anyone noticed how closely we stood? Father's back was to me as he and my chestnut tree's father talked with a few men in tricorn hats—new arrivals. Nobody was looking our way.

"I leave tomorrow," my love said quietly. "If you wait for your father's permission, we may be separated for months."

"Tomorrow!" I ordered my hands to grip each other—not his arm.

"Ever since I received the appointment a few days ago," he said, "Father has insisted I see every patient, gone over my supplies with me, and then taken me on good-bye visits to all of *his* friends. I could not call on you. He suggested that I not come today, but I had to see you." Everyone knew that women as wealthy as I did not marry men who needed to work—even well-bred men who worked as physicians. His father probably had no more notion than mine that my love and I hoped to marry.

"But what will we do?" I whispered.

"Here comes a vulture!" He loved birds, particularly the colorful species like the bluethroat and the citril finch, so we called all men who pursued me "vultures" because their goal was my too-generous inheritance.

Several others had arrived, and one man was heading our way. Our tête-à-tête needed to end before someone wondered whether my chestnut tree was up to something, such as trying to convince me to elope with him. He bowed and I curtsied, and then he stepped away.

Black-haired Rójeran approached me—one of the duelers, so a sword hung from his belt. We were on a first-name basis because our fathers were so close that Rójeran and I grew up like family. Everyone assumed we would marry. When Father looked at Rójeran, he saw a smart, wealthy and educated young man who was almost like a son to him.

But long ago, Rójeran bragged to me about cheating in school. Later, he spoke of using marked cards against his friends. More recently, he had crowed about bilking his companions. He was a tree I had read about that grew in the New World, with sap that brought blisters to a person's skin. Manchineel trees' sap could be fatal. Rójeran was such a miscreant, I could almost believe that an embrace from him would leave me blistered. Was Rójeran his father's get?

"My dear Abbéat," Rójeran said, doffing his cap and bowing his head, "It is good to see you." He was twenty-eight years old—the age a man's family decided he should marry. My love was much younger.

"Rójeran," I said, curtsying too shallowly.

"Never fear," the Manchineel tree said, "I will be victorious."

I nodded—the outcome meant nothing to me. Weeks ago, another of the vultures, Mister Anéjoss, had accused Rójeran of cheating at cards. Rójeran then claimed that Mister Anéjoss had cheated. But neither man was worthy of the air he breathed. Mister Anéjoss probably fantasized that the duel would dishonor Rójeran, thus removing him as a rival for my hand. But, of course, I would never marry either worthless man.

"Rójeran!" someone called.

"I will be back," he said, with a bow to me.

"Do as you wish," I said. He was as blind to my lack of encouragement as Father was to Rójeran's character.

My chestnut tree was speaking with someone else. Father was still facing away from me. As my only family, he did much to take care of me. Ever since I came out a year ago, he no longer attended his club, nor took in boxing matches, nor went shooting. In order to protect me, he sacrificed his enjoyment of activities in which I could not participate. Meanwhile, I looked after the servants and organized social gatherings. He depended upon me. I could not elope.

But what would my life be like if I awoke every morning, knowing there was no possibility of seeing Dávun? There would be no reason to rise from my bed. If we were not engaged, I would not even have the hope of a letter. Would I waste away from heartache before Father gave his consent? My throat ached. My eyes tried to tear. I dropped my gaze and looked at the English ivy around my boots. I struggled to breathe deeply, with only marginal success. I needed an Alfr to help me, because we could not soothe our own energies.

Men talked and drank beer from bottles—what kind of secret, illegal duel was this? A dueler always asked a friend to be his "second." There should have been the two combatants, the two seconds, one physician and just a few witnesses—a handful of people. Father had come to support his friend. I was there because Father kept me nearby. But there were at least two dozen men, if not more.

Probably they were all useless men leading frivolous lives who had wagers on the result. Too like the so-called "tree of heaven"—those trees matured quickly, depriving other plants of sunlight, but worse, those horrible trees poisoned the ground around them so other species could not grow.

Before any fighting took place, the two seconds were supposed to attempt to negotiate a settlement. The duelers would check their weapons and prepare themselves. If no agreement was reached, the duel would be to first blood. In a sword fight, someone would be scratched—bringing first blood and ending the duel—almost as soon as it had begun. Where were the seconds?

Father turned and I smiled.

"Dear, there you are!" Father said. Five years ago, I possessed a respectable dowry until a fire devastated our home. Only a handful of us survived—Father, myself and a few servants. Mother, my brothers and sisters, gone forever. The loss of my siblings meant that I would inherit everything that belonged to Father, as well as Mother's entire dowry. My inheritance was large enough to tempt an unscrupulous man to kidnap me and force me to marry him—the reason Father stayed nearby.

"Yes, Father."

"The duel will begin soon," Father said. "You should say a few words of support for Rójeran, and give him your handkerchief." He began moving toward Rójeran.

"Neither dueler is honorable," I said, walking alongside him. "I do not care who wins."

"Abbéat, how can you say such a thing?"

"Because it is true. Both duelers are profligate spenders, gamblers and cheats. Look at their friends—drinking and carrying on early in the morning."

"They will mature," Father said. "Give them time."

"Your friend is a good man—but his son is not."

"Enough, Abbéat! Such ill humor does not become you," Father said. "I am disappointed. Very, very disappointed."

Once again, he refused to listen. It was *Father's* fault I could not marry Dávun. It was *his* fault my love and I would spend months, if not years, apart. Father was the cause of my problems.

I would not let him ruin my life—and my chestnut tree's life. I would elope. Whether Father disinherited me or not, at least I would be with Dávun.

But my love would depart the *next* day. There was no time to create a clever plan. It was no use! I could not elope.

"Wish me luck!" Rójeran said, putting his hand on my arm. His energy was so churned up, I could sense its restlessness without trying.

Wait—in order to elude Father, I needed chaos. Instead of calming Rójeran's volatile energy, I irritated it until it was akin to tree branches during a thunderstorm.

"May you always be rewarded commensurate with your merits," I said.

Father looked down and gave a tiny shake of his head, as if he knew his words had not changed my attitude.

"You will make me proud, son," Rójeran's father said, clapping him on the back.

How could I sow more chaos before the duel began? I took a step, pretended to stumble, and caught myself on Rójeran's father. I misused my sixth sense again, until his energy swirled like snow during a blizzard.

But my heart pounded. What had I done? Misusing my training as an Alfr was forbidden. The Sixth Sense Society was secret because very, very few people in the world had special abilities. Those without might fear us, declare us witches, and then burn us. I had been taught to make people's lives better—not do things one might believe a practitioner of black magic might do!

And to what purpose? Dávun stood across the clearing, talking with his father. Supposing the situation became chaotic, how would he know to escape with me?

"When is this going to start?" Rójeran's second asked. He tipped his beer bottle over, showing that it was empty.

"I was wondering that myself," Father said.

I took a step as the men talked. Then another. I stood close to Rójeran's second.

"There is something on your coat," I said to him as I brushed at his sleeve. I whipped up his energy, too. Using my sixth sense against the rules was having its own consequences—I was tarnishing myself. I needed to stop doing it—but I also needed a distraction so that I could elope.

"Are you ready to admit your failings?" a man hollered. It was Mister Anéjoss, over on the other side of the clearing.

"You lying, cheating son of a whore," Rójeran yelled, "I hope your pastor has written your eulogy!" He stormed towards his opponent, his second keeping pace with him.

"*You* are the swindler!" Mister Anéjoss said. "You and your associates!"

Rójeran's second slugged Mister Anéjoss. I gasped. Rójeran punched one of Mister Anéjoss's friends.

Other men charged forward, their boots pounding against the dirt. Thwacks. Grunts. Someone's hat rolled on the ground. Chaos!

"Gentlemen!" Father yelled, "This is not appropriate—"

Nobody listened. Rójeran's father rushed in. Father followed. I needed to leave. Where was—? My love was watching the fight!

I tried to recreate the call of a citril finch. He turned my way, a frown on his face. I gestured with my head towards the trees between the open land where the brawl was and the riverbank. His eyes widened and a smile spread across his face. He began walking.

I did not wait—I walked, too. If anyone saw us together, they might try to interfere. No, they *would* interfere. I increased my speed and was soon amongst the trees.

Twigs snapped nearby. In fear I sucked in air, then it whooshed out—it was Dávun, making his way through the trees from a slightly different direction.

"If we leave now," I said, "Pushing all the other boats into the river, they will not be able to catch up to us."

"You will elope?" His eyes wide.

"Yes, but we do not have much time."

We hurried down to the river. So many boats! We began shoving them into the water.

Shouts! But we had not escaped!

As we pushed one of the last boats, the rustle of leaves and the snap of twigs announced someone's approach.

"Abbéat, what are you doing?" Father demanded. His face was red.

"Eloping with Dávun," I stated the obvious. I strode to one of the remaining boats.

Dávun hustled to me and offered me a hand.

"Abbéat," Father said, "Stop this foolishness!" He was hurrying down the riverbank.

"Foolishness?" I turned to face Father. "*You* are the one who thinks cheating Rójeran is a paragon!"

Dávun stationed himself between Father and me. I put a hand on Dávun's shoulder and stepped into the boat.

"Stand aside!" Father said.

"Only if she—" Dávun said.

"Do not try to stop me, Father," I said.

"What is going on here?" Rójeran bellowed from up by the trees. "Move away from my fiancée!" He was hatless and without a coat, his hair disarrayed, and a line of blood slid down his cheek. He rushed down the bank.

"Climb into the boat!" I said to Dávun.

"Walk away from her!" Mister Anéjoss yelled, racing after Rójeran, also disheveled and bloody.

"What are you doing with her?" Rójeran challenged. He threw a punch at Dávun, who ducked and stepped back.

"Stop this!" Father commanded.

Dávun stood, fists up, ready to defend himself.

"Rójeran," I said, "I will never marry you. Leave Dávun alone."

"Then marry me!" Mister Anéjoss cried.

"She was promised to *me*," Rójeran claimed, shoving Mister Anéjoss.

"Stop this right now!" Father demanded.

"I will *never* marry either of you," I said.

Dávun shoved the boat into the river. I fell onto the rear seat—better than becoming submerged. Dávun waded after the boat, but Rójeran and Mister Anéjoss both jumped him and all three went down, thrashing in the icy water.

The current tugged at the boat, so I picked up an oar and worked to bring the boat closer to the riverbank. Dávun freed himself and lunged for my boat. The small craft rolled crazily, almost capsizing. I leaned far to the other side, barely managing to keep us from overturning. The boat drifted into the current. He was more in than out, so I focused on counterbalancing him. His hat floated away.

"But you were promised to me!" Rójeran screamed, standing in the water.

Mister Anéjoss tackled Rójeran, and they crashed into the river.

"Father," I said, gesturing at the two fighters, "Look at them. Selfish. Unprincipled. Undisciplined."

He looked towards them.

"Dávun is upstanding," I said. "Reliable. But he is leaving for Sathá. Come with us!"

"Sathá!" Father said, looking at me again.

"He is a colonel, but he leaves tomorrow—so we must marry today. Come with us!"

"Come," Dávun's father said. Where had he come from? I hadn't seen him come down the riverbank. He must have arrived after the others, but had somehow managed to commandeer one of the drifting boats. He held a hand out to Father, whose attention shifted between me and the soaking miscreants.

"What?" Rójeran's father cried out when Father took the extended hand, "You are going to support this?"

"Look at your son—gambling, fighting," Father said. "I had hoped he would mature, but I will not pressure Abbéat to marry him." He climbed into the boat with Dávun's father.

Father spoke against Rójeran! He climbed into the boat!

I turned to Dávun, who had made it fully into the boat. We would be together, and our fathers supported us.

# FICTION

TIMES OF TENSION

# Diamond Shine

by Tara Maher

Medora perched on a satin bench in front of a mirror, debating the mood for her face. She fingered a smokey palette of eyeshadows, choosing. There would never again be a day quite like today in her marriage. She picked through a dozen cylindrical tubes, rolling out each lipstick to survey the varied reds: Ruby, Bubblegum, Dusty Rose, Froly, Coral and Scarlet. Not certain yet which tube would best suit after she'd slipped on a dress and stepped into the stilettos that Hugh found irresistible, she set both Froly and Scarlet aside. Then she turned back to the mirror, her attention captured by how the morning sun bounced off the glass, dispersing jags of light that glittered like diamonds onto the soft gray walls of their master suite.

Medora took her time applying makeup. She rarely hurried now that she'd tipped into her forties. The frenzy of youth—landing a job, a partner, and filling up a home with offspring—were all past goals, with two of the three achieved. After too many sad drives home from the fertility clinic, she'd struck children from the list.

From a velvet pouch, Medora fished out a platinum necklace Hugh had gifted her a decade ago on their tenth anniversary. She hooked the choker around her throat, imagining Hugh behind her, dark eyes narrowed in appreciation of her swan-long neck. Over the years, Hugh had possessed many exquisite collectibles, like gemmed cufflinks, custom guitars, cigars from Castro's personal stash, auction-won Masters golf clubs, ivory chess sets and more. But whatever his current obsession, Hugh cooed that she remained his favorite treasure and showered her with extravagance.

Unlike other women, Medora didn't shame her own image in the mirror's reflection. She simply observed the gentle sag of her breasts, and the waist widened with age. Then she was off to rustle through dresser drawers. Today's event, dreamt up late last night when the moon had highlighted her husband's vacant side of the bed, required special preparation.

Hugh's top drawer was in its usual uproar. Whatever Hugh touched, he left stirred. He affected people too, especially women. When Hugh entered a room, the atmosphere changed. Maybe his silver-fox looks brought the blushes that pinked other women's cheeks. Or perhaps his stormy effect came from how he sauntered into a room, ambling on long legs at a pace that spoke confidence. People remembered Hugh long after he vanished, often leaving charged hearts in his wake.

Medora sifted through piles of photographs that Hugh coveted––shots of himself with a variety of busty younger women from the years before Medora. Love letters, creased with age, marked by lipstick smears from the cast-aside, lived next to his black boxer briefs. At the back of the drawer, tucked in a forgotten corner, Medora found what she needed.

She took out the napkin served long ago on a now-defunct airline, with "Dinner in Paris?" scrawled in Hugh's hand and a pair of her silver crew wings. She placed both on top of the dresser.

Medora tugged an all-occasion black dress from its hanger. She slipped on silk lingerie and stepped into the three-quarter sleeve sheath. While she worked the garment's zipper to a close, she wiggled her feet into well-fitted stilettos. Her plan included plenty of walking, and she knew from her sky days that comfortable heels paid off.

Medora trotted up a narrow staircase to the third floor. Once a week, along with the rest of the house, Medora swiped a feather broom over the built-in shelves that housed her books on travel. She raced the ostrich sweeper over other treasures, too, taking care to dust her favorite paintings that waited for a day in the spotlight. Mostly oils and watercolors of faraway oceans leaned against walls, scenes she'd chosen while searching for tranquility. Her themed collection of cuckoos and bird-shaped timekeepers, purchased while traveling with Hugh, also rested along the room's perimeter, championed and displayed until Hugh banished the clocks from view, citing their lack of taste.

In an attic wing out of sight, blue and white patio cushions and her other favored items yearned for their season in the sun. In a heap, Medora spied her long-saved Rollaboard suitcase that Hugh badgered her to drag to the curb on garbage day. Though pushed to toss her bag, she'd rescued it with logic, pointing out that two decades without abuse kept the durable siding shiny and unmarred. She'd only been a fledgling flight attendant when Hugh had plucked her from the skies, grounding her with a heavy diamond.

Medora wrapped her fingers around the suitcase handle and clipped back down the staircase. The Rollaboard thumped along, happy to be back in motion. She laid the bag onto the master suite's rug and worked the zipper until the two halves spread wide like butterfly wings, ready for flight.

Remembering her sky days, and how she'd packed smart for assigned trips, Medora began gathering essentials like swimwear, running shoes, a smattering of jewelry and a versatile dress.

In the canvas box marked "summer," Medora found the navy bikini she liked best. But instead of tossing the swimsuit into the suitcase, she set it on Hugh's side of the bed. She added a few other items she'd need later, like sunglasses and the tube of Froly. Within minutes, the bed housed her folded cashmere, an umbrella, workout gear, and other necessities like her passport and a thick wad of cash.

Medora didn't waste time choosing between pairs of rare cufflinks. Hugh owned dozens because he valued variety. When she opened up the custom wall safe, she didn't dwell over which pearl-handled handgun he preferred. She grabbed both and carried them to the suitcase along with boxes of cufflinks.

Her stomach growled. She checked her watch—nearly ten—but Medora didn't slow her pace. She could go hungry but eventually would need to fuel with caffeine. As soon as she'd gathered the "best of," she'd brew the coffee that started each morning, even bad ones, like yesterday.

Twenty-four hours prior, she'd gripped a cup of dark roast and stared out at a cold rain, the truth of her marriage uncovered. Hugh's disregard for the heart-healthy snack she'd prepared for his flight to New York had been in character. As was her chase after him when he'd rushed to his electric auto, leaving the snack without thought. Thunder cracked when Medora shouted at Hugh, trying to catch his attention. But only another lightning strike answered her calls. She'd stood in a downpour, alone and unheard, while his car rolled out of their drive.

Medora might have dashed indoors, damp and defeated, to clean and dream of Hugh's return. But her husband didn't zip off as usual. His car crept up the block at the pace of a slug. Medora guessed he'd noticed her and waved an arm. But Hugh's car didn't reverse. Instead, it snaked up a neighbor's drive, two houses down and across the street.

Medora closed her eyes to wish away the inevitable. But when she raised her lids, their recently divorced, leggy neighbor raced out into the storm. Had Medora not stared, she might have missed the travel bag slung over the woman's shoulder or how Hugh's hand pushed the passenger door wide. If lightning hadn't flashed in the next moment, she wouldn't have witnessed the intertwinement that drove her destiny. But with the storm's illumination, Medora caught their kiss like a punch to the gut.

Medora let the bite from the memory fade. She had work to do. In Hugh's second-story shrine-office, she lifted a signed Super Bowl football from its brass stand. At charity events, Hugh loved to brag about the day the ball had been brought to the private box where he'd lounged and snacked on caviar with Medora seated by his side. When Hugh ogled the young wife of the quarterback who'd handed off the ball, he hadn't noted his own trophy wife looking on.

The football sailed across the room and landed in the suitcase on top of the firearms. Medora grinned, pleased by her powerful arm and the lack of explosion. Then she gripped the neck of his favorite custom-made guitar. Though Hugh had several built over the years, the replica George Harrison model alone had been his bitch when he strummed. Since she couldn't shove the guitar in the suitcase, she slung the instrument across the room in the general direction of the bag. The Strat met the floor with a twang.

Next, she pulled a dozen framed and signed vinyl record albums from the wall. They were inches too wide to stow in the bag, but with a mess of broken glass from her efforts, they fit inside the suitcase. Before she skipped from Hugh's office, Medora eyed his retro Fender Vibroverb collector amplifiers. They were too heavy to lug down the steps in heeled shoes.

Medora recalled the golden rule she'd learned twenty years ago when she'd been in flight attendant school.

Push, never pull.

With both hands, she shoved the two amplifiers over to the hallway window that hovered above the bluestone front steps.

With a hard push, the sash shimmied upwards, glad to release winter's stagnant air. Medora crouched low and tucked her palms under the bottom of the first amp. She carefully checked for the mailman who delivered on weekdays at eleven. With the mail truck only halfway up the block, and the sanitation engineer not due until two, the coast was clear. The first amp landed on the ground with a satisfactory thud. Its sister amp didn't disappoint and cracked up like the first on impact.

In a fit of glee, Medora glided from room to room and picked through Hugh's beloved. There were many souvenirs, but only certain ones he would miss. She rambled around the second story and admired collected artifacts from various global escapades. While rummaging through a closet that housed a Redford Cigar Humidor and candles to set the mood for nights when they perched on their balcony, Medora found the Castro stash. She removed the Cubans, but rather than saw them in half with Hugh's Gentac Limited Edition Knife or use them as scented kindling for a fire—though the idea delighted—she tossed them into the suitcase. Satisfied with the contents, Medora zipped up the bag and tugged it down to the first floor.

On the rare occasions that Hugh wasn't away for business, they'd sit shoulder-to-shoulder in the living room on a cognac-colored couch and dream about paradise destinations. To honor their shared love of travel, she chose this spot to stage and sort the collectibles. But before Medora shook the treasures from the suitcase onto the couch, she covered the cushions with Hugh's favorite blanket from his university days. It wouldn't do to stain the leather if things got messy.

Medora found the linen tablecloths from last summer's tented backyard Junior League luncheon. From the bar, she removed a bottle of Old Rip Van Winkle 10-Year Bourbon and a Roederer Cristal Champagne, both saved for special occasions. She flung the bottles simultaneously at the couch to see which traveled faster when airborne. Neither bottle won first prize. Both landed on the pile of treasures, and miraculously, neither broke into shards.

After downing two cups of coffee, the garage was next on her agenda.

Medora stood for a beat with her face tilted in adoration towards the sky, appreciating the warmth of the late April sun. Then she pushed the code into a keypad, and all three garage doors raised up in unison. She surveyed Hugh's beloved outdoor gear, picking out the best, but first, she needed the props.

Push, never pull.

Abiding by her safety rule, Medora pushed two heavy tables purchased for outdoor entertaining to the end of the driveway. She gathered the goods from the cognac-colored couch in the blanket and dragged it outdoors. She tooled Hugh's wheelbarrow back and forth multiple times, whisking the treasure to the curb, always using good form. Hard work paid off. In less than thirty minutes, she'd cleaned out the garage of valuables and, for an extra bit of fun, added sugar to the fuel tanks of both the lawnmower and snowblower.

By eleven forty-five, she'd erected both tables and dressed them in skirts. Their surfaces overflowed with rarities, but that didn't deter Medora. She borrowed Hugh's blanket to display larger items on the ground—golf clubs, a pro-bowling ball, an assortment of drills and saws, and the custom bike painted in a girl color that Hugh rode for fitness. Next to the table, Medora arranged a cooler to chill the Cristal Champagne and hide the pair of handguns. Now she only needed signage for the event to begin.

Back inside, Medora danced up the flight of stairs to the second story. She scooped the sunglasses from the bed, slid them onto her face, and stowed the tube of Froly in her purse. From the dresser top, she snatched the scrawled airline-logoed napkin and crew wings, pocketed the napkin, and pinned the wings to her chest.

Inside a hallway closet, Medora foraged through a forgotten picnic basket loaded with airline-logoed dishware borrowed long ago from a Paris-bound flight and fished out a single glass. Next, she dug through her acrylics and a stack of canvases. She chose a sturdy brush and a tube of sky-blue paint.

Medora relaxed in an Adirondack chair, admiring the canvas she'd tacked to a tree that bloomed on a prominent corner.

## ESTATE SALE – FREE!

She popped the cork of the Cristal and poured herself a glass. Though she'd never smoked, the idea of a cigar was irresistible. Medora fired up a Cuban when the first customer pulled up in a pickup truck.

"You got good stuff."

Medora nodded and took a swig of champagne. The bubbles floated over her tongue and down her throat, bringing a warmth that competed with the beating sun.

"How much for the guitar?"

"My husband found everything here priceless," she said. "I can't charge. Take two of anything you like."

By the time the pickup man popped the cost question, four other lurkers had arrived.

Medora sipped the champagne, enjoying the crowd through dark glasses. Every few minutes, she'd repeat "take two" like she did on Halloween when doling out candy to herds of eager-eyed youths. Muscled men with construction hats and maids in marked cars made up the bulk of her customers as the hours passed.

Only one neighbor walking a Terrier paused.

"Hugh's gone now—" Medora said, bringing a hand to her face. "So sudden."

"I'm sorry," the woman replied while flipping through a stack of collector vinyl albums. When the dog-lady trotted off, she carried The Beatles White Album—signed—and a rare John Coltrane.

By one forty-five, the tables were nearly empty, as was the bottle of Cristal. Medora knew that every party ended. She could toss the rest of the goods in the trash. Then a Harley flew down the road and roared to a stop.

"I think you're the man I need." Medora wagged a finger at the biker to come close. "My husband—" she kicked the lid from the cooler and pointed inside, "left those behind."

The biker let out a low whistle.

"Maybe you'd have a use?" To Medora's surprise, when the biker leaned in to lift the pearl handle pistols, he smelled like fresh pine, reminding her that not everything was what it seemed.

Ten minutes later, Medora had stripped the tables and rolled the linens, readying them for a future woman to wash. She'd taken down the sign and pushed the broken amps to the curb. Rather than return the tables to the garage, she left them on the grass. Maybe the divorcee who lived two houses down and across the street could come by when she had her children and conduct a lemonade stand.

Before she returned to her house, the vehicle she'd been waiting on rumbled up.

"Roy!" Medora breezed over to a man who'd rung her bell on Fridays when she'd forgotten to drag the trash bins curbside. "Are you still dating the girl from Christmastime?" The chore of tipping workers weighed on Medora since she mostly spent her holidays alone. Each year, she chatted while handing out hundreds: Roy was in love, their gardener had nine children, and the mailman survived cancer.

"Yes, Ma'am," Roy said. His jade eyes shined.

Push, never pull.

Medora pushed her diamond ring over her knuckle and tucked it into Roy's hand. "You might need this?" she asked, feeling a burn of excitement. Roy's face mirrored her own jubilation when, six weeks after she'd met Hugh, he'd surprised her with the ring.

As Roy pocketed the diamond, a lone cloud blotted out the sun. Medora studied the finger she'd relieved of Hugh's ring, noting the lack of sparkle. She shivered in the shade, with no coat to protect her from an unexpected wind gust and the weight of her choices. But by the time Roy lugged the broken amps, trash bins and ring to his truck, the sun and her resolve had returned.

Medora didn't mind the light turbulence that rocked the plane on its descent. She rested in an exit row, with her legs stretched long. The jet's silver wing shimmered in the sunlight, reflecting rays through an oval window and onto her ring finger like a sun jewel. Below, the destination city's skyline became visible under the wash of light. Soon she'd picnic at the foot of the Eiffel Tower on a blanket with a simple meal of wine and cheese like she'd intended twenty years ago before Hugh whisked her away from her layover plan and into a five-star life.

Medora watched a flight attendant push a garbage cart down the aisle.

"Trash? Anything to toss?" the young woman asked. Her name bar read: HOPE.

"Garbage?" Hope asked Medora.

Medora pulled the crumpled napkin from her dress pocket and dropped it into the bin. "That's the last of what I don't need," she said, smiling up at Hope. Medora took out the tube of Froly, rolled the paste over her lips, and turned back towards the window, ready for play and the seemingly endless blue-sky day.

# Milk

by Polly Hansen

Aggie shook the carton again, as if shaking it would make more milk magically appear. Outside, the rain was turning to snow and chips of ice tapped against the windowpane. Her son Danny tugged on her dressing gown, demanding Cheerios in the insistent, petulant manner of a three-year-old. Aggie looked down at him, dreading his protest if she suggested toast instead.

Damn her husband, Rick. How could he be so selfish? She pictured him at the breakfast table blithely crunching away while they slept, and then slipping out the door before sunrise to head downtown to the radio station. They had agreed he wouldn't wake her and the kids on these early morning shifts where he was the engineer for the morning drive show. Aggie imagined calling the station, pretending to be a call-in guest, and then cussing Rick out on the air. But it was her own damn fault, forgetting to buy milk when she had the car yesterday. Still, she wished Rick would have noticed there wasn't a new carton in the fridge, that he would have left what was remaining for the kids.

Her daughter, Celia, 20 months, happily beat her spoon against the highchair tray. At least someone was content. But how long would that last? Aggie placed her hand firmly on Danny's back, guiding him to the kitchen table. She placed a plastic bowl in front of him, shook cereal into it and dribbled the last of the milk over the little brown o's.

"More milk!" Danny demanded, slapping his pudgy hand on the table. He caught the edge of the light-weight bowl, sending cereal flying into the air and onto the floor.

"Goddammit, Daniel!" Aggie yanked Danny's chair away from the table. "You are going to pick up every little piece, young man!" The corners of Celia's lips drew downwards; her forehead dimpled. Aggie covered her ears against the high-pitched wail. Dear God, not one of those days again, please!

Yesterday when it was Aggie's turn with the car, she'd left the shopping cart half-filled in the cereal aisle, Celia shrieking under her arm and Danny dragging on the floor behind her all because she wouldn't let him put a box of Count

Chocula in the cart. Out in the parking lot, Aggie had sat in the car while both kids screamed, praying for them to shut up, praying some kind woman would knock on her window and ask, *Are you okay?* To which Aggie would reply, *no, I am not okay.* But no one came.

Aggie lifted Celia out of the highchair, wiping flecks of milk off her tear-stained cheeks. Danny stared up at her from under the table with round, yearning eyes. Aggie patted her thigh. Once her kids were balanced on her lap, she said, "How about we go on an adventure?" Danny's face brightened. "We could bundle up and take the stroller to the pharmacy for milk!" His frown returned. Aggie rushed on. "And maybe we can look at Beanie Babies." She regretted this as soon as she said it.

"Yay! Beanie Babies!" Danny squirmed off her lap and climbed onto the window bench, placing two small palms on the windowpane, his hands instantly clouding the glass. Thick clots of snow swirled through the air in a frenzy.

Rick had made Aggie cut up the credit cards, saying it'd be easier to stay within budget that way. If they didn't have money for something, they'd go without it. But milk? "You should always have your own money stashed away," her mother had said when Aggie explained how they managed their finances. Her mom had rolled her eyes. "Oh honey, you think he doesn't have his own stash hidden somewhere?"

Aggie bristled at the idea, believing that's why her parents' marriage had ended in divorce. They didn't trust one another; that was their problem. Aggie wanted to show her mom what a trusting relationship looked like. "We don't hide things from one another," she had said.

Aggie switched on the radio and got the tail end of the news. "…President Clinton attended a prayer breakfast this morning…" Traffic and weather was next. She pictured Rick in the engineer booth, and Monica, the gorgeous morning show producer who always wore scoop-neck tops that showed off her cleavage, leaning over his shoulder and laughing with those big white teeth. Sixteen inches of snow predicted by midnight. Blizzard-like conditions. Aggie glanced out the window. A manic vortex of snow reeled down from a steel gray sky though barely an inch covered the ground. Sweet Jesus, they needed milk.

Aggie checked her wallet. A five, three singles, and some change. She could buy a quart and have enough for at least one Beanie Baby. After plonking her children down in front of the television, she checked underneath the sofa cushions and found a quarter and a few pennies. She tried the junk drawer in the kitchen. Nothing. She checked all the coats in the front hall closet, then went upstairs.

Rick emptied his pockets at night and swiped change off the dresser in the morning. Maybe he'd missed a few coins, or maybe he'd dropped a few in the faux leather box that sat on top of his dresser. The partitioned tray inside held a few tie clips Rick never wore, a handful of AA sobriety tokens, and an old battery-operated Star Trek pin that made a burbling squawk, but no coins. Hopeful and anticipating being angry at the same time, her mother's admonishment floating back to her, she lifted the tray, but found only receipts for past Christmas gifts in neat stacks. But underneath the pile of receipts was a small silver key she'd never seen before. She held it up, miffed that Rick might lock anything without her knowledge, and surveyed the bedroom, the cut sharp against her fingertips. Muffled television sounds and Danny and Celia's whines traveled through the air vent. She needed to be quick.

Aggie opened the bedroom closet. Her clothes were crammed in tight on the left, blouses and sweatshirts mixed together. Rick's side was tidy and uniform, the shirts all facing the same direction. The top shelf was a jumble of shoe boxes and photo albums. On the floor, plastic bins were stacked under Rick's hanging clothes.

She pried off the lid of the top bin filled with her shorts and sleeveless blouses and longed for days when she could wear them again. Would they still fit? She pinched a layer of tummy fat between her thumb and forefinger and let go in disgust. The second bin contained old tax returns and insurance files.

She worried the sharp key edge against her thumb and was about to close the third bin of Rick's neatly packed and folded T-shirts when she noticed the stack at the back of the bin was taller than the one in front. Curious, she reached under the shirts and was shocked to touch a cold, hard surface towards the back. Aggie tossed the T-shirts to the floor and lifted out a black metal box with a slender silver handle on top.

Hot with anger and heart pounding with excitement, she fit the key into the lock and lifted the lid. Inside was her missing souvenir tea towel from their trip to the Indiana Dunes last summer. What the hell? She'd been looking all over for it and had asked Rick repeatedly if he'd seen it.

It was wrapped around a videocassette. That sonofabitch. She'd seen ones like this before. After Danny was born, she'd made Rick get rid of his stash of porn, dozens of cassettes hand labeled with names like "Pussy Willow" and "Peaches and Cream." He'd done so reluctantly, complaining that Danny was just a baby, but she'd insisted. This one had no label. Why her tea towel? That meant the videotape was relatively new.

Boiling inside, Aggie flung the videocassette away from her in disgust. He said he'd gotten rid of them. She rose on stiff knees, ripped off her bathrobe and dressed in a fury.

She thought back to last summer camping at the Indiana Dunes. Rick had left them for one day, driving back to Chicago for some stupid radiothon he said he couldn't get out of. And then he'd returned the following day morose and irritable. She'd been hoping they would silently make love in the dark of the tent while the children slept. But the whole rest of the week he barely spoke to her and snapped at the kids. She'd tried to ease him out of his bad mood, thinking he resented his job. But now she wondered, was it her and the kids he resented? She wanted to go downstairs, slip the videotape into the player to see what was on it. But the kids were getting louder. She'd have to wait until nap-time. Leaving the bedroom, she kicked Rick's T-shirts across the floor.

Aggie stuffed Danny and Celia into their snowsuits, snapping at them to quit fussing and hold still! Shoved on their boots, fastened their hats and gloves. By the time they were dressed she was sweating. Danny was so bundled up he looked like a tiny punching bag. Horrified by the urges she felt, Aggie bent on one knee and wrapped her arms tight around his solid little body, the musty canvas of his hood filling her nostrils. She kissed his soft, pudgy cheek and wiped away the sheen of tears left there.

The instant she opened the door slivers of ice hit her eyes. Goddamn Rick for leaving them without a car. Aggie maneuvered the double stroller down the two steps to the walkway of their small bungalow. She picked up Danny and put him in the back of the stroller, then nestled Celia between his legs. She tucked a blanket around them then draped a poncho and another blanket over the hood of the stroller. Peeking in at them as the wind whistled around her, she asked, "How you doing under there? You two warm enough?" Danny nodded and grinned. Her daughter bobbed. Aggie lowered the poncho and blanket and tucked them into the sides of the stroller. She pulled her fake-fur-lined hood far forward, muffled her nose and mouth with her scarf, pushed down on the stroller handle to lift the wheels and headed into the wind.

She was glad to have the stroller to hold onto as her boots slipped on the slick sidewalk. Cars passed slowly, a soft muffled purr under the sharp wind, the rear lights pink through a slick layer of snow. She wondered what the drivers must think of this crazy woman taking her kids out in a blizzard. But they needed milk. She'd get it and then they'd get home and she'd make hot chocolate. The kids would be fine. She could do this. She wondered if she could distract Danny once they got to the pharmacy to keep him out of the toy aisle.

One block. Two blocks.

Aggie kept her head down. Why had he wrapped it in her tea towel? Was it a sick joke? She remembered buying it in the souvenir shop the day he was gone, how rebellious she had felt spending money without his permission, the feeling of triumph and freedom. He'd held up the tea towel the next day and questioned her. Had she not seen it since then? She couldn't remember. The stroller wheels hit a curb hidden under a snowdrift and she went skidding.

Three blocks. Four blocks.

The parts of Aggie's face that were exposed were numb and wet. She gripped the handlebars and gathered momentum for the incline past the bank, losing her footing a few times. At the intersection, she negotiated cars spinning their wheels as she crossed to the pharmacy, feeling victorious that they had made it. The crotchety old guy who delivered prescriptions came to her aid as she struggled to get the stroller through the door. "No mother in her right mind would bring children out in this weather!" he scolded.

"They're fine. They're having fun!" she snapped, swallowing the thanks that had been on her tongue, her face hot with shame.

She'd barely parked the stroller just inside the pharmacy door when the kids scrambled out and made a beeline for the toy aisle. Danny held up a white unicorn Beanie Baby and handed Celia a green-hued rainbow bear. *Five dollars each*, the sign read. Aggie took the toys from them, giving her children a stern look.

The dairy case was almost empty. There were only two gallons of milk left. Aggie went to the register and spoke to the heavyset woman behind the counter. "Do you have quarts of milk?"

"Sorry. That's all we got."

Aggie felt uncomfortable under the woman's stare. Was she judging her, too? "How about in back?"

The woman shook her head. "You're lucky we got that. Been a run on milk this morning."

Aggie's heart sank. She counted her money. The kids had been so good. "Is this enough for one Beanie Baby and a gallon of milk?"

The clerk peered at Aggie's outstretched palm. She sniffed. "Doesn't look like it. Not with tax."

Danny pulled on Aggie's coat, his face a pale circle in a muffle of gray. "Mama."

"Just a minute, Danny." He tugged again. "Danny, stop it!"

"Celia went outside."

Aggie dropped the cash and raced for the store exit. Celia stood beyond the glass door inches from the curb, her pink snowsuit a blur in the buffeting snow. Cars slid through the intersection, not stopping. "Celia!" Aggie screamed. She raced outside, grabbed her daughter, slipped, and landed on her back. Celia howled against the wind as Aggie held tight, furious with herself and hating her situation—no car, no money, always alone at night when Rick moonlighted at other stations. Someone gripped her elbow and forcefully pulled her up. It was the pharmacist in his white tunic, his head and arms disembodied against the snow.

"You had quite a scare there, ma'am," he said kindly, helping her back into the store.

A small crowd was standing by the entrance. "How did she get out there?" the cash register lady asked.

"I was at the counter," Aggie stammered, aware of the few customers eyeing her. "She was right next to me and—she must have followed someone out."

"You're lucky she didn't get hit by a car," the crotchety man said.

"Yes, I know, I know," Aggie said, apologetic and fuming at once.

The pharmacist reappeared with two lollipops, one purple and one red. "This okay, Mom?" he asked.

Aggie hesitated, hating to soothe her kids with sweets, then nodded. "Yes, that would be great, thanks."

When Celia had calmed down and was sucking on her lollipop, Aggie gathered her cash from the counter and went to the pay phone, holding Celia in her arms and taking Danny by the hand.

"Who are you calling, Mama?"

"I'm calling Daddy. You stand right there."

Danny's face brightened. "I want to talk."

"We'll see."

Aggie slid two quarters into the slot and dialed the studio.

"Down!" Celia whined as she squirmed.

"Not on your life, little girl."

Aggie bit back vitriol when Monica picked up. "I need to speak to Rick... I don't care if you've got Bill Clinton on the air. Get me Rick now, Monica." Celia writhed in her arms. Aggie squeezed her daughter tight as sweat trickled from under her bra and down her back. She wanted to unbutton her coat but didn't dare put down the phone or her daughter.

Rick came on the line. "Aggie, I'm in the middle of the show. What the hell?"

"How could you not leave us any milk this morning, Rick?"

"What are you talking about?"

"You left one gulp of milk in the carton. Nothing for the kids. I had to come out in this weather and now we're stuck at the pharmacy. You have to come get us."

"Are you crazy? I can't just walk out. I'll get fired."

Danny yanked Aggie's coat. "I want to talk to Daddy."

Aggie covered the mouthpiece. "Hush, Danny! Rick, we can't get home. I can't push the stroller through the snow."

"You walked to the pharmacy?"

"You think I called a cab? With what money, Rick?"

"Why didn't you buy milk yesterday when you had the car? That's your job, Aggie. Not mine."

Aggie closed her eyes and tried to keep it together, not wanting to have a meltdown right there in the store. She trembled with the effort. "Yes, I know it's my job, but the kids are your job, too, Rick. You're never home anymore. You're always working. Shouldn't we have extra money with all the moonlighting you're doing? Are you, Rick? Are you really picking up extra hours?"

"What? Aggie, I have to get off the phone."

Aggie gripped the handset slick with sweat. "I found my tea towel, Rick. My missing tea towel from the Indiana Dunes you claim not to have seen. The one you wrapped so carefully around your precious little videotape." Silence. She could tell he hadn't hung up because the morning show hosts were jabbering in the background. She let the silence spin out between them and had not the slightest urge to fill it with her words. She waited, certain of herself. When Rick spoke, she could barely hear him.

"I'll come get you."

"What's that you said?"

"I said I'll be there to get you in about an hour."

When Aggie hung up she felt oddly tall, as if she was seeing everything from a great height and clearly for the first time. A feeling of calm rested across her shoulders and her abdomen relaxed. She felt strong, as if she could walk for miles and miles if she cared to. It was an odd sensation, alien, yet familiar, and entirely thrilling, like meeting up with a beloved friend she hadn't seen in a long, long time.

# On Squirrels &
# Other Interlopers

by Della Leavitt

irst-time homeowners Gus and Jill Kaplan soon learned that even in the heart of the city, nature had her ways. The couple contended with field mice, horse flies, carpenter ants, hornets, and the occasional wasp in their 100-year-old frame house where something always needed to be fixed. But none of this prepared them for human interlopers, Carrie and Paul Bishop who bought the house next door, after the O'Reillys, who had become the Kaplans' dear friends, moved out to the suburbs seeking a good Catholic high school for their eldest child.

The Kaplans' introduction to the Bishops began with Paul Bishop barking orders to the movers while Carrie flounced up their front stairs without even a shake of her highlighted, Julia Roberts-esque, cascading tresses for Hello. Amid the gaggle of neighbors gathered on the sidewalk, Jill predicted that this new couple would become the Neighbors from Hell. This standoffish behavior was sure to clash with life on North Seeley, an old-world Chicago block of narrowly spaced, single-family homes where everyone knew everyone else's business. Gus urged Jill to go easy on the new people.

Amid the gaggle of neighbors gathered on the sidewalk, Jill predicted that this new couple would become the Neighbors from Hell. This standoffish behavior was sure to clash with life on North Seeley, an old-world Chicago block of narrowly spaced, single-family homes where everyone knew everyone else's business. Gus urged Jill to go easy on the new people.

"C'mon, Gus," said Jill. "Get real. A white BMW SUV? On our block?"

"Give them a break," Gus said. "Moving day is hectic. You're just missing the O'Reillys."

Jill did miss them. Ten years earlier, Eileen and Ed O'Reilly, who had both grown up nearby on Hoyne and Oakley, had run interference for the Kaplans, the first Jewish homeowners on the block. Not until the block party when Gus brought a case of Stiegl beer from Meyer's Deli did others begin to warm up. When an old-timer shook Gus's hand, admitting he had once worked for Jewish people who "weren't too bad," the Kaplans were tacitly accepted, forgiven their hubris to dare to move in and pay $75,000 for the charming, painted-over, asbestos-sided house they loved: $20,000 more than anyone had paid before.

At that same party, Jill made friends with Tina, who, like the Kaplans, had moved in recently. Tina worked from home as a freelance writer and was an ever-reliable source of information. She passed on news to Jill that Carrie Bishop was an interior decorator and her husband Paul was a real estate developer, a most sinister profession amid the rapidly changing housing landscape. Jill could imagine Paul, a short, scowling man, knocking on doors, gloating as he swindled properties from senior citizens, while twirling a waxed, handlebar mustache with a snide, *Nya-uh-uh*, under his breath.

When the Bishops arrived, gentrification in Lincoln Square was accelerating. A grand Starbucks sprouted overnight at the corner of Lincoln and Wilson, replacing the grimy laundromat that had stood there as long as anyone could remember. Gus and Jill, an accountant and systems engineer, respectively, weren't flashy. By necessity, they parked their cars on the street: an aged silver Skylark and a three-year-old, navy-blue Toyota Corolla. Jill's father, proud to have raised his daughter as a first-generation suburbanite, lamented: "How could you buy a house without a garage?"

The next fall, the Neighbors from Hell planted a wall of tall, white poplar trees abutting the Kaplans' house. It was their first act of encroachment.

"Too close!" Jill complained to Gus. "They've got a double lot. Why are they crowding ours?"

"Calm down. They can do whatever they want on their side."

"Are those trees really on their side? Do you know that for sure?"

Gus gave Jill a quick hug. "Pick your battles, honey."

Over lunch on the patio at Café Selmarie, Jill and Tina discussed the intruding poplar trees.

"They've got their nerve," said Tina. "Those trees are practically crawling up the side of your house."

Tina wasn't the only neighbor to notice. On his walk to the grocery store, old-timer Mr. MacGregor interrupted Jill who sat reading on her front porch.

"Watch out for those pushy people next door to yez," he said, jerking his thumb at the offending trees, "We don't need no one who won't be neighborly living here."

When Gus reminded her that neighbors should get along. Jill considered softening her stance. Until a few months later when she watched Carrie supervise a crew sinking concrete posts deep into the ground to support a ten-foot-high iron filigreed gate, complete with a menacing padlock to create a grand entryway into the side yard between their two homes.

"Where do they think they are, Lake Forest?" asked Gus.

Jill appreciated his humor. "More like, Lake Forest Lite."

Sauntering down the sidewalk, Tina's husband Brad offered his view of this latest makeover. "Maybe they'll want to turn Seeley into a cul-de-sac."

Jill said, "I think they'd like to annex the whole block for themselves. Don't you think their poplar trees are too close to our house?"

"Jill, don't make a big deal about this," said Gus.

"She's right," said Brad. "I'm headed to the Ward office; I'll ask around."

He returned saying they'd need a formal survey before any further investigation. Gus wouldn't hear of it.


Two years later, a development group demolished an old house next to the alley and built a McMansion on spec. Rumors flew that Paul was one of the partners and by the following autumn, the Neighbors from Hell embarked on a major addition of their own, without permits. They began by dismantling the O'Reillys' deck, built by hand by Ed and his brother, complete with outdoor power outlets. Gus and Jill wistfully remembered Ed generously powering the sound system for the Kaplans' long-ago, blow-out "Name That Tune" backyard party with an extension cord across their yards.

Late one afternoon, upstairs at her desk, Jill panicked at the smell of smoke and ran downstairs, coughing furiously. Haze engulfed the first floor. Grabbing the fire extinguisher, she checked the stove. Off. Throwing open the back door to bring in wafts of chilly November air, she spotted the problem immediately. Next door, construction workers chatted idly in an Eastern European language while filling burning steel barrels with discarded wood, ignoring ordinances codified after the infamous 1871 fire burned Chicago to the ground. Even burning leaves was illegal now. Jill waved her arms, shouting, "Stop!" but the workers ignored her, kept yakking, and tossed more wood into the flames.

When Paul Bishop appeared, Jill let him have it.

"You're just jealous," he said, "because your place is a dump."

"Go to hell!" she said.

Paul gave her the finger.

When Gus came home, Jill tearfully relayed what had happened.

"Those jerks," he said. "I'm going over there."

Unable to hear their exchange, Jill watched from the porch as Paul pointed at her, while Gus gesticulated at the smoldering barrels. Finally, Paul threw up his hands and went inside.

When Gus returned, Jill asked, "What did you say?"

"I told him he's lucky we don't nail his ass."

A few days later, Carrie rang their bell, mumbled "Sorry," and handed Jill a box from the overpriced Pottery Barn. Inside was a green china serving platter, cracked perfectly in half.

Jill showed it to Gus. He asked, "Do you think she knew it was broken?"

"I'd put money on it," said Jill. At least Gus hadn't offered his usual: *Nothing we can do about it.*

Jill took Carrie's apology "gift" back to Pottery Barn, explaining this was how she received it.

The clerk eyed her dubiously. "We haven't stocked this item for two years," she said, but issued a twenty-five-dollar store credit nonetheless. Jill selected two tiny blue soup bowls and promptly donated them to The Ark's resale shop to purge the memory of her smoke-filled kitchen.

By the next spring, Bishops' monstrous addition was complete, destroying the sanctuary of the Kaplans' screened-in back porch which had long been Jill and Gus's cozy refuge to relax with a bottle of wine after long work days, chatting and sharing dreams for the future. Jill remembered when the O'Reillys would spot them there and call out, "Enjoy! We're jealous! You're living the life we had Before Kids."

Now, new outdoor speakers blared unwanted country rock at all hours. Soundless programs continuously flickered across a big screen TV in the Bishops' oversized bonus room. Oblivious to what was around them, the Neighbors from Hell had overstepped their boundaries once again.

Although the addition obliterated Gus and Jill's view, nature's soundtrack remained: trilling cardinals, chirping chickadees, buzzing crickets, and peeping sparrows. Blocked was a chance to track gracefully swerving nighthawks as they swooped across their yard on through to the next, an occasional raccoon sighting, or that cranky opossum scurrying from hidey-hole to hidey-hole after his hasty exit from the hollowed-out domicile in the base of the ancient catalpa tree adjacent to the Kaplans' porch. Animals couldn't know where one lot began and another ended. After the Bishops' major construction project disturbed the ground, giant rats began popping out of the earth, their hairless, skinny tails swinging as they battled each other to feast on refuse from the trash bins lined up the alley.

"Where are the feral cats when we need them?" asked Gus.

"Or a pied piper," said Jill, "to lead the rats straight into Carrie and Paul's new den."

"You are evil," said Gus, kissing her.

One year later, Jill showed Gus how roots from the offending row of the Bishops' Maginot Line of poplar trees were snaking through cracks in the Kaplans' foundation into their unfinished basement. Again, Gus told her to back off. About that same time, for reasons no one ever discovered, Paul Bishop took to placing their overflowing trash bins to the Kaplans' side of the fences between their lots. Jill pushed them back. The cycle was repeated several times until Paul complained to Gus.

"Your crazy wife is at it again."

"Who's crazy?" retorted Gus. "Keep your stinking garbage behind your own f-ing fence. Or is your lot too small for you, like your little dick?"

But that didn't stop Paul. In the morning, their bins would again be on their side, until Gus urged Jill, "Leave them be. It's a no-win."

"They're pigs," said Jill.

Tina stirred her iced tea as she sat with Jill in the newly claustrophobic screened-in porch while Jill told her about Paul Bishop's latest alley shenanigans, and added, "I hate staring into their den."

"I can see why," said Tina. "I'm going to tell other neighbors."

"What can they do?"

"For one, Mr. MacGregor has friends at Streets & Sanitation."

Everyone knew better than to rile up that rough-and-tumble city department. Don't mess with anyone there, especially the tough guys who piloted the garbage trucks.

At that moment, Carrie and Paul's pair of Labradoodles began to howl.

"There they go. Those annoying Rich People Dogs," said Tina.

"Barking all day and all night," added Jill.

The curly-haired creatures roamed free on the Bishops' double lot, touched off by anything that moved: trash-talking teens, screaming children playing freeze tag, unmuffled low-riders booming through the alley, rabbits chomping on greenery or squirrels leaping through tree branches. Akin to rodents, lithe as trapeze acrobats, pesky squirrels traversed the expansive network high above Seeley Ave.

Old houses are plagued by myriad weak links. The Kaplans' home was no exception. Routine maintenance was never-ending. They covered the asbestos with charcoal vinyl siding, repainted the white trim, and replaced the newel posts to secure the railings on the front stairs—futile attempts to catch up.

One day, at her attic desk, Jill's stomach clutched when she heard intermittent scrabbling on the other side of the wall. Afraid of what she might find, she held her breath and opened the door of the rarely used crawl space. Peering into the dim light, an overpowering, sickly-sweet stench engulfed her. When her eyes adjusted, she found crap everywhere. Not the expected crap: a moldy accumulation of unneeded papers, cast-off clothing, and Gus's forgotten Cubs hat nailed to a rafter. Instead, she saw globs of guano. Bird shit? Worse. A bushy tail scampered outside through a crack of light. Oh, God. Squirrels. Droppings drenched the bare wooden planks and scads of chewed-up papers were strewn willy-nilly.

Returning to her desk, Jill's fingers shook as she dialed the city's animal control center. The no-nonsense operator was emphatic: no dispatches for nuisances inside a private home. Jill discovered a promising Internet listing with an 800 number called Critter Control. In a friendly voice, Jayson explained his charges: $35 for each animal caught and removed alive to the wilds of McHenry County.

"How soon can you get here?" asked Jill.

Jill called Gus downtown. He applauded her resourcefulness, and said, "You hired Trapper Jayson!"

Jill loved Gus's clever nickname for the Man from Critter Control.

Problem solved.

Within the hour, a black Ford Bronco with Xtreme wheels pulled up to the curb, and out stepped six-foot-five Jayson in a red, long-sleeved shirt. After one glance, he traced the squirrels' route. Jill followed his outstretched arm and shuddered. Why hadn't she noticed this before?

He pointed to the blanket of sugar maples across the street that formed a canopy connecting with curbside, mature mountain ash trees. A conga line of squirrels danced an identical choreography: up the maples, leaping onto the ashes, landing one-by-one on the Bishops' Lake Forest-wannabe iron gate, hopping around the ornate curlicues, then up one specific white poplar tree, onto the Kaplans' shaky gutter, and easily entering a breach in their decayed wooden soffit. Once inside, Jill imagined wildly gyrating victory dances, producing heaps of scented refuse to brand the space, until lickety-split, in reverse, they bounded out in gleeful escape.

Trapper Jayson chuckled. "Nothing I ain't seen before. I'll put a trap up high in this tree," pointing to the gateway poplar, "and catch the little buggers before they can get up in there."

Retrieving a wire cage and ladder from his vehicle, he climbed up to mount the trap at an optimum level to catch the unending streams of marauders. At the moment Jayson was high over the Neighbors from Hell's side yard, Carrie appeared, trowel in hand.

"Take it down," she said. "That's my tree. Trapped squirrels could bother our 'Doodles."

"Are you kidding, Carrie?" said Jill. "We've got a mess from squirrels getting inside by going up this tree."

Carrie smoothed her designer gardener gloves. "Your problem. Not mine."

"She's an A-hole," said Trapper Jayson, with Carrie still in earshot.

"You got that right," said Jill. "Those damn trees were a nuisance from Day One. And their roots are growing into our basement."

"I'll tell you what I'd do," said Jayson. "Put copper nails into the roots. It'll kill those damned trees. Learned that from my dad."

Jill considered this, but couldn't willfully kill a tree. Even if it were the inconsiderate Bishops' trespassing tree.

As it turned out, Trapper Jayson was worth his weight, not in copper, but in gold. Without access to the poplar tree, he climbed three flights inside the Kaplans' home to squeeze into the enclosed overhang from inside the attic and set the traps. At the sounds of flailing, captured rodents, Jill called Jayson back to retrieve the intruders. Jill paid him extra to temporarily patch the breach and clean out the poopy mess the squirrels had made. Another animal control professional might have refused that dirty job. What a gem. When Trapper Jayson's work was done, Gus and Jill hired a contractor to replace the rotted wooden soffit with a metal one.

Game Over for squirrels.

Problem solved.

A few months later, after five years living in their now-expanded home, the Neighbors from Hell became curiously absent, but suitcase-toting folks streamed through their high-and-mighty gateway at all hours, right past Jill and Gus's front porch. Gus warned Paul that non-owner-occupied Airbnbs were illegal in Chicago, after which the Bishops left threatening notes on the Kaplans' windshields when they parked in front of Bishops' house. The Bishops claimed those spaces were "reserved" for paying guests.

Over dinner at the Daily Bar & Grill, when Gus showed Tina and Brad the "Move Your Car or Else!" notes, Tina decided to spread the word. Brad agreed. After dinner, Jill went over to Ace Hardware to buy light bulbs. In the next aisle, a packet of sparkly copper nails caught her eye. She hesitated, then picked it up and took it to the register. Why not?

At the next block party, the public defense lawyer who lived across the street spoke up.

"We all know about their Airbnb," she said. "But threatening notes? This time those Bishops have gone too far! Even with Dibs after a snowstorm, we all know it's legal to park anywhere. Seeley Avenue belongs to the People, not to an entitled few. I'm filing a formal complaint with the City!"

Cheers erupted.

"Let's go tell them now!" The lawyer marched a group up the Bishops' front stairs.

No answer.

At the edge of the crowd, Jill recognized Herman, the alderman's muscle. "Would you like a beer?" she asked, in an innocent-sounding voice.

"Sure. I heard all of yous. We's been watching that house. Now we's got the goods on 'em."

While doing laundry the next day, Jill remembered the copper nails. She pushed several into each of the tree roots swirling into their basement. A few weeks later, two of the poplar trees turned brown. Trapper Jayson had been right. One night during a thunderstorm all hell broke loose and one of the poplars toppled and crashed through the largest window of the grandiose addition.

Timing is everything.

The next day, a city official arrived to shut down the Bishops' Airbnb.

"Bad luck," said Gus. "Even if they did have it coming."

"I love your soft heart," said Jill, kissing Gus full on the mouth. "That's why I married you."

# Off Course

## by Beth Lewis

Lisa craned her head to look out her kitchen window after hearing something whir across her lawn. She watched a chrome-trimmed golf cart zip across her next-door neighbors' backyard and then careen through her flower bed and crunch off the curb. As she watched, the cart casually pulled onto the driveway across the street. Lisa took another sip of her coffee to ensure that she was, indeed, awake and not imagining or dreaming.

When Lisa and her husband bought their house on the golf course, the large backyard with many trees to offer privacy from the eleventh hole was one of the things Lisa loved the most about it. However, in eight years of living there, she had never seen a rogue golf cart.

A neighborhood social media group had been created for safety alerts and general communication, so she messaged the group to ask if anyone else had seen the golf cart and knew what was going on. About ten minutes later she saw a reply. It was from Melissa, who never said hello even though they'd been introduced before. She lived at the opposite end of their long, winding road. Each house was on at least a half-acre so people who lived a few houses apart didn't always see each other on the street. Because the road curved, the distance was shorter between back yards.

> That was me. Dropped off my daughter
> across the street from you. Takes too long
> to get in the car and I know the Rogers
> aren't home anyway.

While Lisa was reading it again to make sure she had understood it correctly, a message came from Jennifer, who lived across the street from Melissa.

> That's terrible! You shouldn't cut through
> people's private property!

Melissa immediately responded.

> I used to go through your yard until you built
> the fence. Ha Ha

There was no reply after that, but Lisa couldn't stop thinking about it for the rest of the day. Her left eye twitched every time she thought about Melissa making her own rules.

The next morning, she saw Jennifer driving past her house and waved her down to ask what she was going to do about it. "Well, I told Melissa that I would open the gate for her if she let me know in advance."

"What! You would let her go through your yard because she's too lazy to drive her car? I won't even ask why her kid can't just walk or ride her bike."

Jennifer shrugged. "I talked to her yesterday after posting to the neighborhood group. She is uh, in a hurry sometimes…."

Lisa couldn't believe that Jennifer was okay with this. Did Melissa's husband know she was doing this with his beloved, limited-edition golf cart? Did he care that the kids might scratch the luxury leather seats?

That morning Lisa took the garbage bins out and almost tripped when she saw a foul pile of dog poop marring the green expanse of her front lawn. All of the dog owners in their neighborhood were very diligent about picking up after their dogs. She looked around to see if the perpetrator was still out anywhere. At the far end of the street, she saw a fluffy white ball shuffling along next to someone wearing a black jacket with a hood. While she couldn't positively identify the human from that distance, she was pretty sure that the mobile marshmallow was Norman, who belonged to Melissa.

Lisa ran back into the house and collided with her husband Pete, who was leaving for work. "You are not going to believe what she did now! We need to do something about her!"

Pete sighed and got into his car. "I'm sure it was a mistake. Probably won't happen again. Gotta go." He blew her a kiss and backed out of the driveway.

Why did no one else seem to be bothered by Melissa's exploits? Lisa couldn't understand how they were okay with this behavior. Were they all afraid to say anything about it? She would need to be the one to fight back.

After her kids left for school Lisa got ready to head to her yoga class. She left a few minutes early and drove in the opposite direction, toward Melissa's house. Lisa wasn't sure what she was looking for and really didn't see anything other than the trash bins by the curb. As she backed her car up to turn around, she smirked as an idea came to her. While reversing the car, she backed into the garbage bins just hard enough to tip them over onto the lawn. Confirming that no one had seen her, Lisa then proceeded to her class. She was definitely in need of some deep breathing.

Later that afternoon, the message was posted to the neighborhood chat.

> Anyone else have their garbage bins tipped
> over?

The only reply came from Jennifer.

> Wow, sorry that happened to you. We
> need to make sure this doesn't happen
> again. Everyone please check your security
> cameras and let us know if you see any
> suspicious drivers around here!

By dinner time, Lisa was wondering what would happen next when the whole family was startled by the "Beeeeeep ... Beeeeeep ... Beeeeep ... Beeeeep" right outside her window. This time the golf cart was going in reverse from the street, right over the edge of her freshly emerging tulips, before heading forward and sideswiping the Rogers' rosebushes. As it sped away through their backyards, Pete asked "What just happened? Was that a golf cart?"

"Yes!" She slammed a pot down on the counter, "and it will be the last time!"

Lisa's eye twitched as she finished cleaning up. After stepping outside to survey her perfectly aligned tulips that were now flattened, she informed her husband, "I need to go over there right now. If I don't stop her, she'll continue ruining people's property for no reason."

"What are you going to do?" Pete sounded concerned. "Please don't get into a fight with them."

"I'm not getting into a fight. I'm just going to tell her face-to-face that she can't cut through people's yards with her golf cart and that she needs to pick up after her dog like everyone else! Why does she think rules don't apply to her?"

Lisa stomped halfway down the street with her head jutting forward and her eyes squinting to match the hard line of her mouth. After a few puzzled looks from children playing outside, she settled into a purposeful stride. She had passed Melissa's house in her car before, but she'd never seen it close up. As she approached it on foot, she noticed that it looked well-cared-for although a bit worn. The paint was chipping around the pillars on the porch and the brick driveway had a couple of dangerous crumbled spots. This seemed pretty selfish to her. They probably had someone scheduled to fix the driveway but couldn't be bothered to put a sign up so people wouldn't trip on it. The yard was empty except for a lonely soccer ball in the corner.

She then realized that she probably should have made sure someone was home before walking all the way over here. Well, she was here now so she may as well try. Lisa strode up to the front door and rang the bell. After a minute, when she was about to turn around and head home, the door slowly opened a few inches.

Melissa's blonde hair was in a messy ponytail and her makeup didn't hide the dark circles under her eyes. "What's this about? Why didn't you text me? No one just shows up here without prior notice."

"Well, I'm here now." Lisa folded her arms "And I came down the street, as opposed to trespassing through your yard." Her voice escalated. "Which is what you're doing when you can't be bothered to drive your golf cart on the road, or here's a thought—*on the golf course!*"

Melissa's jaw clenched and something went dark in her eyes. Lisa continued her rant. "If you drive through any of our yards again, I will contact the police. And by the way, Norman's shit is no different from any other dog's. Pick. It. Up."

At the mention of his name, Norman appeared in the doorway and wagged his stubby tail. Melissa gently pushed him back with her foot. "Get...," she shouted, then stuttered, "go...just..." She turned away from Lisa.

Lisa exhaled. "Um, sorry...that was a little strong... But you really can't um..."

Melissa slowly turned back. "Listen. I'm just trying to...to..." Her lower lip trembled and then a torrent of tears raced down her cheeks, dragging black eye makeup with them. "Ever since Richard left, stuff has been really weird. I don't even know for sure if we can stay in the house long term." She hiccupped as loud, ugly sobs began to escape.

Lisa had been trying to tamp down her anger and was now completely unsure of how to react. "Left? When did he leave?"

"Stuff was going on for a while, but about six months ago we officially separated. That's when I started my new job. My kids are friends with your neighbors across the street, and they said I could bring them there when I need to go to work early or stay late."

Norman kept trying to squeeze out of the door, so Melissa motioned Lisa to come inside. When Melissa closed the door, her shoulders slumped, replacing the usual swagger.

Lisa's eye started twitching. "I'm really sorry about Richard leaving. But you're ruining people's lawns when your drive over them. Can't you drop them off in your car? Or can't your kids walk there?"

"We tried having them walk but they either take too long to get going, or it's raining, and I end up being late. I tried dropping them off on my way, but it really does take longer in the car." Melissa shrugged. "Also, they keep wanting to go on the golf cart. I guess if they can't have their dad here all the time, they can at least ride on his golf cart. He hasn't got around to selling it yet."

Lisa uncrossed her arms and Melissa continued. "Jennifer is the only other one who knows. I'll have to tell other people eventually, I guess."

"And as far as not picking up after Norman, I was in such a hurry to walk him after dropping my kids off, and before going to work, that I forgot the poop bags. I was honestly going to come back later and pick it up. I guess I should have told you, but I was kind of embarrassed."

Lisa tried to ignore the little white head with pleading eyes thrusting a toy at her knee. "I wish I'd known. I wouldn't have, well, I was really angry, and I was going to say something to you the other day. I drove by here and it seemed like no one was home and when I turned around I…may have backed into your garbage bins. I thought you felt like you could do whatever you wanted with no regard for other people's property."

Melissa wiped her tears and took another deep breath. "Well, knocking down the garbage bins was *not* cool, but I get it. If I drive my kids on the golf cart, I guess I don't need to shortcut through people's backyards."

Lisa shrugged and almost smiled as she offered, "If there's anything I can do to help, let me know. Really."

Melissa pulled out her phone. "I think I have it covered for now." Shortly a message popped up on the neighborhood chat.

> Please do not drive golf carts through
> private yards. Also make sure not to
> accidentally tap garbage bins with your car
> when turning corners.

Lisa tossed the toy for Norman, and as he waddled after it, Melissa opened the door.

After Lisa stepped out, she turned back. "I came here to tell you that you don't own the neighborhood and can't just cut through people's private property, but I guess I shouldn't make assumptions about people. Thanks for chatting with me."

Melissa started to shut the door and then paused and smiled at Lisa. "I'm glad you came. See you around."

As Lisa walked home past the perfectly landscaped yards, she heard a slight rattle in the distance. She caught her breath as she looked around but then she relaxed. It was just people in a cart on the golf course heading toward the next hole. Continuing toward her house, she narrowly missed tripping over a skateboard that someone had left on the sidewalk. Lisa moved it onto the grass and kept on walking.

# The Draft

by Margot McMahon

## 1850 – ALDER BROOK, ADIRONDACKS, NEW YORK

John McKillip was arranging woven-seat stick chairs around two large council tables that had been pushed together into a "T" shape. Amber sunlight splintered the room as John's younger brother Hugh ducked through the tavern's front door. John straightened up to give his dark-haired brother a bear hug.

"Good evening, Hugh," John said. "The banking-account proposal is on tonight's agenda."

The town of Alder Brook was growing fast. The stagecoach brought new settlers and visitors daily; grocery and tavern businesses were booming. John was convinced a community banking account would reduce risk to townsfolk, encourage more development, and provide funds to supply a volunteer militia.

"I'm opposed to lumping our savings together, Brother," Hugh said.

"Yet sharing everyone's labor for your hall, meals, and home is fine?" John answered. "We're stronger together. We've built this town together."

"I didn't run from the shortest war in Britain's history," snapped Hugh. John had immigrated to avoid the Opium War.

"I stayed home to keep Da's kelper business afloat," John shot back. It was an old conflict. John smarted at Hugh's accusation that he had avoided conscription into the British Navy and Hugh chafed under his elder brother's mantle. John calmed himself. He needed to gain common ground with all the McKillip brothers for the forthcoming vote.

"I sustained our parents and the business," John reminded him. "And I bought your ticket to America."

They were joined by two more McKillip brothers—Archibald, the youngest, and paunchy, freckle-faced Patrick. Patrick passed John and sat next to Hugh while Archibald took a seat across the table.

John fumed. His auburn hair bristled above his stocky shoulders. When they were young, John, Hugh, and their younger brothers had bonded like a flock of birds. Now they bickered like magpies over shared territory. John was irritated with himself that he expected loyalty. He was more irritated with Hugh for creating their divide. John had shared his good fortune with all his brothers: giving them a cabin, credit in the grocery store, and stone foundations to help them build homes. Now he needed them. Tonight's vote was crucial.

As John placed pitchers of ginger beer and spring water on each table, a horse neighed outside, followed by a chorus of men greeting each other in cheery tones reserved for a Sunday picnic. The smell of pine from freshly milled boards permeated the large room. Lingering mint essence kept ants from devouring the enticing pine. Hugh waved off John's offer of ginger brew and poured himself a noggin of spring water. After months of conversation, writing, discussion, and editing, Patrick brought in the final draft of Alder Brook's bylaws. It was finally on the agenda for a vote. Unfortunately, Hugh and Patrick opposed what, in John's mind, was the most essential component: the community banking proposal.

Growth had brought business and residents to Alder Brook, but it also brought thieves. Most residents understood the need for a sheriff or some kind of militia, and that would take money. John was confident he could make the case that security was a top priority, and paying for it would require a community bank. This would avoid having to tax the citizenry, many of whom had fled Ireland to escape excessive taxation. Everyone who attended tonight would have a vote. Those who didn't attend would have to abide by their decisions. What John could not predict was how hard his brother would try to influence others to turn against him.

Stocky men in their Sunday suits—all immigrants from Northern Ireland—filled the tavern. John mentally tallied the votes of those in favor of protecting their settlement from intruders with a savings account. The settlers were now busy baptizing infants, educating children, confirming youth, and celebrating weddings in the growing Catholic parish above the AuSable River Valley.

Before the meeting was called to order, a calico water bird flew in the open door.

"Mind the Bishop-bird!" Cornelius, the tavern owner, called.

"Nah, that's a chuckatuck," called another voice. Soon many voices filled the air.

"Nope, a creddock."

"A Jinny."

"A sea quail!"

"A rock-bird."

"A Red-leg."

"Calico-jacket."

John listened with growing irritation. How could the town agree on anything if they couldn't agree on what to call a wayward bird? He shouted above the ruckus, "Archibald, what is that bird's name?"

"The great ornithologist Alexander Wilson named it a Ruddy Turnstone," his youngest brother said, adding in jest: "Who would like to make a motion that Wilson was correct?"

"I move that we all agree on Ruddy Turnstone," Cornelius yelled. He used a fish net to capture the bird. One by one, fifteen men hung their wool coats below beaver caps and settled into chairs. The regular attendees took places at the council tables, the others along the walls. Harris Hammill, the scribe, opened his inkpot and whipped a sharpened quill from his pocket. John, Cornelius, and Harris made a governing triumvirate. Hugh and Patrick sat together facing them. None doubted Hugh and Patrick were the finest authors of the lot. On the other side of the intersection, Archibald sat next to a man named Jay who was self-taught in the law. They made quite the pair: Jay was revered for his clarity, Archibald for his wit. They were seldom united in their views, but together brought an air of wisdom to the conversations.

"Well, fellas, no gains without pains, wouldn't you agree?" said Archibald as he relaxed into his pine chair.

Cornelius stood and the room quieted.

"Public business must be done by somebody," said Cornelius. "Let us bring this meeting to order as self-elected representatives of Alder Brook. Let our business be done and agreed upon by those gathered tonight for the good of all." He thumped his noggin so that it splashed. "Everyone here has an equal vote. If you choose, you may briefly state your intentions." At that, every man in the room gave his name, which was writ by Harris into the record log. Some offered intentions.

Jay said, "No power on earth, including the great state of New York, has a right to take our farms from us without our consent."

John nodded, for in the Adirondacks, labor signified ownership.

Hugh rose and stated, "When a man assumes a public trust, he should consider himself as public property. I vow to consider the community over my personal gain."

*Like hell you will!* thought John. Hugh's statement flew in the face of his selfish actions. It was clearly a ploy to win sentiment among the undecided voters for his position against the community bank. Hugh had gained a following by bringing a sawmill to Alder Brook.

Patrick shuffled papers and read, "We must first enable this governing body to control the governed and, in the next place, oblige it to control itself."

Harris restated the pecuniary importance of protecting the community: "In our deliberations, let us remember, if we give all the power to the many, they will oppress the few. Give all the power to the few, they will oppress the many. A militia protects our labor."

John stood. "It is my honor to associate with you men of good quality, for I'd rather be alone than in poor company. It is our combined labor that keeps alive in our breasts the little spark of celestial fire called conscience. That we have shared a cougar's portion of perspiration, our combined work ensures our conscientious and honorable interdependence." The men stomped their feet in agreement.

"If there are no more introductions," Cornelius paused, "then let us begin. First order is an accounting of our unified savings. John, please report your findings."

Cautiously, John took a breath, smiled, and looked around at his quiet audience. "Would you look at the passel of us who have monetary concerns?" John said. "We've come a long way, men. Remembering that some of us fled excessive taxes, some left war or hunger, we move forward for a vote of our community earnings. By the grace of God, we now have savings to guard. A few of us visited the Franklin County Emigrant Industrial Saving Bank branch in Malone to enquire about a community savings account. We were informed that our community could share an account managed by our council. Several signatories will protect our shared savings." John felt a drip of perspiration on his graying temple. The crowded room glowed from a roaring fire.

"Why should we trust this bank with our hard-scrabbled savings?" Patrick prodded.

John wasted no time responding, "The esteemed New York Attorney General Thomas Addis Emmet, leader of United Irishmen since the 1790s. His Irish Emigrant Society founded the Emigrant Industrial Saving Bank this year. Each of you is free to open your own account, but tonight we're voting on a community account. We'll agree on one amount for each family to deposit and the interest will be used for community expenses." John sat with a thud. The heat from the crowded room was tiring him.

"What if we are to move out of Alder Brook?" an agitated Hugh asked. "Will our compensation include interest?" Hugh was showing his true colors.

John controlled his frustration. A line from *Hamlet*, the one book he packed from County Antrim, flared in his mind. *What is the reason that you use me thus? I loved you ever: but it is no matter.* "Hugh, you have just arrived from our mother's bosom," said John. "Where do you intend to go so quickly?"

"If I choose to move to…perhaps…Illinois…or Colorado, could I extract my contribution with its full interest?" Hugh's question was louder than the room required. Sheets of the draft blew under the sweep of his arm. "Would it be only my portion or from the joint interest accrued?"

Patrick put the papers back in order. A murmur of surprise rippled through the men seated along the wall. Hugh had just lost his followers. John sensed the momentum build towards approval of a joint account.

"Hugh, we must invest in the community," said John. "Roads, helping the infirmed, supplying a militia, keeping up the school, the church, and its yard. With a group account, more interest will accrue, and Alder Brook will avoid having to impose taxes. You have embraced and contributed to our community with your labor." John looked around the room. "As have you all." Continuing to look as many of the men in the eye as possible, he added, "Our best option is for a community savings account to ensure a future for all in the event of injury, age, or illness." Zeroing in on Hugh, he said slowly, "Alder Brook cannot be siphoning off community savings for your next conquest."

In Vermont counties, the Know-Nothings had burned Catholic churches and kept Irish folk from working. What was Hugh thinking? Here was abundant land for farming, materials for building and for fuel, and the freedom to prosper! All around the room, the men's expressions showed that Hugh had lost their loyalty.

Nonetheless, he struck back: "If I contribute my hard-earned savings, I do not want to be conscripted to live in these backwoods forever," said Hugh hotly. Men murmured again. The word "conscripted" still made John's nape bristle.

"Then you are profiting from a community of settlers and *our* first chance of getting ahead." John tried hard to keep his composure. If Hugh were able to lead a majority to vote his way, Alder Brook would not be able to avoid taxes, and surely the town would collapse. "With the interest from the community account, we will not need to tax anyone."

Another Hamlet line popped in from John's memory: *Popp'd in between the election and my hopes. Thrown out his angle for my proper life... To let this canker of our nature come in further evil?*

"Then I will leave with my family's meager fortune and open my own account," Hugh snapped. And there it was, now, Hugh's true intentions, out in the open. *And a man's life's no more than to say "One."*

John's mind filled with outrage. What an ungrateful louse-about! He builds his home on *my* stone foundation after living in *my* homestead, builds a hall with the labor of all these men and now he's going to sell the hall and move to Illinois? The nerve. *...let a beast be lord of beasts.* I've offered him the coat off my back, yet he sneers at my buckskin.

Though it was clear that Hugh's position would be voted down, John could foresee endless bickering to follow.

"It's enough that New York State taxes us for our shared land!" shouted Patrick, suddenly in agreement with John. Sensing agreement in the room, John remained standing and signaled Archibald with a nod to hurry the vote.

"Do you love life? Then do not squander time, for that's the stuff of which life is made." Archibald stood. "Let us vote!"

Harris counted the yeas and nays. The councilmen at the table were counted first, then the men along the wall. Two-thirds of all the men in the room voted in favor of a community bank account.

"Let us consult our means rather than our wishes," John said. "Harris, please share the accounting." Harris laid out the financials with his expected acuity and confidence as the men nodded in agreement.

"Let frugality and industry be our virtues," Cornelius said. "As night is descending, we must efficiently attend to the bylaws. If we do so decide, an agreement might be reached. Patrick, would you please present the latest bylaws draft?" Patrick rose to empty a buckskin pouch of his handwritten document. "The Alder Brook government is intended to last for the ages, while remaining adaptable. Our conversations culminated in a government with three natures of power: the legislative, the judicial, and the executive. Members can serve on only one branch of government at a time, for a term of seven years. The judiciary department will be separate and distinct." As usual, the whispering and mumbling in the room erupted as they sorted their differences from a monarchy. As he listened, John wasn't sure Alder Brook would last seven years. If even a few changed their minds in the future, there would be conflict.

"Executive magistracy is the foetus of monarchy!" Hugh cried out. Sparks flew from his blue eyes, humiliation of losing the bank account battle fueled his anger.

"The check and balance of our government branches ensure little room for monarchies to develop," Cornelius retorted. "The sooner we have these bylaws defined, the sooner our designation as a village will be recognized by the great state of New York. I move we elect John as the Executive—and as the delegate to the Irish Emigrant Society and the Emigrant Bank. He will keep a finger on the pulse of change."

Three-quarters of the men voted in favor, and resounding applause shook sawdust from the rafters. Without pause, Cornelius called for a vote on the bylaws. Everyone at the table voted for the bylaws, with nearly unanimous yeas from the perimeter.

Cornelius gathered his notes and struck the empty noggin. "If there are no more comments, we will adjourn!" The room resounded of rousing rumbles as a quick-footed Hugh led his followers outside. Cornelius noticed and whispered to Harris: "It's better we rushed the bank vote. Opposition may still show itself." Harris nodded as he hung his chair on the wall. John hurried out, hoping to speak with Hugh.

Outside, John was surrounded by well-wishers and couldn't reach Hugh, who spoke quietly in a circle of men. Others who still had doubts questioned John, and to those who were unsettled, he spoke calmly to reassure them. "What is wrong with leaving some decisions to be sorted out by time?" He went on about the virtues of democracy, which he hoped would also assuage his supporters, so their minds might not be changed on the way home.

As the tavern yard emptied, Harris and Cornelius locked the door and joined John. Cornelius gave John a hearty pat on the back and shook his hand, saying: "John, it seems you are the First Father of Alder Brook. How does seven years of service settle with you?"

"I am not going anywhere," said John. "We can be pleased there is agreement on the main issues." His deep concern was with the minority opposition. "Our ongoing differences may yet split our village in two." He congenially slapped the two men's backs. "But let us give it a try, and we shall see how long we can sustain our republic, eh?" Sustaining the vision of Alder Brook would not be their problem, after all, but his. As he slipped a bit into his gentle mare's mouth, he saw Hugh's mount kick up stones as it galloped up Rock Road.

Leaping on his horse, John cantered after Hugh. He understood that winning over his brother was now more than just a familial responsibility, but his sworn civic duty, one that may well determine the fate of Alder Brook.

# A Perfect Angle of Light

by David Alan Pelzer

It is June 21st, another unseasonable scorcher in northern Wisconsin. Charlie Preston stands at the trailhead, his neck still sweating from the sweltering church. The hot sun plays peekaboo with the clouds as it slips toward the jagged outline of white pines. Charlie's left hand dangles a near-empty bottle of Leinenkugel, while the right hand loosens the top of his white dress shirt. He jams the bottle between his legs, freeing up both hands to roll up his sleeves to the elbows and curl the cuffs of his black wool pants past the top of the too-tight dress shoes, taken from his father's closet.

He enters the forest in search of a phenomenon his father, the great Royce Preston, had talked about but had never seen. Because solstice comes but twice a year, and the day must be crystal clear for the light to get through. At the reception following the funeral, his sister Rose handed him the hand-drawn map she had found in Dad's desk drawer. An attached note read, "Charlie track this down."

Rose nudged him, saying, "Get out there today, Bro. It could be your last chance."

The brown bottle is the lone survivor from a full case he and Rose lugged up from the basement for the well-wishers. Charlie takes a final swig of ale, then readies his arm to tomahawk the empty into a snarl of blackberry bushes. It would be a perfect hatchet throw, just as Dad had taught him. Then he holds back, recalling the old man's words: "Don't shit in the woods. It's your home."

The bottle, whose face shows the original satisfied smirk of an Indian Maiden, could be worth real money to a collector someday. Even so, it hardly compares to the one he'd seen resting on Dad's bookshelf: the hand-crafted emerald apothecary flask Charlie and his girlfriend Sally Jennings had uncovered in the riverbank mud the summer after high school, ten years before. Charlie had assumed that, once he left home, his father would have tossed it in the trash. Dad probably had no idea a savvy collector would readily part with a few Andrew Jacksons to claim it.

A passing cloud casts a deep shadow onto the hood of his rented black Camaro as Charlie opens the passenger door and tosses the bottle on the floor mat. Maybe he will stuff it in his duffel bag and start a new collection someday. The car is due back at the airport in three hours. That's when a puddle jumper will whoosh him to the Twin Cities, where he will catch a big jet home to his trailer outside Reno, then head to his blackjack job at the casino.

The afternoon stays hot and muggy. The locals at the reception complained it has not rained in nearly a month, the longest drought in a decade, or more. Charlie dips into his pocket for a bar napkin to wipe his brow. Instead, his fingers latch onto the map and note, scribbled on the back of an electric bill from Wisconsin Power. *Charlie track this down.* Aye aye, sir. As if he were still at his father's beck and call. The map looks like a child's doodling. It shows a forked trail, the river, the downstream bridge and a big black X next to an inclined mark showing the crested boulder Dad claimed to be as tall as himself, and nearly as long and wide as a pickup.

As Charlie moves along the trail, he sees signs that the drought has already devastated these woods. The landscape is more brown than green, the path more dust than mud. Gaping cracks in the clay soil. Each time he steps on a downed maple branch, it cracks under his feet. High in the canopy, a lone warbler croaks its parched song.

Charlie reaches the wooden bench at the river's overlook, where he and Sally had once set up a telescope to gaze at the sky. On clear nights, they could see Cassiopeia, the bright Summer Triangle, and old Arcturus, guarding Ursa Major, 37 light years away. This is where he told Sally about his dream to study the stars someday. But that dream got sucked into a deep, dark hole. He sold the telescope to fund his trip to the Sierras—and score a little weed. Now he can't afford a scope, not when a third of his bi-weekly pay slides into the slots.

The river is even lower now than it was back when he and Sally first found the flask. That was the summer he decided to head west. Sally declined to go with him—she had to tend to her diabetic mom. Johnny Cain, his wayward pal from high school, tagged along instead. When they reached Truckee, Charlie called to wish Sally happy birthday. She fell quiet, then whispered she had missed her period. When he called again the next day, she told him not to worry, it had only been a false alarm. Within a month, Charlie found work at the casino as a bouncer, then a dealer. Johnny, thirsty for a bigger fortune, began cooking meth

119

for some Mexicans in an old chicken shack south of Fresno, until one day the shack exploded. Had Charlie been a little less wary and a bit more greedy, he, too, could have ended up a smoldering corpse.

Sally came to the funeral this morning. She sat silently in the back row in a plain black dress, squished between a balding guy in a shiny blue suit and a sandy-haired boy who leaned his head on her shoulder. Maybe she was married now. Maybe the boy was her son.

Charlie and Rose sat in the front row. He marveled at how the two of them were a bizarre blend of their parents. Rose's wide hips, double chin and winning smile all belonged to Mom. But her squared shoulders, gnarly brow and mottled skin were distinctly Dad's. Charlie had Royce's hazel eyes and stunted growth, stopping at five foot eight. Rose was wired more like Dad, intense and determined. Charlie was more like Mom, shy and compliant—except when he was pressed. Then, he could become a caged badger.

By the time he realized he was a rebel, it was almost too late to forge his own path. Rose was the courageous one, returning home after her first semester to announce that she and Allyson were an item. Dad stayed boiling inside. When Rose returned to school, Charlie was left alone to face Royce's wrath.

Rose should have been the one out here in search of the old man's stone. She was the one who had interned at Xochicalco, the one who grew orgasmic when she learned that ancient Mayan astronomers had spotted a beam of light streaming through a hole in the ceiling rock, forming an imprint on the dusty floor of a cave. "It's not just a legend," she said, pointing to pictures on the Web. But neither she nor Dad had ever seen the light going through. Her work—digging up rocks—is all about the past. Dealing cards is about the present. It's about real people—a few lucky winners in their most ecstatic moments, the rest losers, in their ugliest. Yeah, Rose should be the explorer today.

Charlie has a plane to catch. He has no compass, no canteen, no digital camera. Only an Android with spotty service. And there is no App for finding spirit rocks.

This patch of woods is both familiar and strange to him. It's like returning home to find the scarred and charred remains of the place where one grew up. Over Royce Preston's long career as county game warden, he would bring Rose and Charlie to see patches of trillium, jack-in-the-pulpit and other wildflowers. He had them stand on the rock piles lining the riverbank to hear the roar of the falls. In summer, they brought grain to the deer feeding stations and inspected the traps he set to tag lynx and bobcats and fishers. In winter, when it was too cold and snowy to go into the woods, Dad huddled them by the fireplace and told them about the wild animals he had seen, the strange plants he had found. He told of a bear called the Blueberry Bandit that broke into locked cabins in search of its favorite pie, and a beaver with teeth so strong it could gnaw through the trunk of an ironwood, and a ten-point buck that darted around with an arrow stuck in its flank. When Charlie asked Mom if the stories were true, she winced and said, "Your father is prone to embellish a bit."

In summer and fall, Dad brought him and Rose to powwows on the reservation. There, Charles Cariboux, the Ojibwe game warden Charlie was named after, chanted and danced to the sound of drums with other members of his tribe. Dad told his children how, in the old days, Ojibwe wayfarers would stop at manitou rocks to leave tobacco and other offerings. If the rocks were ever broken, they might spill out human flesh and blood. Some Ojibwe hid food, and even messages, in the crevices. They formed signs with wood or stones or plants. To them, these rocks were not only waystations, but storybooks.

Dad had first told about finding his spirit rock three years earlier, when both Charlie and Rose returned home early for Christmas. Mom had made a big pot roast and a German chocolate cake to honor his birthday, and they all waited around the dinner table for him to return home. Mom sat wringing her hands. Charlie knew she had to be fretting that Dad might be at Tubby's Tap, pounding down Brandy Manhattans with Gracie Peterson, his latest honeydew. Then Dad came through the door, raving about the giant stone he had seen in the woods.

At the funeral this morning, Pastor Paul, newly transferred from the Ozarks, recounted the accolades he was told about Royce Preston, the renowned county game warden who supported hunters while protecting the wilderness. An icon of justice: fair to all, partial to none. The congregation was not aware of Royce the house devil, the one who beat, belted and belittled his son. They did not know about the time he called Charlie a coward for not pulling the trigger on an unsuspecting doe…the time he locked Charlie in his room all day after he and Johnny Cain were busted for smoking weed in the county park…the time he slapped Charlie for quitting the wrestling team, after making it to the state tourney the year before.

121

Pastor Paul asked Charlie to stand and say something about Royce, but Charlie waved him off. Most of the congregation stayed silent. Only two people stood to speak: Rose said, "Everyone knew our dad, warts and all. He loved his town, these woods, and us, too." Charles Cariboux stood up in the back row and said, "Royce was our brother. He looked out for us. He valued our ways."

Maybe the throng of mourners had come as a make-good for Mom, who was loved by all. She died the previous December, a few days before Dad's birthday, and a bad blizzard caused both Charlie and Rose, along with most of the town, to miss her funeral. The old man, so dependent on her, could only hang on for a few months after that. In a way, then, Charlie and Rose had returned home to mourn both of them. The morning of their father's funeral, they had first gone to Mom's gravesite to place white lilies and red roses by her headstone.

Charlie had told Rose, "Admit it, he led her to an early grave."

Rose shook her head. "She wasn't perfect. No one is."

"You're wrong. Our mother was an angel, sent down to look after us. She never should have died."

"She made choices, just like all of us."

"What choices? She was stuck with him. You and I were lucky to escape."

It was no use arguing. Rose never had to battle Royce like Charlie did. And he hated the way Mom always caved.

Rose looped her arm around him and said, "Remember the day Dad found the rock? The time he came home late for dinner and Mom scolded him for dragging snow into the house? Remember how she told him to shut up, sit down and eat?"

Together, they raised their fists and mimicked Dad's deep, impassioned voice: "Good God, woman, this is more important than pot roast!"

When their laughter trailed off, Rose said, "Remember how he described the rock as being split open, as though some giant had pierced it with his sword?"

Of course he remembered. Dad had been out tracking down two doofuses from Chicago who were hunting deer out of season and had gotten themselves lost. It was ten degrees out, and the sun was lowering in the sky. He said he heard water trickling—in the dead of winter!—meaning there must have been an underground stream somewhere.

Standing right in front of him was the rock. A glimmer of light struck it at a nearly perfect angle, so close to piercing the slit. Dad had meant to return the next day for the winter solstice, so he could see the light pouring straight through the opening and onto the ground below. But that day it snowed all morning and afternoon. Dad had missed his chance. As it turned out, he never made it back to the stone again. Discovery, he said later, was more about luck than persistence.

Charlie traipses for another mile or so down the overgrown path, then stops to watch the northern sky darken. A storm is coming. The wind has shifted, and the air has turned cooler. When the trail splits, Charlie stops to check his bearings. He lowers his head to read the map and a bead of sweat drips onto the paper, smudging the ink. As he checks his phone for the time, the screen goes blank. No more juice. Bad omen. Maybe this is all for naught. He could end up wandering through these woods only to emerge like a drenched otter, without ever having found the stone. Maybe the rock is another one of Dad's tall tales. What if it isn't even there?

His feet are swollen and aching from the ill-fitting dress shoes, but Charlie pushes past prickly shrubs and circumvents tree limbs downed during spring storms. He wades through an undergrowth of invasive plants that harbor swarming thrips and biting flies and thrashes down the slope through an entanglement of roots, rocks and overhanging branches.

Pausing where a huge oak has fallen, its blackened trunk split by lightning, he swats away a flurry of gnats that swirl in the light pouring through a hole in the canopy. In church this morning, as Pastor Paul blathered about how the Lord Almighty had poured down his blessings on the congregation, rays of heavenly light filtered through the stained glass. Mom used to say she thought of God not as a person, but as a patch of pure light streaming through, making everything clear.

Charlie's entire face is sweating. He slaps at the gnats again, then fishes in his pocket for the bar napkin to wipe his brow. The map reappears in his hand. Another bead of sweat falls squarely on the paper, smudging the ink so much that the markings become useless. His mouth is parched, but he has no water. Pressing on, he comes upon another fork, which the map never showed. What now? A soft voice says, *take the river trail.*

As Charlie moves deeper into the forest, he hears the caw of a raven in the canopy. The ferns whoosh in a sudden breeze. Water ripples in the distance. Ahead, he eyes an outcrop of rocks bordering the river. Maybe the stone is nestled among them. If he locates it and sees the light pouring through, maybe he will amaze Charles Cariboux's clan with the telling of his find. Maybe Charles will place his hand on Charlie's shoulder and say, "Well done." Over the years, the tribe has kept the locations of the manitou rocks secret, to keep punks like Johnny Cain from defacing the surfaces. Maybe the Ojibwe think Charlie is like Johnny. A doper, a drunkard, a deserter. Maybe he has been all of those. But he has never been a defacer. He would give anything to assure them that, should he ever encounter the rock, he will keep their secret safe.

In the sky above there is an impending battle between light and dark. The sun has been hiding behind a thick cumulus cloud, but when the cloud slides past, it peeks out again. Light streams through the canopy, forming tiny twinkling stars through the rustling birches, then shines through an opening like a sparkling sword. In the next moment, a low rumble in the distance. A tumble of dark clouds has amassed in the north. It's too late to turn around now.

Following the sound of the river, Charlie slides past a rotted-out birch whose white bark has peeled away. He climbs over a fallen limb, caught by the finger-like branches of an aspen, and wades through a bundle of pink thistles, mingled with white daisies and purple blue bells whose petals crumble at his touch. When he comes upon a patch of low-lying ferns, he stops to take a leak. When the flow stops, there is still a distant trickle.

Charlie wades through the brambles in pursuit of the sound, until he comes upon a sloped clearing. In front of him lies the stone. It is angular, and taller than the surrounding rocks, just as his father had described it. At its peak, a jagged ridge that resembles the angled head of a giant bird poking through. A toppled cedar rests against its side; young saplings have sprung from a mound of humus. Charlie steps back, trying to assess whether the rock may have been ripped from a massive outcrop, or if it may have been a chunk of meteorite that had fallen from the sky. He descends the slope toward the rock, but stumbles over a downed log. He grabs a sapling to brace himself, but his hand slips away, and his leg crashes against the jagged corner of the stone, driving both of his knees into a deep decay of leaves. At the base of the slope, defying the drought, the trickle makes its way toward the river.

The sinking sun, defiant of the oncoming storm, has aligned with the tree-tops overlooking the west side of the river. Its rays poke through the barren pines like shiny daggers, nearly blinding him. Charlie scrambles around to the illuminated face of the rock. He reaches out to run his hand along the stone, cold and damp and smooth. He uncovers no wads of paper, no secret signs wayfarers may have left, but, feeling along the edge of the rock, his fingers find the deep crack where the shaft of light will pour through. Peering up at the threatening sky, he holds on, waiting for that brilliant beam, that flash of perfection, before darkness swallows the light.

# FICTION

THE TROUBLED NARRATOR

# Trouble

Sunrise in the east, shining off the struts of the bridge ahead. I'm thinking that's why they call it the Golden Gate. We'll be in San Francisco before long. Should I wake Cerise?

No, I think I want it quiet for a little longer. Though I am sleepy, driving almost seven hours straight through the night from Brookings. I guess it'd take longer in daylight, coming down Route 101. I could sure use a rest stop. We only took the one, filling up on gas. Something like 380 miles, a bit more from where Mom and I live.

Driving my mom's old Chevy Equinox, hoping it won't break down like happened once before. Mom's away this weekend, up in Vancouver, Canada, which surprised Cerise on Wednesday when I told her, that mom would leave me on my own.

Mom's boyfriend, Phil, taking her to Vancouver in his airplane. A get-away she called it, saying I'd be fine for a couple days. Otherwise, I couldn't have the car. SUV, I guess I should call it.

Cerise says this is our get-away.

With Cerise asleep, not looking at me, I've had time to think. This all happened kind of sudden. I think maybe she's in some kind of trouble, somewhere behind us, back in Brookings.

Mom says I'm a slow but steady thinker. Kids back in Brookings-Harbor High School used to say I'm just not bright. Maybe so. But I get there, eventually.

I'm pretty sure driving Cerise south isn't too bright, not knowing why she had to leave so quick. Yet what could I do? She asked me. She's always been kind, never made fun of me, back when we worked together at Kroger, her a cashier and me bagging.

That was my second job, after the car wash. Now, I work at the pharmacy as a clerk, which Mom says is a step up. I called in sick so I could drive Cerise.

I think she's seven years older than me, Cerise I mean. Maybe eight or nine, I'm not sure. I'll be twenty later this year, and looking forward to being twenty-one, but I have to wait for that.

"Morning, Richie."

"Oh, you're awake."

She stretches and I'd like to watch but I'm driving.

"Need money for the toll, Richie."

"Sure." Mom keeps coins in the center box or whatever they call it. I start fishing them out. "How much do you think it is?"

"Eight dollars."

"Oh, that much? There's not enough coins."

She chuckles, "It's alright." From her purse she gives me a ten-dollar bill.

I like it when she laughs. It's a sound better than our cat's purr.

Once through the toll, I say, "Cerise, I'm going to need to stop."

"We both do. Let's find a restaurant. Get some breakfast."

A good idea. "Okay."

■ ◆ ■

Not much is open this early. Cerise directs me down Park Presidio to Geary Boulevard, then west. We find a Starbucks she knows about that opens at 6:00. We wait, parked on the street. I can't help yawning.

I'm worried about spending money. Whatever I earn goes in my savings account or to Mom, except for my allowance and the change I put in the piggy-bank. Allowance is $15 a week, though I usually only spend about half that so it does build up. I like one meal a week at McDonald's, that's where my money goes. Mom says if I eat there too often it wouldn't be healthy. Anyway, I have $61 on me. I thought about raiding the piggy-bank, too, but Cerise was in a hurry and it takes too long to get the coins out unless you bust it, but I've had the piggy-bank since I was eight so I didn't want to break it.

I guess if I never go back, I should have busted it. Is this forever with Cerise? I've been afraid to ask.

"What's the matter, Richie?"

See, she knows me really well, can tell when I worry. "Nothing. Just what happens after we eat?"

"Then we get some sleep."

"Oh, sounds good." Do we sleep together? I'd like that. Cerise is...well, I mean...she's sexy. And I, well...sometimes dream about her and me.

"You're blushing, Richie."

I'm embarrassed, so I say, "Look, I think the Starbucks just opened."

※ ◈ ※

Well, we do sleep together, sort of. Cerise says she doesn't want to stay in a motel, so we drive into Golden Gate Park, find a quiet area and sleep in the car. Let the seats go back and try to get comfortable, which is difficult since I'm six foot four. I fall asleep pretty darn quick; I don't know about Cerise.

When I wake, needing to find a bathroom again, Cerise is sitting up making a list. It takes me a while to realize she's torn out the last page of my book to use for paper. I don't like that; it's the first nonfiction book I've ever read completely, all about dogs and how to raise them. I've always wanted a dog. Still, I don't say anything to Cerise.

"You okay now, Richie?"

I must have scowled. She leans over and kisses me on my cheek, "It won't hurt your book. I just needed a sheet of paper. It's a blank page from the back."

I fear my bad breath from sleeping might offend her, despite the kiss. "That's okay. If you needed it." It's not the first time she's kissed me. It's the fourth. Once on the forehead and now three times on the cheek, always my right cheek.

"We need to drive further south. We can leave the park and fill up on gas. Remember, no credit card. We use cash for the gas. Alright?"

"Use their restroom, too."

She laughs, "Yes, that too."

Though I do wonder why only cash. My mom mostly uses a credit card. Maybe that's just Cerise's way.

※ ◈ ※

I met Cerise at work two years ago. Well, really two years and seven months, plus, I think, six days. Brookings is a town of old folks mostly, that's what Mom says. Lots of retirees come up from California to live in Brookings because of its mild climate and reasonable cost. Brookings is peculiar climate-wise. The

131

furthest north you can go on the coast and get the Medi…darn, what do they call it?…Medi-something climate. Mediterranean, right?

Cerise said she'd come to Brookings three years earlier with an older fellow, but he died and she didn't inherit anything, so that's why she got the job at Kroger.

I know she dated around. Likes what she calls older gentlemen, well-off widowers ideally. I guess she's kind to them, too. Maybe even more than kind, like kissing them, too.

After we gas up, we go down Route 1 to the 280 Interstate, then on to 17. I was in San Francisco once with Mom when I was twelve, but I've never been further south. Cerise says we're going to Monterey. I've heard of it. There's an aquarium there that's famous. She promises I can go see it.

She has us stop in Santa Cruz, which is on the north side of Monterey Bay. We have lunch there. She wants to find a place where she can buy a phone, one of those temporary kinds. I know she has her own phone, and I offer my cell phone, too, but she insists. I tell her I'm going to a drug store or supermarket to buy toothpaste and toothbrush since I didn't have time to pack. We agree to meet at the car in half an hour. "Don't leave without me, Richie," she laughs.

"I wouldn't, Cerise. Not ever."

She makes sure I lock the car. She's got two duffle bags and a briefcase in there. Had them with her when she showed up at home at eleven on Friday night, wanting my help. Wanted me to drive her out of town.

As I start to walk away, she asks, "You have money, Richie? Don't use a credit card." She comes to me, digging in her handbag, gives me a hundred-dollar bill. Says, "Here, take this." Then pats me on the shoulder, more a rub than a pat, maybe what's called a caress.

Looking for a drug store, I'm thinking I've never had a hundred-dollar bill of my own before. I've seen them many times at Kroger and at the pharmacy. Then I think about Cerise touching me. I have to quiet that thought or I could embarrass myself, being all stiff.

Not that I will use the hundred. I still have the two dollars change from the toll booth, plus my own money. Anyway, the hundred has a corner that's purple and purple is my favorite color.

After the drug store, I find the public bathroom, just where the clerk said it would be. I brush my teeth, not really liking the Colgate toothpaste but they didn't have my favorite, Pepsodent. Look at myself in the mirror. Mom says I'm handsome if I don't let my mouth hang open. I try not to. Not sure I look handsome today, mostly tired despite the hours of sleeping at the park. I should have bought shaving stuff, too.

When I get back to the car, Cerise isn't there yet. I can see where she spelled her name on the window at dawn, going through the toll booth. In the damp dust on the window, though it's not damp anymore. It makes me smile seeing her name even if it's faint now. A smudge, I guess.

I'm tempted to look in Cerise's bags, mostly just to smell her scent on the clothes. She doesn't use much make-up or perfume. What she uses, though, has a spiciness to it. It kind of turns me on. She noticed that when we worked together. I once got stiff right there in Kroger, but she was nice about it, sort of brushed me down. Said it wasn't the time or place.

I'd like us to have the time and place.

The briefcase has initials on it: GEP. So I guess Cerise must have borrowed it or got it second-hand. We get a lot of things second-hand at home. Not so much lately, since Mom and Phil have been dating.

I see Cerise coming down the street. She's wearing black Capri pants, like Mom wears sometimes only Mom's aren't as tight, with a white button blouse that has three buttons undone over a red tank top, black low-heel shoes, the leather looking soft, earrings but no other jewelry. Her long dark brown hair is swept back with a red cloth headband. She's five ten, I know. Slim but muscular. She works out at a gym, I think. Pretty much perfect. I can feel myself getting a little stiff just seeing her.

"Time to head south, Richie," she calls, a big smile.

Another hour's drive, then we go to Cannery Row and the Monterey Bay Aquarium. I admit I'm excited. Cerise pays our entry using her stack of hundreds. She even holds my hand for a bit, then we agree to meet a half hour before the café closes.

I try to visit as many exhibits as possible but barely get through the first floor, liking the sea otters and the tentacles exhibits best. I probably spend too much time watching the octopuses.

When I join Cerise at the table, she's on her new telephone saying to someone, "I've got to go, my beau is here."

I think she says boy at first, so she explains the word beau. That pleases me, her beau like in boyfriend. If she is my girlfriend, then maybe it could be forever. Like, might we marry?

We have a snack, a coffee for her and a hot chocolate for me, and we share a poppy-seed lemon cake.

"Do we sleep in the car tonight, too?" I ask.

"Not tonight."

"Where do we go from here?"

"You want to stay together."

"Sure. Forever."

"What about your mom?"

That does bother me. I don't really want to leave my mom. At least I need to say goodbye properly.

"Trouble will find us," she says. "If we stay together."

She's right. My mom will be really upset with me. "Maybe I could call my mom."

She sighs, takes my hand. "No matter where we go, trouble's right behind us."

I like her taking my hand, it makes a flutter in my stomach, but I don't know what to say. I could ask what trouble, but maybe I don't want to know. Does she mean with my mom? I don't think that's it; it must have to do with why she needed to leave Brookings. I'm not sure.

Still, I probably need to explain to Mom. For now, Cerise does need my help, and she's my girlfriend—I think. All I finally say is, "It will be alright." My mom says that a lot to me.

Cerise smiles, pats my hand, "Sure it will." Then she excuses herself to go use the ladies room.

I wait. After a little while, I get worried about the poppy seeds. Could they be stuck in my teeth? So I go to the men's room. I guess I didn't have to worry, the hot chocolate must have washed all the poppy seeds down.

When I go back, the café has closed. It's maybe an hour until the aquarium closes. Since Cerise is not here yet, I think I could go back to the second floor and see more of the exhibits, so I do.

Even when the aquarium closes, I can't find Cerise. I go to the car, she's not there either. I can feel my breath come and go in quick bursts, and I'm all sweaty. Could something have happened to her? The trouble she talked about?

Then I go back to the aquarium but I can't get in now. So back to the car. When I go to unlock it, I find it's not locked. The spare car key is on the driver's seat with a folded note, another page from my book. I read it: *Thank you, Richie, for helping me. C.* Her bags and the briefcase are gone.

I don't know what to do. I'm close to crying but Mom says big boys don't cry. On the back of the note, it reads, *PS Drive back home, Richie.*

I'm not sure what PS means. Is there someone with those initials I'm supposed to drive?

Then it hits me, she can't be walking with the duffle bags and briefcase. Somehow she got another ride. With someone else.

I don't cry, but my eyes get wet. For a moment I think I might heave up lemon cake and hot chocolate.

That night I sleep in the car again. On Sunday, after getting gas with the hundred-dollar bill, which I didn't want anymore, I drive north. It's a long way, ten hours plus with stops for lunch, restrooms, and more gas. Summer, so it's still almost light out when I pull into our driveway. Mom's not home yet. She said not to expect her before 11:00 tonight.

I know I was peeved for much of the ride. Peeved is a word my mom uses sometimes, it means angry, like in an irritated way. Peeved with Cerise. Maybe more than just peeved. I thought a lot about her, our times working together, how she said I was her favorite bagger, and even at the pharmacy she'd come see me sometimes, like last Wednesday to say hello, how are you, Richie?

I make a supper of scrambled eggs and toast. Hot sauce on the eggs. Chocolate ice cream for dessert, with sprinkles. Then I go to bed, just too tired to stay up for Mom.

Morning, and Mom is real chipper. "Did you enjoy yourself this weekend, Sweetie?"

I think about that. It was an adventure, I guess. I don't know what to feel about Cerise. She wasn't really a girlfriend. She needed help, so I helped her. And, anyway, I got to see the aquarium. I wish I could tell Mom about the Monterey Bay Aquarium. Normally I tell her about everything I do, but I'd be in trouble with her for driving all that way. Also Cerise is kind of a secret, and I'm guessing it could make trouble for Cerise if I tell. "It was…just okay."

"You missed me, Richie?" she asks smiling, as she cuts her grapefruit in half.

I say "Sure" even though it's not true. I don't want to lie to Mom. Not wanting her to ask me more, I say, "Tell me about your weekend."

# Man of the House

by Moira Sullivan

"Robert, I worry about you ending up old and alone," said Mom, growing quiet, her large violet eyes starting to tear. We were sitting on white wicker chairs on the front porch of her Wisconsin home after dusk, watching the sky fade from yellow to orange, to bright red, then purple. Amid cricket chirps and the snorts and snuffles of grazing cows, the day came to a gentle end.

"Don't worry. Everything is fine the way it is." It was my standard response.

"But it's not fair to you," she said. "And what about Iris? Your father thought you two were so, so…"

"Until we weren't," my cryptic response was designed to stymie further conversation. How could I explain Iris' refusal to understand my familial duties? Mom and I had become especially close during Dad's decline as I assumed his responsibilities, like mowing the lawn, maintaining the garden and orchard, and repairing damage from the occasional storm. Now that he was gone, I felt responsible for Mom's safety and happiness.

What were my siblings doing to help? Quite a lot, they would claim. My older sister Em and her family lived in a posh suburb. A dramatic redhead, she devoted herself to managing her family and coaching girls' soccer. My oldest sister Jo was just weird—all brain embedded in a pale, pudgy body—obsessed with completing her arcane PhD thesis.

When I asked Em to visit Mom on holiday weekends, she claimed to be too busy with family demands. She suggested I ask Jo, who always bristled at Mom's unwelcome advice about her romantic pursuits.

Clipping my words, I said, "So, I guess it's me. Again. This weekend."

"Rob, don't be such a martyr. After all, you are the favorite son," said Em with a dry laugh.

"And the only one to my knowledge," I noted.

"You're racking up the cosmic points."

"You mean karmic?"

Her mood shifting, she snapped, "Look, I don't have time to argue with you."

"I thought we were talking," I said, adding, "Well, then I'll bring Greg with me for company."

"That loser?"

"He's a nice guy in a difficult situation. And he's been out of work for a while."

"I hope you're not lending him money."

I didn't answer.

"You are, aren't you? Dammit, Rob!" Retreating slightly, she said, "Okay, it's your business. But he can't hold down a job."

"Em, I told you what happened. Not his fault; the world isn't kind to dreamers."

"Oh, is that what he is? I think there's more to it. You always try to see the good in people, but this guy? He doesn't seem to be the kind of guy who exerts himself."

I fell silent as Em began to mutter under her breath, a sure sign of irritation. I caught something about "picking up strays," which I didn't dignify with a reply.

That night, I called Greg to make plans. He told me that he appreciated everything I was doing for him. This made me feel good. The next morning, I drove to Evanston to pick him up in my SUV. Smiling, he emerged from his apartment, a gray beret surfing his thick and unruly black hair, a Hawaiian shirt covering his generous frame, the beneficiary of too many double cheese, triple garlic pizzas. He apologized as always for not having the money to pitch in for gas and, without asking, tuned the radio to the local classical music station. On the way, we called Mom on the speaker phone.

She sounded excited. "I'll wait until you boys get here to fire up the grill." I could almost hear the tremble in her voice when she said, "Maybe you'll want to wear your father's grill master apron and hat. You know how he loved to barbecue."

"We'll see," I said, without enthusiasm. I wanted to make her happy, but there was no way I was wearing that cheesy thing.

"Mary, we'll be there in an hour," said Greg.

I felt a twinge of irritation when he called Mom by her given name, but I let it pass.

During the drive, Greg shared his ideas for a TV sitcom. He showed me his new business card with the job title "Imagineer." I'd always admired Greg's artistic talent during our time working for a nonprofit publication. Unfortunately, his alcoholic boss had written him up (unfairly, he told me) for missing a major deadline. After losing that job, he was never able to land another worthy of his talents.

We traveled country roads past a strawberry farm, fields of corn and soybeans, and meadows with grazing cows, sheep, and horses. Windows down, we enjoyed the grassy fragrance of freshly mown alfalfa and the changing scenery—rolling hills, small maple groves, and wetlands with wading birds.

Approaching the 600-foot drive, I beheld Mom's rectangular limestone behemoth and the surrounding four acres of land. The grass was long and thick enough for our neighbor to harvest for his dairy cows, once I'd cleared the branches left by the windstorm. The lilac bushes were still exhaling their heady perfume along the driveway and behind the house. How could anything disturb me this close to heaven?

Mom was so happy to have company that she had bought brats, beer, and sauerkraut—the Wisconsin trifecta. Before we started the fire, Mom insisted on bringing out Dad's grill master garb. I held out my hand to take it but then, in a move that surprised everyone, even myself, I handed it to Greg. As he happily donned the official uniform, I took Mom aside and explained that Greg had lost his parents early in life and I wanted him to feel that he belonged. She teared up and hugged me, telling me that I was a good friend.

We set up the grill, then put on the brats and burgers. Mom's spread included German potato salad with bacon and vinegar, broccoli raisin salad, coleslaw, and, for dessert, Racine Danish Kringle. We drank cold Sprecher root beer rather than the local brew because we'd be driving home that evening. As Mom had never met Greg, she asked him a million questions about himself, discovering their shared passion for classical music and opera. She even found the photos of his tame squirrel charming.

The visit was so successful, our trips to Mom's became a regular weekend event and I enjoyed Greg's company on the long drive. Greg had a bad back in constant need of adjustment, so I tackled the heavy work, while he consulted with Mom about energy meridians, furniture placement, and *feng shui*. Mom and Greg would drive into town to look at paint or wallpaper, and leave me to clean the furnace, whack weeds, or burn trash—things I enjoyed doing.

I was so happy to be taking care of Mom and bringing a friend who was such good company that I must have missed something. A lingering glance? A hug that lasted a little too long? I just didn't see it.

Greg looked forward to our visits and began sending Mom cards, starting with her birthday in July. Mom loved the company as well, waiting on us hand and foot. On the rare occasions when Greg didn't accompany me, Mom became irritable.

She'd ask me, "When are you bringing Greg again?" followed by: "It's not the same without Greg" or "I need Greg's help."

███

One night in late August, Greg and I were sitting on the front porch after one of Mom's delicious meals. It was after dusk, so the mosquitoes weren't biting. In the kitchen, Mom was busy making the iced organic tea that Greg preferred. As he smoked a cigar—one of his small indulgences—he advised me to exercise more and find time to relax and meditate. It was true, my middle was thickening and my blond hair thinning like Dad's. On the other hand, it was hard to take advice from someone who had so little going for himself.

Greg sighed. "This is a beautiful place, Rob. You sure no one in the family can take it over?"

"No, Greg, we all have jobs in the city. I've tried commuting, but it's too far from the train."

He sighed again. "It's a shame it'll pass out of your family."

We fell into silence as a thousand fireflies exploded on the front lawn.

███

By early fall, I didn't have much time to visit or take care of the grounds. I convinced Mom to find someone local to do the yard work while I was traveling on assignment. I can't remember who suggested that Greg stay with Mom on weekends. Maybe it was after she tripped on the carpet and broke two ribs. Mom needed help and Greg was available.

After I returned from a three-week assignment in India, I received a call from a worried Em. "Have you heard from Mom?" she asked. "I think your friend is staying with her at the house."

I cringe when I think of it now, but tired and jet lagged, I said, "At least someone is looking after her!"

Em retorted, "I'm not sure who's looking after whom."

"Then why don't you try visiting her? It's all on me." I had my own problems. The constant stress, lack of sleep, and unhealthy food were taking their toll. My blood pressure had risen precipitously, and I'd started drinking a little more than usual just to sleep.

When I phoned Mom, she was unhelpful and unsympathetic. "I told you to take care of yourself. You're going to end up just like your father. Greg walks for an hour every day. He's going to start a walking group in town."

"Mom, I do exercise. Somewhat."

Mom snorted. "Greg told me how he tried to get you to exercise. I swear you're going to drop dead like your father."

"Mom, is Greg still there?"

Mom sounded girlish, animated. "Yes, Honey. He's in your old back bed-room. Want to say hello?"

Greg joined the conversation. "Hey Bro, it's all good. After I couldn't pay the rent, the building engineer let me keep my stuff in storage until I get on my feet. I'm living out of my suitcase now. Mary, er, your mom, gave me a place to stay just 'til I get another job."

"That was certainly nice of her, but I wish you had told me. You're able to help her with things?"

"Of course. I've got Mary, your mom, on a vegan diet. She'd been complaining about her acid reflux. Right, Mary? No more red wine in the evening—"

I heard an "Oh you!" in the background as she and Greg laughed at their private joke.

"When you come up to visit, I'll show you where we're planting herbs next year."

Next year? This was something Mom and I had talked about—growing organic herbs to sell to local restaurants. "Really? Can you put Mom back on the phone?"

"She's in the kitchen, getting the snacks—her famous kale chips! Your mom is a great cook. We just started a movie, so I don't want to keep her waiting."

"Never mind. I'll call back later. Have fun."

⸏ ⸏ ⸏

It soon felt like things were getting out of hand. Mom became harder to reach. She was suddenly involved in renovating the house. Her daily calls were now weekly if I was lucky. Then there was the disturbing porch incident. We had talked about painting the porch before winter but when I called Mom to plan the project, she seemed distracted.

"Well, Dear. I know we discussed it, but I need to check with Greg before you do anything."

"Mom, what do you want to do?"

She seemed flustered at this. "Honey, Greg is much better at—"

I had to interrupt her. "Mom, what are you talking about? How many houses have you owned and restored? Two? Three?"

"Honey, I can't talk about it now."

"Mom, put Greg on the phone, right now."

"Robert, I don't like your tone. I'll have Greg call you later when you've calmed down."

"Mom!"

Click…

⸏ ⸏ ⸏

A week later, Jo gave me an earful. Mom and Greg had driven down to meet Jo's new boyfriend who had volunteered to manage Mom's finances. Greg had nixed the investment opportunity in favor of a plan of his own. Jo reported that Mom had gone blonde, looking ten years younger, and a slimmer, jauntier Greg was now sporting a plaid beret. At the same time, Jo chastised me for having introduced Greg to Mom.

We met at Em's home for an overdue family meeting. Em looked impressive in a blue linen outfit, her curly red hair showing traces of gray. Jo, now on a keto diet, seemed edgy, her hunger intensifying her bad mood. Both sat facing me, sharp-tongued and out for blood.

Shaking her dyed black hair, Jo started the blame fest. "This is your fault, Rob. We'll never get rid of him now. It's up to you to do something."

"What do you expect me to do?" I asked.

Em continued the attack, "More like undo. You're so damned dense, Rob. Nothing matters to Mom except having a man."

I rose to Mom's defense. "It's been five years. Doesn't Mom deserve to be happy?"

Em and Jo paused to consider my point.

I started to pace. "But why Greg?" I continued. "He's so, so—"

"Refreshingly average?" said Jo.

Before I could react, Em grabbed my arm. "Can't you see what's going on here? Look, we've all been replaced—even you, the favorite son. Mom needs to protect her assets and we need to make friends with the enemy."

I was thinking that I was already friends with said enemy.

Jo shifted the focus to Mom, her favorite scapegoat. "She's betrayed us! And you most of all, Rob. You need to get back in circulation. We have lives. All you have is your job and Mom."

Em chimed in, "and us."

Jo nodded.

I must have seemed unconvinced because Jo added, "Really, Rob," and gave me an awkward hug.

"I need time."

"Don't wait too long," said Em.

■ ● ■

I drove up to Wisconsin that weekend, a cold lump in my stomach and adrenaline surging through my veins. The neighbor's daughter, who'd been watching the house while Mom and Greg cruised the Caribbean, told me that Mom had become the talk of the neighborhood. She had been seen drinking wine on the front porch with a younger man, maybe two. On my way out of town, I stopped at the hardware store where the owner asked about Mom, as usual, but was too curious about "her young fella." I cut the conversation short, probably exciting even more speculation. I fumed all the way home, earning a speeding ticket for my trouble.

When we received postcards signed "Love, Mary and Greg," I knew it was too late. My siblings were of two minds: *Let her enjoy herself*—from Jo; *I don't want to see her on Dateline*—from Em. When the house sitter said they had returned relaxed and tan with matching tattoos, my heart sank.

The next weekend, I drove up to see for myself, bringing my own brats this time as Mom was now vegan. The change was startling. Mom was vibrant, full of life, and Greg seemed to have purpose. I should have been happy for them, but I felt a sour taste in my mouth and a bitterness in my heart. I felt old and alone, an empty husk.

I joined Mom in the kitchen to see if I could help. Seeing my pained expression, she put her arm around my waist and squeezed. "Don't be so sad. I'm doing this for you too, Rob."

"What do you mean?" I asked, feeling my body stiffen.

"You need to live your own life," she said. Just then Greg shouted something and Mom handed me a plate of corn for the grill.

Greg was smiling at me in his grill master apron and hat. As I silently, deliberately placed the corn on the grill, he pulled me aside to hug me, saying, "I have to thank you, Bro."

Escaping his grip, I shouted: "*Do you think I planned this for you*? You don't deserve her!"

Greg put his hands up and backed away, "Whoa, whoa, wh—"

Then I lunged at him. I ripped the apron from his body and bloodied his nose. The hat ended up on the grill, seared to perfection.

I walked away without looking back. What had I done?

But what had he done to me? Whatever small injury I inflicted was nothing in comparison. Greg was looking for a soft place to land and, thanks to me, he found one. How did I not see my role in this? A little later, I walked back to the house to find Mom and Greg sitting on the white wicker chairs on the front porch, waiting for me. Mom was silent, even grim, as she applied a bag of ice to Greg's swollen nose as dark bruises bloomed under his eyes.

Wincing with pain, Greg asked, "Are we okay?"

"I honestly don't know, Greg. But I am sorry."

Greg made a gesture like, forget it, and continued to speak, "You don't have to worry about Mary. I'll take care of her; I want to take care of her."

Mary took his hand and smiled, apparently believing this comforting fiction.

But I knew better. He wouldn't be able to take care of Mom like I could. It was in that moment that I decided on my course of action; I'd become a master gardener, a gardening angel so to speak.

I'd take care of Mom's property like I've always done. It's a big place, so I'd have to live onsite. Resurrecting those lilac bushes will be a full-time job. I won't say anything about that now. Let things settle down. Best just to smile and stay friends with the enemy.

"Hey, Bro, how about that hug?" I asked.

# Doe

by Cathy Chester

The sound of tumbling pebbles bouncing off one another suspends my thoughts of life and family. Turning towards the source, I gaze upon a magnificent brown doe. She isn't large, but I still keep my distance. I watch as she paws her way toward me, stopping every three or four steps to munch on the sweet white clover covering the landscape. I am close enough that my scent gives away my presence, yet this beauty continues to come closer. Inexplicably, the doe sighting calms me and brings me to a place of contemplation.

I started the day with thoughts of my sister's recent death. I can't believe how much I miss just holding her hand or sharing family happenings even though she understood little of what I was saying. I would smile when she responded in what we lovingly called Lynisms. She would roll her eyes or shrug her shoulders with a questioning twist of her hand. Other times she would utter her infamous line, "yeah, right," at just the right moment. To us, they were pieces of remembering Lyn.

Still dealing with the grief, I question my own life. How much more do I get? More importantly, what have I done with what I've been given? That's the one! Have I done anything with my life? Have I lived a good life? Adding more mayhem to these thoughts is my rejection of established religion, compromising my essential nature of embedded beliefs.

I had to get away to sort out my thoughts.

A six-hour drive did not have the hoped-for effect. I checked into a motel overlooking the Pennsylvania hill country and went for a walk.

Which is how I got here. The area reminds me of a camp I explored as a child. I fell in love with legends of crooked trees and sacred sites. I was enthralled by dew-dampened mornings and anxious over the prospects of finding new paths to follow and creating new tales to share as shadows crept around each tree when the sun began to set.

The walk turns into a lengthy hike, and now I am sitting on a fallen log admiring a doe.

Watching the doe, I feel a strange connection. She edges closer until she is only a foot away. I smell the earthiness of her coat and feel the warmth emanating from her body. I stand up, step forward, and stroke the soft velvet-like hair on the doe's forehead. She looks directly at me.

"Who or what defines a 'good life?' There are many scholarly beliefs. Go ahead, pick one." It's as if she is speaking to me.

I peer into the doe's eyes, my mind a tangle of confusion.

"Pick one? How can each person choose their own definition? Chaos would reign."

The rebuttal comes instantly. "And there lies the center of your questions, Terri." Along with, *is this doe real?* "Are we actually speaking, or are you simply talking to yourself?"

Skeptically I reply, "That last part goes without saying. How do you know my name?"

She casually goes back to grazing. After a few minutes, I turn to walk away, knowing that all of this is in my mind, but Doe draws me back, "I know you recently experienced a loss."

As tears fill my eyes, I respond, "I said goodbye to my sister years ago as she drifted away, suffering with dementia. A few months ago, we lost her physical being. Family makes up a large part of the labyrinth of my life, and losing a sibling has led me to much soul searching."

"You don't handle loss very well," replies Doe, "yet that is the very thing that brings you here. You seek things that I cannot answer. You don't receive wisdom; you discover it for yourself."

I look away for a second. I can't believe I am still standing here talking to an animal. I turn back, but Doe is already scampering off.

When I return to my motel room, I turn on the TV. It pains me that many of the same issues I protested and fought for in my youth are now resurfacing on the nightly news: wars, discrimination, injustices, political mayhem. I jerk the plug out of the wall socket, and silence and darkness fill the room with a sudden spark.

Opening a window, I peer at the sky. The stars shine brighter than I've seen in years. I stare at them for a long while. I listen to the calming sounds of owls hooting and feel the wind blowing gently, causing the curtains to sway back and forth. The energy here is the antithesis to what is happening in the real world. I soak in as much as possible until I finally lie down and sleep.

The next morning, I follow the path to where I think Doe and I came upon one another. The woods all look the same. What if we don't reconnect? What if it really was all in my head?

Doe comes strolling down the hillside and chides, "You need to learn patience, my friend. Nature does not hurry; everything is accomplished in its own time."

Gently Doe nudges me toward a tree stump. She curls up with her legs beneath her and continues. "Terri, what is it that you're really looking for?"

That stopped me. What indeed? Not wealth, not power. Certainly not immortality. Then what? And it came to me. "I want something that I can leave for the future. You know, a lasting legacy."

Doe's eyes closed, but I could hear her thoughts. "Really? I'm not sure that is what life is about: leaving something."

"Okay, then what is it?" I wonder.

"Knowing yourself is the beginning. You continue to be consumed by events that have led you to this point in your life. That is where you should begin."

Doe nuzzles my hand. Suddenly I am back on the Edmund Pettus Bridge in Selma, Alabama, March 25, 1965, waiting for Dr. King to speak. He stands on a box at the front and begins leading us in prayer. "Be jubilant, my feet! Our God is marching on. Glory, hallelujah! His truth is marching on." His words ring out, and we link arms showing our united front as we begin to walk. With all my heart, I believe that by breaking through the police barriers, we can break through the walls of racial discrimination. We are full of hope and determination. Fear envelops me with every step as armed Klansmen and State troopers surround us. Only a week ago, the beatings and deaths of Bloody Sunday are still uppermost in our minds. However, the outrage we feel instills us with courage, and we walk boldly toward whatever fate lies ahead. Others are overcome with fear and retreat seeking safety in the anonymity of the crowd. Many who try to melt into the crowd are met with violent blows from the butts of the Klansmen's rifles. The loud snarls of the dogs nipping at our legs echo the screams of those being beaten and deepen our resolve to continue.

My body shakes as I sob at the memories and anger of that day. I feel the coolness of Doe's nose returning me to the hillside. I ask her, "Why did you take me there? I have worked for years trying to forget the memories and pain. What gives you the right?"

"I don't control your memories. The interpretation is yours."

Doe is still lying on the ground. I look for solace as I lean into the curvature of her body. She brushes her head against me. I am in Washington D.C. with the masses at the Lincoln Memorial listening to Dr. King. "…When we allow freedom ring from every village and every hamlet, from every state and every city when all of God's children will be able to join hands and sing in the words of the old Negro spiritual: Free at last! Free at last! Thank God Almighty, we are free at last!"

People are jumping into the Reflective Pool to escape the intense heat. I join them. Water splashes everywhere. It cools my physical and inner being. I float, bouncing off others. I shout, "Free at last, Free at last," wanting it to be more than a dream. But as in real life, dreams are usually short-lived, and suddenly, I am back with Doe.

"Why did you pull me away so quickly?" I ask. "That is a comforting memory."

"In dreams, we enter a world that is entirely our own. Come back tomorrow, and we'll continue."

With a heavy heart I respond, "I'm not sure I want to."

Doe walks away, then turns, "Terri, you always have a choice."

I stomp back to the motel kicking at every leaf and stone I can find. Doe thinks she has all the answers. She doesn't feel my anguish. My thoughts are more chaotic than when I got here.

This night I find no peace, no gentle breeze. I struggle to keep my eyes open because I know what the next memory will be and I don't need a touch from Doe to remember it. It is the one that haunts me the most. It took place in my city, where I grew up with life-long friends, feeling safe, and learning my core values.

The attendees enter the hall for the 1968 Democratic National Convention in Chicago as protesters shout their opposition to the war in Vietnam. I hear a voice booming over a bullhorn; "Disperse, or you will be arrested. You are breaking the law!"

I can feel the intense heat of the horses' breath streaming from their nostrils on this humid August night. I hear agitated stomping of the horses' hoofs beating against the ground. I hear the shouts of the police. We are shoved across Michigan Avenue and pushed further into Grant Park. The scared horses rear up on their hind legs and trample anything below them when their forelegs fall back down. A man runs past me, his head bleeding profusely from an indentation above his eye. The cut matches the curvature of a horseshoe. He runs a few more feet, then collapses. A peaceful protest quickly becomes a chaotic melee. Bottles are thrown, explosive thumps are heard as tear gas canisters erupt and fill the air. The chasing, swinging, and clubbing is indiscriminate, and tensions rise on both sides.

Jolted awake from a car's backfire, I touch the deep, jagged scar on my shoulder, reminding me of the blows from the nightsticks wielded by the police. I remember the intense pain as my open wound filled with the burning chemicals of the tear gas. The dream stirs up so many heinous memories that I can't close my eyes for the rest of the night.

At sunrise, I walk into the woods where Doe is waiting for me. She quietly says, "I wasn't sure you would come."

"To be honest, I wasn't sure either."

I begin telling Doe my dream and flashbacks. I attempt to keep all the details correct as my mind speeds on and on. I grab paper and pencil from my backpack and start to write. I write about the gay rights movement in June 1969. Police arrested patrons for their mere presence at a gay bar during the raid at Stonewall Inn in Greenwich Village. I write about standing silently in solidarity with other protestors along the sidewalks of Chicago's Clark, Diversey, and Halsted Streets. That was only a beginning. Since then, doors have opened and some have slammed. The struggle goes on.

"Why do you feel the need to write?" asks Doe. "You have the memories."

I stop writing and look at her. Why indeed? It takes me a minute. "I need to share the story! We still face these same injustices sixty years later. There are some issues where we have taken steps backward. I feel society is failing."

Doe responds gently, "What matters, Terri, is what you have done. Your legacy is that you believed in doing the right thing."

I begin to gather all my papers. "Why do I still feel like a failure? None of this has ended."

"At the center of your being is your answer; you know who you are and what you want. A journey never comes to an end; it goes on in others. Let your family continue walking the labyrinth. Be here for them; support them, love them. Help them see what is essential and that neither success nor failure will ever define them as well. Let that be your legacy.

"Terri, it's time for me to go."

"But I have more questions."

"And you will find the answers."

I wake, finding myself in a hospital room. I push a button, and a nurse appears in the doorway.

"Glad you finally joined us."

"Where am I? What happened?"

"You're at Allegheny General Hospital. I'll be right back, let me get your doctor."

I turn my head, and a shooting pain stabs my temple. I carefully lower my eyes and see that my arms are bruised. I look into a mirror and am shocked at my reflection. My face is swollen, and my head is bandaged. I try to get up just as the nurse comes back. She caught me as I was about to fall from dizziness.

"You're going to be woozy for a while. Call if you need to get up; better yet, don't get up. You were in a car accident. You swerved to miss a deer running across the road and crashed into a tree. You have a concussion and bruising but luckily, no other injuries."

The nurse continues filling me in as she checks my monitors. I've been in a coma for three days and will have to stay a few more days before I can be released. My family is on their way. The nurse leaves.

In the silence of the room, I realize Doe actually was a figment of my imagination. But my memories aren't, and neither is the message I come away with. History is not there to like or dislike or to use as a tool to determine our life's value. But it is how we learn. If we are offended by it, all the better; we are less likely to repeat it. At least, that is my hope.

One thing I've decided: I'm going to return here every year or two. That hillside is my place for sorting things out. Perhaps generations from now, my family will find me here in dreams, circling on the wings of soaring birds or, by chance, feeling a warm breeze twisting through the branches of billowing trees. And if they are lucky, in the company of a young doe.

# The Unraveling of Sylvie Plum

by Meg Salzman

"Morning, Sunshine" are the first words I hear most days. Harry makes the coffee the night before, the timer set for 6:00, at least an hour before I wake. We are not morning chatterers, but each day I pad downstairs in my too-large slippers, smell the welcoming aroma of dark roast coffee, and look forward to Harry's loving greeting. That morning was different: total silence, no greeting at all.

Finally, Harry handed me the coffee, just the way I like it—sweet cream, extra hot. "You may want to have a good gulp, Dear. Trump did it. He won."

I laughed. "Good one. You got me!"

But then I saw his face. Immediately my limbs felt heavy. As I slumped in my chair, my kitchen felt unfamiliar. Later I went to the gym, talked to no one, took an extra-long shower, and handled every task with Herculean effort.

That night I watched Harry divide his pork medallions, potatoes, and asparagus so they do not touch. I have been watching this for about 35 years. I used to find it endearing, a quirk, something that makes him who he is. After all, I like quirk. But lately quirk annoys me. The months of screaming at the news, uttering profanities, once throwing a shoe at the TV, have accomplished nothing. My threat to move to Canada is moot—I can't cook and Harry is an excellent cook. I didn't want to move anyway.

My husband, Harry J. Plum, is a balding, past-middle-age man, my *only* love. Harry is a man of few words, which made him immensely attractive to me. He is a Data Scientist, which according to *Harvard Business* is the *Sexiest Job of the 21ˢᵗ Century*. Harry has always been sexy.

Our friends like to call our little group "the nearly elderly." My dear partner in crime, Dorothy, coined the quaint term when we all turned 50, which was a while ago—but who's counting? Dorothy likes to send me witty poems and satirical essays from *The Paris Review* and the *The New Yorker*. We met at a baby shower 30 years ago when I mentioned loving my visit to Monet's garden at Giverny. She handed me a glass of chilled white wine and said, "Thank God you're here. I'm so sick of oohing and aahing over tiny clothes."

Dorothy and her husband Desmond never had children, and I never asked why. I've always figured people tell you things they want you to know. To our daughter, Sadie, and our son, Luc, our friends are Aunt Do and Uncle Des. Dorothy and Des have been present for most birthdays, communions, graduations, and weddings. Our relationship with them goes beyond friendship. Beyond words, even.

The day of the inauguration was bleak. I busied myself painting and listening to Beethoven. Mozart was far too tame for the occasion. I splashed bright colors on the canvas, my small version of revolt, the cell phone set to vibrate. Nothing could tame my thoughts. Even the squirrels playing tag in the garden annoyed me. The persistent hum of the vibrate sound startled me and I ignored it, but when I saw who it was I reluctantly answered.

"It's me. I'm taking the train to Chicago tomorrow for the Women's March and you're coming with me. I'll pick you up at 8:00 am. It's going to get busy."

Dorothy always got straight to the point. All of my other friends texted to see if I was busy. Dorothy just figured, hell, what could I possibly be doing that was more important than talking to her?

"Alrighty then." Suddenly I felt happy, like a schoolgirl. With giddiness I added a large crimson brushstroke to my canvas. Beethoven matched my mood, so I cranked up the volume and threw the cell phone in a drawer.

The next day, Saturday, was warm for January. The Metra train was packed, and when Dorothy and I filed out of Union Station we joined a flood of marchers—white-haired grandmothers, young mothers with babies strapped to their chests, and couples holding hands. People were smiling, chanting, even dancing. Just as the rally in Grant Park was about to start, someone shouted out, "Ready to go! Fired up, Chicago?" My senses were overwhelmed in the best possible way as I stood a little taller and screamed to the sky, "Yes!" I felt fierce, shameless, powerful.

That night Harry made me seared Ahi Tuna and Lemon Coconut cake. When I first met Harry I fell in love with his bedroom eyes…right before I fell in love with his lemon coconut cake. I savored small bites, wanting to memorize the meal, the moment.

"Honey, I know you've been upset lately," Harry said. "I thought this might tame the beast inside."

"You are better than I deserve, Harry. And this is better than I deserve." And I meant it with all my heart.

We lit a fire in the dining room, and I began the ceremony of making Harry's favorite cocktail, The Last Word. We only had it on very special occasions because it called for a sinfully expensive green chartreuse liqueur made by French monks.

"I guess we're in the money, Honey," he chuckled. "What bank did you rob?"

"You're hilarious. Sweetheart, I want to tell you about the day. It was impressive." I proceeded to spend the entire evening recounting every detail, every encounter, every speech.

"It sounds like you had a good day, Dear. Mine wasn't nearly as exciting. I think I'm going to read a bit before bed. Join me?" He patted my head.

"No, I'll clean up the kitchen. You go ahead. I'll be up later."

I reflected on the day, wrote in my journal, and trudged upstairs, surprised to see Harry already asleep. When had he started snoring so badly? And why did he pat my head? What was I, a toddler?

That fall I arranged a surprise retirement party for Harry—the least suspecting person in the world. I could have hidden a corpse in the linen closet for decades, and he wouldn't have noticed. But—modest as ever—he took it all in with great humility and appreciation as his bosses and colleagues toasted him again and again.

By 10 pm Harry had nodded off by the fireplace, and most of the guests had left, except for a small group of bigwigs at the dining room bar. As I approached one of them said, "Well of course we can't let in those people. That's why he's building the wall."

Someone else chimed in, "That's why I voted for him. We finally have a guy who knows how to get stuff done."

Stunned, I fumbled for my manners. The feelings—the numbing silence from that post-election morning—flooded back. I marched to the closet with as much speed and determination as I could muster, and threw the heap of coats at them.

"Thank you all for coming, people," I said. "But I'm afraid the guest of honor is sound asleep."

"Shouldn't we say goodnight to Harry?" mumbled one frizzy-haired blond.

"I'll give him your regards." I overheard them talking as they walked to their cars. These people were co-workers. But they weren't friends: not my friends, not Harry's friends.

"Well that party ended quickly," said one of the men as he approached his car. And I shrieked down the sidewalk, "You're welcome!"

The next few years things really fell apart. I did not recognize the world anymore. A president who tweeted? Bans on Muslims entering the US? Treating Nordstrom's dropping of Ivanka's fashion line as big news?

Harry and I eventually stopped watching the news together. He once tried to calm me during a commercial, and I seethed at him: "Do you have a pulse? How can you not react?" I immediately regretted the outburst, but the damn thing had been said and the hurt was done.

I found myself less interested in going to the gym, less interested in painting, which had always been my refuge and my passion. Friends called and I didn't pick up, I waited days, sometimes weeks, to call them back. Laundry piled up in baskets, Christmas decorations in March, no apologies.

Harry had no problem filling his time. He read old comic books, bought an electric bike, volunteered at church, and built a fort for the kids next door. He always invited me to "share in the fun," but I always had an excuse. Even though Harry was not a couch potato, he was at home more. I began noticing small things, like his grunts and groans when he exercised, his throat-clearing, his little piles of stuff seemingly everywhere.

January 6, 2021, a day etched in memory for everyone. My mind was a mess; images of the Capital building being stormed by angry mobs, five people dead, Congress hiding, nobody in charge to say no, this is not what we're about. Harry and I held hands on our worn sofa, stuck together like glue in disbelief. He softly cried.

"Sylvie, this is not us."

"We have had greedy, power-driven people at the top before, Harry. What scares me the most is this mentality, that anything is okay to get what you want. People have given themselves permission to say anything, do anything. The *it's all about me, and screw everyone else.*"

Months went by, warm days of summer, fall colors, Christmas, and someone at the top who looked like what we were used to. He was calm, he rarely tweeted, and he didn't spread hate or call himself a genius. But people stayed in their corner of the ring, people talked about those damn liberals, those out-of-touch conservatives. People were still hungry, or just power-hungry. People shot each other, old wars, new wars.

The novel I was reading seemed more realistic than the world around me. It was about a woman who time-traveled from the 14th century, and was now navigating the technology, culture, and mores of the 21st century. The protagonist was coping far better than I, and I fantasized about swapping lives with her. The 14th century had Black Plague and we had Covid. People isolated, people wore masks. I had been preparing for this for several years, I guess. It seemed as if everyone else joined my world—the world of being alone. The anger continued, boiling, boiling.

I took a break from the novel I was half-heartedly reading to check Facebook. I hoped to read something uplifting, but instead found a poem from a young woman who sat next to me in Figure Painting class. Andrea and I had not talked in several years, though I often thought of her. We normally painted in silence, but after class she had shared her plans to go to college. I read her Facebook status slowly.

> I never thought it would happen to me
> Feeling like a prisoner and having to flee
>
> Born and raised here in the States
> Hiding with people, like fish bait
>
> We waited for this for about three years
> To do the right thing only left me in tears
>
> If only the world knew how I felt
> No amount of advice could ever help
>
> A forced separation between mother and
> child, like dumping a baby alone in the wild
>
> I understand the way that this works, but I'll
> never forget how much this just hurts

For a long time I was motionless. My cell phone squeezed in my fist, I wanted to pulverize it. I held my breath, tried to control something. Maybe when I started to breathe again this horrible thing would not be true. I pictured Andrea's sweet face, and her mother who picked her up after class each week, always apologizing for being late, though she wasn't. Mrs. Martinez cleaned houses during the day and studied English at night. It was obvious that in addition to being her mother's English tutor, Andrea was her sun, her moon, and her stars. I called Andrea but the phone number I had now belonged to someone else. I asked around and found out that Mrs. Martinez, who lived for 20 years in our little town, had returned to Mexico. One person thought Andrea had moved away, but didn't know where. Was Mrs. Martinez afraid of being deported? Was she deported? My anger stewed bright red, further consuming me.

One gray Monday morning Dorothy called. She was her usual perky, *I have something to tell you that's really going to wow you* self. "You're never going to guess our luck," she whispered. "Des's uncle died and left us his cottage in Ireland. We're all going. Start packing."

I had barely gotten off the couch that week, and the thought of packing almost did me in completely. But I packed.

The flight was uneventful. The thatched roof cottage, nestled in the countryside just outside of Monkstown, a village on the Lee River in County Cork, looked like something out of a postcard. The kitchen Dutch door opened up to hills of green and a flock of bleating sheep. Our bedroom window in the loft overlooked Monkstown Bay. The first Sunday we were there Harry roasted a whole lamb in the stone fireplace. In true American fashion we made too much food, so the next day Dorothy invited the neighbors for "leftovers." The neighbors, Maude and Patrick McGinty, had known Des's uncle, and they came with an assortment of homemade cheeses, which they proudly placed in the center of the table.

The McGintys had a good sense of humor, teasing us about our custom of potluck, apparently unknown in Ireland. Des's Uncle Fred had initiated them to this custom, thus the platter of cheeses. Patrick patted me on the back as he left. "Sylvie, your first time in Ireland, you'll have to come to the auction in Cork. It's a fine affair." Four days later the rest of our group played golf and Patrick kept his promise, educating me on livestock auctions as we drove.

Patrick dropped me off at the entrance to the fairgrounds, and as I looked back at his trailer, filled with sheep to sell, I was thrilled to be on my own, welcoming the adventure. I soon realized that the livestock auction was a social event in Ireland. There were families gathered around picnic tables, munching on sandwiches and crisps, a male quartet singing something called "The Boys of Fair Hill," which I learned was a Cork favorite. A woman handed me a bidding card. I tried to explain that I was not here to buy but she was already on to the next person. The auction began with a group of five sheep entering the pen while the auctioneer chanted rapid-fire gibberish. I remembered Patrick's advice, "Don't scratch your head or raise your hand unless you want to bring sheep home in your big fancy American airplane."

Once in the car, he said, "Sylvie, I have one more stop to make before we go home." The constant light rain stopped, so we opened the truck windows. I felt lulled by the landscape that swept by—the gentle glens, mist-chilled fields of green, wooden bridges, poky sheep in no particular hurry to cross our path. We approached a town whose square was flanked by rainbow-colored buildings, and Patrick pulled around to the back of a shop.

"Patrick McGinty, I was beginnin' to think you were swallowed whole. I was expectin' you hours ago," a large woman shouted.

"I'm sorry, Mary, but the auction ran long, and I wanted to show our new American friend, Sylvie here, all the glory of our bit of heaven." Mary and I exchanged quick hellos and the two of them began unloading boxes. And I thought there were just sheep in the trailer—I counted twelve boxes in all.

When we entered the shop I saw a large hand-painted sign: "Welcome Friends from Ukraine. Everything is Free." Mary explained to me that the community was tired of just watching the news and decided this is what they could do to help. The shop was set up for anybody who arrived from Ukraine, many who came with nothing but the clothes they wore. There were dungarees, pajamas, coats, baby clothes, car seats, strollers—everything you could imagine. I spied a small play area that had toys, began tinkering with the miniature cash register, and picked up a baby doll that said "mama" when I held her.

All of the toys had hand-written, signed notes. The children in the local school wrote the notes to welcome the Ukrainian children.

A strong longing danced around the edges of my soul, a longing for this rarified feeling to last as long as possible. I shouted out to Patrick that I was going to sit in the truck while he finished up, and to take his time. Patrick had the grace to pretend not to notice the tears that rushed down my face. It was all too much for me. And then it seemed plain as day that I had to sort myself out. I feigned sleep and Patrick let me rest for the journey back home.

When I returned to the cottage I sat in the fading light and thought about the small town of farmers who had few possessions, who came together to help strangers from halfway around the world. I wrestled with my shame—disgusted with the cocoon I'd created, and I resolved to change this.

After supper Harry and I took a walk down a narrow path and sat together in the tall grass, sharing a tartan to keep us warm. The quality of the air made me feel light, lighter than I had felt for a long while. Here I was in a country that was not my own, and yet I felt more connected: connected to Harry, to the people around me, and especially to myself. I felt a renewed hope entering time, and space, and me.

"You seem happy, Sylvie. I'm glad you're back."

I caressed Harry's bald head.

# Journey Interrupted

by Carol Orange

Peter's phone call disturbed me. He confided he needed to get away and asked if he could visit us in Mijas this July. I let my kid brother know that I'd love to have him join us. I detected a downbeat tone in his voice. When I asked him what was wrong, he told me that his principal had sent a written warning about his sixth-grade classroom being out of control. He was afraid of losing his job.

I assured him he was a wonderful teacher. I had visited his classroom this past spring and watched him inspire his students, making sure each kid had an opportunity to shine. The noisy classroom was a result of interactive learning activities.

Peter thanked me for my encouragement but admitted he really blew it by telling his principal she'd done an outstanding job. She'd misinterpreted his compliment as manipulation, making her even angrier.

"Are you sure it's okay to come? I won't be sparkling company."

"She's nuts. I don't care what other people think. I love you."

After our conversation Peter wrote that he hoped to ease into European life in Mijas. He intended to explore Spain by train for the rest of the month—visiting Ronda, Seville, Granada, Madrid, Toledo, Salamanca and Barcelona, places he'd read about in Hemingway's stories. Europe had been a fantasy for Peter ever since he became a sixth-grade teacher.

I prayed Peter's spark would return by spending a week with us at our summer rental, an old adobe house on a cobblestone street in Mijas—an Andalusian village perched on a mountain overlooking the Mediterranean. Mijas—where the former liberal mayor hid in a family closet for thirty years during the Franco regime, his bravery giving the town a heroic luster. Mijas—where Steve and I hoped we could revive our marriage. If we couldn't recapture our passion in this scenic village, with our young daughter Gracie, when and where could we ever be happy?

Gracie turned four a few weeks before Peter's arrival. Already she knew how to count to ten in Spanish, and sweetly inquire, "*una coca cola, por favor.*"

The night before Peter came to Mijas, Gracie sat on my lap for her bedtime story as the summer light flooded the room. When I kissed her goodnight, she imitated the way her uncle wrinkled his nose. "That's what he does when he sings."

I pulled the drapes across the windows and laughed at how my daughter was fast becoming a crackerjack mimic.

Gracie and I waited for the plane to arrive at nearby Malaga airport. Steve, the quintessential university professor, had decided to remain in our parked car where he could read his book in peace. He wasn't missed. Gracie sat still for a short time; barely enough to calm my frayed nerves. She played with her stuffed elephant and every few minutes popped out of her plastic seat in the arrivals lounge to ask if Peter had arrived.

"Hope he likes it here," I said to her.

"Will he sing?" She squeezed my hand.

"Your favorites."

"Uncle Peter," Gracie yelled out loud.

Sure enough. There was Peter ambling toward the arrivals lounge. He carried a leather suitcase in one hand while his guitar case lay slung over his other shoulder. As he approached, I noticed his eyelids drooped. He seemed oblivious to the two attractive American girls with backpacks who stared at him as they walked by. This was not the Peter I knew.

He lifted Gracie up for a hug and nuzzled her ear. "Gracie baby," he said… with less than his usual enthusiasm. After she wiggled from his arms back down to the linoleum floor—her body propelled into its perpetual state of motion—he reached up and hugged me.

"Stacy-Macy," he said.

That affectionate nickname started a long time ago when we played Monopoly as teenagers. I recalled how seriously we once took the board game, as if we were playing for high stakes instead of paper money.

When Peter and I no longer lived in the same house, we shared our lives via weekly calls. I worried our close relationship made Steve jealous. Instead, he isolated himself by using our sibling chats as an excuse to board himself up in his office, researching his "bestselling" books of political essays.

Steve strode into the arrivals lounge, much to my chagrin. I feared he'd ruin our reunion, but when he greeted Peter by punching his arm as a sign of affection, I felt relieved. Peter released Gracie's hand to give his brother-in-law a bear hug.

"He's here," she said to her daddy. "See Mommy's smile."

I felt happy for the first time that summer.

"You must be tired," Steve said, offering to carry Peter's bag. Although Steve hated small talk, he asked Peter about his trip.

"Met a pretty stewardess."

Steve perked up. "What did she look like?"

I rolled my eyes, thinking how it was just like Steve to fixate on a good-looking woman he didn't even know. My husband had perfected a knack for irritating me.

"Let's go, Honey," I said, grabbing Gracie's hand.

"I want Uncle Peter," she balked, looking back at him as I pulled her along.

We piled into a white Siat. Steve and I sat in front while "Gracie baby" and Peter relaxed in the back. We rolled down the car windows to catch the breeze. I turned around in my seat and asked my brother for news. He spoke about his favorite student, Ernestina: how she had agreed to write one paragraph a day during summer break. He felt proud of Ernestina's talent, thought her stories showed promise.

I reached back over the gearshift and patted Peter's knee. "Those kids are damn lucky."

"Not really." He looked down at the floorboards as if they contained something of interest. "The principal berated me for my out-of-control classroom."

"You don't deserve this. I've seen how much those kids admire you."

"Are you going to lose your job?" Steve asked.

Peter shrugged. He made funny faces for Gracie. Theirs was a familiar routine. He raised his eyebrows, then poked his forefingers into his cheeks. She giggled.

Steve drove along an old road, winding through adobe villages nestled in the scorched hills. We passed shimmering olive trees bordering small vineyards. I noticed my clenched fists and realized the landscape's pastoral beauty could not dispel the underlying tension between Steve and me.

We reached the high midpoint of the mountain road to Mijas. The Mediterranean appeared as a wavy blue-green stripe, jumping out from the dry landscape as a horizontal brush stroke in an abstract painting.

Peter stuck his head out of the car window. He gasped at the view and said, "Let's stop for coffee."

The midday sun beat down on the red tile roofs of the whitewashed houses in Casares. A few steps into the village we found a small café with outdoor tables under canvas umbrellas. A radio blared inside. Peter sat facing the sea and put his arm around my shoulder.

"You did it, Stacy-Macy," he said.

"Did what?"

"Got me out of the Upper West Side."

Steve complained about the heat, pulling each sticky T-shirt sleeve away from his skin. "We need iced coffee," he whined. "Bet the bartender won't know the right way to make it."

"*Una coca cola, por favor,*" Gracie asked the young waiter who had appeared. Peter applauded his niece's Spanish.

"How did she get it?" he asked me.

"Get what?" I asked. But I knew he meant Gracie's self-confidence and felt troubled he seemed to have lost his.

"She adores you," I said.

Peter sat back in his chair, puffing on a cigarette. Then he blew three smoke rings, delighting his young niece with this small piece of theater.

"Do it again," she begged, jumping out of her chair, and throwing her arms around his knees.

Steve had followed the waiter back to the café's bar and emerged with a satisfied expression. The bemused waiter served us three glasses of iced coffee and a Coke. He made a fuss over the pretty little *señorita*.

"I was blown away by your book about why the working class supports the Tory party," Peter said to Steve.

"Why thanks," Steve said. "I hadn't realized you read it."

The drive to Mijas took another half hour. After we parked, Peter sighed, "I need to pinch myself." Upon crossing the threshold Gracie slipped her hand into his, and with her leather sandals slapping on the tiles, they raced to the upstairs kitchen. By the time I caught up with them, Gracie had already introduced Peter to Ana, a diminutive, dark-haired Andalusian woman of 50, the housekeeper and chef who came with the rental.

"*Hola,*" Ana said. "*Como estas?*"

"*Muy bien,*" Gracie answered for her uncle.

Lunch was served by the small pool under a straw-covered breezeway. The first course of cold gazpacho soothed my parched throat. For the next course Ana served *paella*. We scooped up morsels of fried squid, steamed mussels, and *chorizos*. The *sangria*, combined with the afternoon heat, made us giddy. Steve designed a face on his plate, using discarded pieces of *langoustine* tails, while Peter's eyes widened at our gastronomical excess. He pointed to the large number of empty mussel shells on the table. "Never even saw them on the platter," he teased Steve.

Peter seemed more and more like himself, and when Ana brought out the creamy flan for dessert, he compared its smoothness to a woman's belly. This was Peter at his literary best. He worshipped Hemingway.

"*Delicioso,*" he told Ana.

She graced him with her thin-lipped smile before returning to the kitchen.

"So, this is how the other half lives," Peter teased.

Steve picked up the saltshaker, sniffed the air, and said, "All it takes is brains—not that some of you schoolteachers aren't smart." Although Steve respected Peter's dedication to the craft of teaching, he believed university professors deserved their prestige. His tone reeked of condescension. I felt like kicking him under the table.

Before I could say anything, Steve opened his cloth napkin and put it on his head. Peter followed suit. The sangria must have hit them because each man tried to outdo the other by making funny faces for Gracie. Their boyish antics amused me—until they dominated the meal. It dawned on me Peter had been flattering Steve all day, from asking him questions about his new book and saying "Wish I could write like that" to imitating his zany behavior.

Ana came to our rescue with espresso.

"I need a nap," Peter said after draining his cup.

I looked at my watch. "Wow…three o'clock."

It was late for Gracie's siesta. I excused myself and put her to bed. Then I went to my room to lie down. I had a headache.

Steve, who adapted to a slower Spanish rhythm despite his ambitious drive, also thought a siesta was a good idea. Finding me lying on our bed, he pulled me to him, reached under my T-shirt, and fondled my breasts. I winced, pointing to my forehead.

Steve's recent overtures had felt more like expressions of his physical need than real passion for me. What happened to the sensitive lover I had met at Cornell? We'd had so much fun making out in the back seat of his Chevrolet.

That evening the four of us visited the fishing village of Torremolinos. Avoiding crowds at the glitzier restaurants, we ate *tapas* outside at a small bistro in the main plaza. Young Spanish men and women paired off in a mating dance called *paseo,* a formal walk around the square in clear view of their chaperones, who gossiped on park benches along the sides while keeping an eye on their adolescents. This style of courtship seemed both charming and stifling. Unfortunately, from my own experience, I knew courtship was not a good predictor of marital bliss.

After dinner we went to a nightclub where we watched a flamenco troupe. Gracie wore her red and white polka dot dress. With her dark hair pulled back into a ponytail and small red plastic hoops dangling from her ears, she could have passed for Andalusian. The dancers' foot stomping and hand clapping pulsated in the room, and as they undulated around each other on the stage, I felt warmed by their sensuality.

During the troupe's intermission Peter and I joined other couples on the dance floor. His head held high and his raised arms clapping, he moved gracefully around me. "You look Spanish," I said.

"It's amazing what a little sangria will do," he said. "Thanks for letting me stay here."

Out of the corner of my eye I caught Steve's disapproving look. I didn't care. I hadn't had this much fun in years.

A few nights later I felt more tired than usual after Ana's curried goat dinner. It was close to midnight before I went downstairs to sleep. As I lay half-awake on the bed an evening breeze, as warm and welcome as my brother, caressed my face. The evening at home had been delightful. Peter told jokes at dinner, making us laugh the whole time. It seemed his depression had lifted. And as our old closeness returned, my mood improved—even toward Steve.

Peter and Steve remained upstairs. I overheard Steve's voice as he spoke. And Peter, always the good listener, said, "Oh really" several times. A few more words drifted downstairs—"beautiful," and then "sexy." When I heard Steve say the name Peggy, I sat up. Peggy was the new assistant professor in Steve's department.

"She's crazy about me," Steve said.

"Have you two had sex?" Peter asked.

"Yes."

"Does Stacy know?"

"Not yet."

"Maybe this will make her appreciate you more," Peter said.

*Damn.* Peter was playing up to Steve, but why hadn't he expressed outrage at his infidelity? His encouragement of Steve felt like betrayal. As I massaged my throbbing forehead, I prayed Steve had invented the Peggy story to impress Peter. But who was I fooling? Steve could turn on the charm. I recalled him telling me our chance meeting at Cornell's cafeteria had been *designed by the Gods.* Now I wondered how I could have fallen for such bullshit.

Peter's words echoed in my head. Betrayed by my brother, the one person in the world I trusted. My stomach cramped, and the joints in my fingers ached as I clasped my mouth to fight off nausea.

I heard Steve bang the ashes from his pipe against the metallic ashtray, his signal for wrapping things up. When he came into the bedroom, I pretended sleep. He lay down beside me, and soon I heard heavy breathing. I wanted to kill him. Instead, I tiptoed into the bathroom and took two aspirins.

The next morning at breakfast I avoided eye contact with Steve. I disregarded the orange juice he offered. As soon as Gracie finished eating her eggs, I asked Ana to take her to the morning market where she'd buy *patatas* for our lunch. I drank coffee with restrained dignity. The only noise in the room came from the crunch of toast being buttered and consumed.

When Peter arrived for breakfast, he gave me a kiss on the cheek.

"How's Stacy-Macy this morning?" he asked. He helped himself to coffee, sat down and stirred in the sugar and milk.

"I want you to leave the house," I said. I stomped my foot as I faced him.

His eyebrows rose in surprise.

I couldn't believe the sound of my voice—as if its disembodied shrillness belonged to someone else. I frightened myself with the string of nasty words tumbling from my lips—"traitor, Judas, male chauvinist bastard—never want to see you again," I said.

"And as for you," I yelled at Steve who sat across the room, staring into his coffee mug. My eyes slanted with venom. "Don't you even try to explain yourself. I'll be civil for the rest of our stay, for Gracie's sake, but when we return home—all bets are off."

I'd made sure Gracie wasn't around to hear me. Exhausted, I sank into an easy chair and cried.

Throughout my tantrum Peter remained silent with his arms crossed. He looked more like an ice sculpture than the brother I loved. His aloof stance resembled our father's. I picked up the woolen shawl from a nearby chair and wrapped it around my shoulders.

The following day Peter left Mijas. He did not travel to the other Spanish cities. He took the next plane directly back to New York.

A few weeks later Peter and I made up. "I'm begging you to forgive me," he said on the phone. "I was stupid to support Steve. I wanted to please him."

"I'm leaving Steve," I said.

"Hope I didn't have anything to do with this," said Peter.

"Not really. It's been percolating for a long time."

"I'm sorry about the divorce."

"We're going to need your support—more than ever."

"I'm there for you and Gracie."

When Peter came to visit me in Boston, Steve and I were filing for divorce. His books had been packed and sealed in cardboard boxes. Over the weekend Peter played Candyland with Gracie. He sang silly songs as he pushed her on a playground swing. He helped me cook dinner and wash the dishes. We didn't discuss the Mijas disaster, yet it lay between us like a submerged island. On the surface we were back to our old relationship of Peter and Stacy-Macy. I'd forgiven him, but I needed more time to heal.

# Like Treasures Guarded by Dragons

by Hugh Schulze

Mom says: "Love is for pussies" which, I admit, I really didn't understand until I was maybe ten years old, the night she locked Tag out of the house.

They had been bickering all morning. Just after noon, he left to watch the game at Madigan's. Usually she'd go with him. After Detroit's winless 2008 season, Tag and Mom had switched from doing shots after every touchdown or field goal to one after every car commercial.

It was bad enough he had left her there for the game with Chicago. It was her birthday, which, of course, I didn't want to mention and make her madder.

If there was one good thing about her staying home and Tag being gone, it meant I didn't have to pick up the empties in the living room or vacuum the Cheetos crumbs and Doritos bits. When she is mad, Mom is a cleaning machine and I know better than to ask if I can help. "You want to help, Nathan?" she'd say. "Go outside. Find a friend."

She turned the TV on as background but shut it off at the end of the first quarter with the Lions up 14 to 7. I could feel the tension building and kept checking my bedroom window to see if Tag might wise up at half time and come home. But he isn't one to wise up about much of anything. That's something he tells other people to do.

I keep my room pretty clean, if I do say so myself. (Tag called me a freak when he saw me use a level to put up my Star Wars posters.) Back then, before I had a computer, I had this little clock radio I found in somebody's trash one day and snuck into my room. Mom would have blown a gasket if she heard me listening to the game, so I kept it under my pillow on low and was able to hear the Lions go from being seven points up to being down 24 to 48. Forty-eight?! I kept doing the math in my head.

I put my coat on and walked to the kitchen where Mom sat smoking a cigarette and sipping a beer in the breakfast nook. I knew she knew the final score and this would not, as they say, "bode well" for Tag's return. Mom stared at me like I had just beamed down from a spaceship.

"Where are you going?"

"Out."

"You got a problem with me smoking in my own house?"

"It's nice out. I thought you'd want me to go out."

She paused a long while, looking out the window like she was seeing if I was lying.

"Good," she said. "Go. Make a friend."

Plan A, as I figured it, was to run into Tag on his way home and remind him that it was her birthday. Things like birthdays and holidays didn't interest him much but we'd all be better off if he remembered this one. It's a ten-minute walk to Madigan's, a straight shot along the two lanes of Elizabeth Lake Road. I also didn't see him face down in the drainage ditch that runs along the road. (It's happened.)

It was cool and gray and damp like the sky wanted to cry. From outside, I could hear that the jukebox was back on. The TVs were turned down to Sunday games only gamblers like Tag were watching. I steered clear of the door as it swung wide and a stew of human voices spilled out. A guy in camouflage jacket and jeans stepped out for a smoke. I froze. I didn't want Tag to think I was spying on him, so I put Plan B into motion.

Plan B was basically Plan A without Tag. Earlier, I checked the refrigerator and saw there was no cake or celebratory sweets of any kind. A quarter mile further on from Madigan's was the Mondo Mart where Mom and Tag buy their vodka, beer, and cigarettes. I had eighteen dollars and thirty-five cents from the money jar hidden in my room.

I thought maybe Tag would go in on the birthday treat. But I figured I had enough money to pull off Plan B on my own.

* * *

I've always found something magical about the Mart. Like one of those caves of treasures guarded by dragons. Before you even enter, there is fire(wood) and ice sold on either side of the front door. And inside?! Inside everything is Gold and Silver, Sparkling and Gleaming, Krispy and Krunchy, Diamond and Starburst, Sun-kissed and Lemon-fresh, Scrumptious and Sugar-coated, Zesty and Sexy, Cheddar-boosted and Hickory-roasted.

Eighteen dollars and thirty-five cents is not nearly enough for so many treasures, so I kept my eyes focused on the floor to get to the rack with donuts and coffeecakes. There, I found the last box of six cupcakes—chocolatey goodness in hard frosting and soft sponge. (I remember checking the Expiration Date which I still think was pretty good for a ten-year old.) I found a small package of birthday candles too. I had enough money for both. As I walked by the candy, I counted the black floor tiles.

The cupcakes had two lines of white frosting twisted like strands of DNA across the smooth chocolate: nine dollars and fifty-three cents with tax and candles included.

Old Man Richter didn't bat an eye, didn't ask where my mom was, just rang me up and asked if I wanted a plastic bag. "There you go, Nate-eroo," he said. No one else ever called me that. Why would they? It made my shoulders hunch up as if I'd shoplifted or something.

I walked back faster than I had come. Down the sidewalk back to Hospital Road, I saw no one else. I wanted to beat Tag home. I didn't stop at Madigan's to listen for his boozy voice. All I heard was the Iron Maiden song I hate on the jukebox and the knuckle-crack of pool balls.

It was possible he was back home, so I paused on the front porch to listen for any arguing before going around to the back door. Unfortunately, my mother was in the kitchen cooking. She'd want to know what was in the bag. I wanted to keep it a surprise until after dinner, so outside the back door, I set it on top of the large antique milk can she and Tag used as an ashtray in the summer. The cool October air would keep the cupcakes fresh.

"Where have you been?" she asked before I even closed the door.

I was surprised she wanted to know. "Went for a walk," I said and hung my windbreaker on a coat peg.

"Everybody seems to have plans today," she said to the spice rack on the wall. Then she stepped away from the stove and the macaroni and cheese she was stirring to slide the deadbolt of the back door into place. It was something she did every night before going to bed, but I'd never seen her do it without Tag in the house.

I was going to ask her if Tag was home, but she left the kitchen, crossed through the dining room and living room to set the deadbolt on the front door.

I could tell she'd been waiting for me so she could lock up the house. I knew better than to ask any questions.

I assumed at least two of the three beer cans next to the stove were empty and felt a tightening in my stomach. Mom calls my worried expression my "whiny bitch face" and when she returned to the kitchen I fully expected her to tell me to "wipe that look off my face."

Instead, she said: "Wash your hands" and stirred diced ham into the mac and cheese.

I quickly washed my hands and brought out two presents from my bedroom. I'm not the best wrapper in the world but I spent five dollars and fifteen cents (tax included) on the tissue paper and ended up using most of it because even with three layers of tissue you could still kind of see the red packaging underneath.

Tuesday through Saturday, Mom juggled full family orders at Dawn's Stacks and Macs, so it was a piece of cake for her to carry my plate in one hand, while balancing her own on a can of Bud Light. She stopped dead in her tracks when she saw the presents.

"What is this?" she asked, setting my plate down to move the presents.

"Happy Birthday!" I announced.

"Why don't you go and grab something to drink?" she said.

It was starting to get dark outside. As I took the last ginger ale from the refrigerator, I counted the four remaining beers and did the math; if Tag wasn't home soon and mom drank them all, she might fall asleep on the couch. Less than four, she'd become a little madder and meaner with each beer. On the other hand, he'd have at least one to wave around like a mood fogger as he rambled and tried to calm her down with stories about some of the regulars at Madigan's. I closed the refrigerator door and returned to the table.

"Thank you for the presents," she said as she lit another cigarette. She shook the match and threw it on her dinner plate.

"Go ahead and open one," I said. I wasn't feeling very hungry.

She smiled and squinted against the smoke. "I'll open one before dinner and one after." I noticed for the first time that she had gotten her nails polished. Blue daggers tore the tissue paper.

I'm sure she could tell from the shape of the carton that it was cigarettes. She got as far as *Pall Mall* when we both heard Tag at the front door.

He jiggled the handle back and forth but found it was locked. Then yanked it harder, but the handle wouldn't budge.

Mom took a long drag from her cigarette. "Go to your room."

I sat there thinking maybe I should stay if Tag was in one of his moods. But by that time, I knew it would only make things worse. I wasn't sure what to do. "Go on."

He knocked a couple times. As I walked down the hall, I saw his shadow as he tried to peek in through the shades. I shut my door halfway and heard him curse, fumbling for his keys.

The key unlocked the door lock, but the deadbolt held solid. He pounded again and called "Meg?" His voice was spongy from the beer and (probably) whiskey.

I kept my door open a crack and listened. I figured he'd go to the back door if she just sat there saying nothing. But I heard the chair squeak as she stood up. "Tag?"

He stopped working the key in the handle. "Who the f____ you think it is?" (Except he didn't say blank.) "Open the door."

"What's the magic word?"

"What?!" he said angry and confused at the same time. "'The magic word?'"

"Yeah. The magic word."

"How about you open it before I kick it in?"

Neither one of them said anything for a moment. Then Tag pounded his fist harder. "Meg!" Then his voice softened a bit. "C'mon. I gotta piss like a racehorse."

"Say the magic word."

He slammed his palm against the door. It sounded like a shot through the house. I could hear him breathing. "Okay, okay. Look. I love you."

I thought she might be putting out her cigarette, maybe reaching for the deadbolt. Instead, the silence after those three words was like a fuse to something more explosive than any missed birthday.

"What did you say?" Mom was not asking a question. She was giving whoever she was talking to an opportunity to take back what they had just said or admit they were wrong. Saying "Nothing" when you were asked only made things worse.

At least Tag was drunk enough not to answer.

"Don't you dare!" she screamed. "Don't you dare use that word to me!"

172

Tag was as quiet as I was.

"That word means nothing. Less than nothing. Show it! Don't you dare say that word. That's all you do is talk, talk, talk! Show it! Show it!"

She waited for some response, then kept on. "All those songs by cheats and selfish pricks? And the movies? God, the movies. Show it! Just show it!"

She screamed the last two words loud enough that I wondered if the neighbors would call 911 again. I quietly closed my door. Outside my bedroom window, Tag peed into the bushes.

Then I froze. I saw his silhouette at the window, hands against the frame, trying to open it. I usually kept it unlocked in case there was ever a fire in the house, but I heard him curse when he found it locked. When I was at the Mondo Market, Mom must have locked every window in the place too.

I heard him tugging next at their bedroom window. I'm sure mom heard it too. In the kitchen, another beer can went *schtock*. Then I heard her drag a chair on the kitchen tile and imagined her sitting in the gathering darkness as he tried the handle on the back door.

I reopened the bedroom door a foot or so to listen. Mom was probably, like me, expecting him to plead a little more. The sun was down. He must have been starting to feel the October chill.

"Mags," he finally called out, then almost like you'd call a dog. "Mag-gie."

I heard her change positions in the kitchen chair.

"Tell me something, Maggie." His voice was a little less drunk and that worried me. "Tell me. How can anyone show you something if they can't *show* you something?"

She said nothing. The chair creaked.

"What if I have something to show you? What if maybe I have a surprise?"

"What are you talking about? I'm so sick of your talking."

"Come to the window.... Come on. You don't have to open the door."

It was only then, like an idiot, I realized he had found the cupcakes and candles.

※ ◈ ※

I imagined rushing out and telling her Tag was lying. That I was the one who bought her birthday treats for nine dollars and fifty-three cents. I imagined having her check the receipt. I imagined her keeping the deadbolt locked. But since my life always turns out worse than I imagine, I try not to believe my imagination.

I closed the door and climbed under the covers with my clothes on. Tag was shouting: "*My* house? You're locking me out of *my* house?"

When he slapped her, I admit I felt some relief. It meant they might talk. If he had punched her, I might have to go into the kitchen. Either way, Mom never cried.

"It's my birthday," she said. I wasn't sure if she said this to stop him from slapping again.

"I know that!" he lied. "I knew that!"

A chair was dragged across the floor.

"Here! Here, have your cupcake. Here. Happy now? Eat it!!"

I lay there for a long time but couldn't make out what they were saying and didn't dare go in the kitchen. Their argument was like a fire going out, then flaring up every few minutes, then dying down again. Their bodies thumped, shifted and settled like burning logs.

I stayed awake not knowing if Tag might come in and swear me to secrecy.

That's why Mom says: "Love is for pussies." I needed to write that down to remind myself that she's not one for talking about it.

I've learned how to read between the lines and am careful not to believe what other people say. I know, for instance, that it wasn't just any birthday. It was her thirtieth. And for her thirtieth birthday, when I woke up at 3 AM, I cleaned up the kitchen. They were both in their bedroom. Tag snoring as if nothing had happened.

I threw out the empty cans as quietly as I could and put the lid back on the bottle of vodka. Most of the cupcakes were broken, crushed, crumbs smeared on the tile floor. Cake was pebbled like black tar on the chair legs. That sweet white filling was smeared in long streaks along the cupboards. Random bits were scattered on the counter.

I couldn't bring myself to eat the last one. I placed it back in its box and set it in the refrigerator. I knew she'd be up before he was, that she'd find the cupcake and know I had saved it. That would show her.

# FICTION

LIFE-CHANGING CHALLENGES

# Bagel Rounds

by Susan Bearman

JANUARY 8 — **Ross**
THE BAGEL RESTAURANT & DELI
LAKEVIEW, CHICAGO

My sister Dina calls it bonding over bagels. I hope she's right. I'm meeting my son, Nathan, for lunch. Brunch. Whatever. Things have been…tense…since the divorce three years ago.

Ah, that's BS. I screwed up. I fooled around once too often and got caught—with Nathan's 20-something Hebrew tutor. Then fooled myself into thinking I was "in love" and married her. That lasted six whole months. Twenty thousand dollars of therapy later and what have I got? Everybody's pissed at me and my only son thinks I'm the world's biggest fool. Actually, that's probably not the four-letter word he would use.

With a lot of encouragement from my sister and his mom, Nathan agreed to meet me at The Bagel. Now I'm standing by the door, freezing my ass off. This is a mistake. Maybe he won't come. Not sure if that would be good or bad.

I'm chewing on what's left of the cuticle on my right thumb when this skinny, bundled Yeti crowds next to me. Guessing I'm blocking the door, I move to the other side, but the guy just follows. I scowl up at him only to realize it's Nathan under the parka. Holy shit. He's at least two inches taller than I am. When did *that* happen?

We get a booth and he sheds the parka, but not the beanie. We avoid conversation by looking at the menu. It's a little early for lunch, but I order matzo ball soup anyway. Nathan is specific: the lox platter with two bagels—one plain, one Everything.

Now comes the hard part—filling the void until the food comes.

"So, how are you, buddy?" is my brilliant opener.

"I'm here."

"Thanks for coming. Why is it you have Wednesday mornings off school?"

177

"Block scheduling," he says. I don't know what that means. I probably should. He clearly thinks it's enough of an explanation.

"You grew a lot," I say.

He smirks. "Mom calls me her grew-some child."

I smile back. "More than just some, I'd say." And...that's the end of that conversation. The waiter fills our water glasses and we both reach for them, sipping slowly.

"This place looks just like the one at Old Orchard," Nathan finally says, looking around at the Broadway musical posters lining the walls. "You know, where we had my bar mitzvah brunch." He's glowering now, probably thinking about his tutor and the divorce. Divorces. We've officially transitioned from awkward to excruciating.

I'm rescued by the arrival of food. Nathan bites into one bagel, practically swallowing it whole while methodically building his other sandwich—a schmear on both halves with careful layers of lettuce, tomato, onion, and lox. My matzo ball is the size of a softball and suddenly unappealing. I concentrate on coffee.

"So, what's new?" I ask.

"Nothing," he mumbles around a mouthful. Of course.

"How's band?"

"I quit freshman year."

So much for the $3,000 saxophone and all those lessons. I try the soup and burn my tongue.

Nathan mostly grunts at my feeble attempts to start a conversation, more intent on inhaling his food than talking to me. Too quickly, he's down to the last bite of pickle, and I haven't said any of the things I need to say.

"Hey, I gotta travel," he says, wiping his mouth, then putting on his jacket. There isn't a single poppy seed left on his plate.

"What's your hurry?" I hope I don't sound as desperate as I feel. "Deb... your mom said you don't have to be at school until one."

"I've got band practice." He's on his feet.

"But you quit."

"I quit school band. Me and a couple guys have a trio. Jazz."

"That's so cool," I say. It *is* cool. At 16, I didn't even know what jazz was.

"See ya," he says, and heads toward the door. Two booths away, he turns and says, "Hey, thanks for brunch."

I swallow a huge lump in my throat as I realize that's all Debbie. She taught him that, not me. If he leaves now, I might not get another chance to know him. Suddenly panicked, I practically shout: "Want to try again next week?"

He hesitates. "Maybe. Yeah."

Then he's gone, lost in the crowd at the front counter. An old lady at the table next to me reaches over and pats my arm. "Such a nice boy," she says, and the lump is back.

## JANUARY 14 — NATHAN
### *JB's Deli*
### ANDERSONVILLE, CHICAGO

Dude's late. I've already ordered when he slams through the door and "excuse mes" through the line to the register.

"There's only one table," he says, eyes darting around.

"No, yeah," I say. "It's mostly takeout." I don't tell him about the other room, through the door between the deli up front and the pharmacy in back. I already checked; it's full.

"Where are we going to eat?"

"I figured we could eat in your car," I say. "You drove, right?"

He tightens his lips and nods once.

Outside, he points across the street. "This way." We turn the corner and he beeps the fob; lights flash on a bright red Corvette. My sister Ellie told me about the car, but this is the first time I've seen it. I want to burst out laughing. She calls it his midlife crisis car. Every time we pass some old guy driving some outrageous vehicle, Ellie does this little bow and says, "Yes, we know, you have a big penis. Thanks for sharing."

I slide in and open my bag, starving. I always start with the plain bagel. That's my litmus test. Is it stale? The right kind of chewy? This one is good. He stuffs his bag into the little console between the seats and shoves a bunch of napkins at me. He's worried about the upholstery. Makes me want to slime cream cheese all over it.

He sips his coffee and stares at me, just waiting for me to drop something. I can be careful. I'm not an animal.

"Tell me about your jazz group," he finally says.

I've moved on to my Everything with lox. This deli calls it a mish-mosh bagel—definitely a better name, with all the seeds and stuff.

"Me, Joey B on piano, and Joey Z on bass," I say between bites. "Sometimes we have a singer, Jackie or Nev."

"You still hang with the Joeys, eh? I don't think I remember Nev."

Yeah, he wouldn't. "She moved here a couple years ago."

"Where do you play?"

"Mostly somebody's basement." That sounds lame, so I add, "We've got a paying gig next month." Joey Z's aunt is paying us in food to play at some fund-raiser, but that counts, right?

"I'm impressed," he says. I can't tell if he means it. "Maybe I could hear you play sometime."

"Maybe?" I say slowly, *not* meaning it. I make a little funnel of the wax paper from my sandwich and pour the random fallen seeds into my mouth. Then I make a big show of wiping my hands on a napkin and carefully putting all the trash in my bag.

He starts the car and says, "Where can I drop you?"

"I can grab the 22," I say. The Clark Street bus has been unpredictable lately, but whatever.

"It's freezing," he says. "Let me drive you."

I don't want to be in the car with him all the way to Evanston. "How about you take me to the Red Line. Bryn Mawr." The L is way faster than the bus and it *is* freezing. Plus—and I'd never tell Ellie this—it really is a cool car.

When we get to the L stop, he asks: "Same time next week?"

"I guess." I don't know what more there is to say, but free food is free food.

He's smiling now. "*I'll* pick the place."


## FEBRUARY 4 — ROSS
*NINI'S DELI*
WEST TOWN, CHICAGO

It's been three weeks since our last brunch. Kid canceled on me twice.

"How'd you find this place?" he asks. He seems in a foul mood as he stares at the chalkboard behind the counter.

At least there are tables here. "Something wrong?" I ask.

"Where are the bagels?" he gesticulates toward the limited menu. "Where's the lox?"

This immature little tantrum is embarrassing me, but the guy behind the counter is grinning. "Lox and bagels are delicious," he says with a chuckle. "But my parents are from Cuba, and this is their deli. Try the goat cheese and guava empanadas. They're amazing. Homemade."

"Or how about *The Kitchen Sink* sandwich," I suggest. "Kind of like a Cuban Everything bagel." A stretch, I know.

"I'm pescatarian," Nathan says, exasperated, as if I should have known. "No meat, just fish."

"Since when?"

He ignores me and orders a plantain empanada.

We grab a booth and wait for our food. "I'm sorry, okay?"

"Why are you sorry?" he says, not looking at me, his beanie low over his forehead. "This wasn't your fault."

Is it my imagination, or did he hit the "this" a little hard? Are we finally going to talk about the real "this?" I feel my armpits prick, not sure I'm ready.

"Nathan..." I put my hand on his forearm, hoping he'll look at me. At least, I hoped he would until he did. Something on my face sets him off.

"Yeah, no," he says. "I'm out." He stands, so I stand, putting myself between him and the door. Our host hovers behind us with the food.

"Sit down and eat," I say. Then add, "Please?" I'm actually shocked when he sits.

The guy serves us, pretending he hasn't noticed anything, and I mentally double the tip I'd planned. Nathan picks at his empanada. The lively Cuban background music plays in odd juxtaposition to the mood at our table, but it reminds me...

"Hey, I got you something," I say. Kind of a bribe, I admit. The guy at Reckless Records picked it out—Coleman Hawkins vintage vinyl. I pass it across the table. Nathan wipes his hands before he takes the album, turns it over, and peruses the liner notes.

"I'm more of a Stan Getz fan," he says, but I can tell he's pretty into it. "Don't know how I'm going to listen to it, but thanks."

"My old turntable used to be on those shelves in the finished part of the basement. Maybe it's still there."

"Maybe," he says nodding, and then looks down at his phone. "That's Ellie. She drove me 'cause this place is so far."

Ellie! I feel terrible. Was she in the car this whole time? I hadn't even thought about how Nathan would get here.

"You haven't finished eating," I say. "Why don't you ask her to come in?" Ellie has always been so much easier than Nathan. She was the first to forgive me. And she can usually get him to laugh, so it couldn't hurt.

"Gotta bounce," he says. "We both need to be at school by 1:00." It's a tiny place; Nathan is already at the door. "See ya," he says with a small wave in my direction.

At least he took the record.

## March 2 — Nathan
### Manny's Cafeteria & Delicatessen
### South Loop, Chicago

After the whole record thing, I was done. I mean seriously, did he think a piece of vinyl would make everything okay? But he kept calling and texting. When I didn't answer, he had Aunt Dina call.

And then even Mom said, "Give him a chance. He's the only father you've got."

"One too many," I muttered.

She gave me a potch on the tush and said, "Don't be a smartass. Everyone makes mistakes. You will, too. The thing is to learn and do better. He's trying to do better."

So we made a plan and he picked me up. We're going to Manny's down on Jefferson. A Chicago institution, or so I'm told. I've never been.

A bunch of guys behind the counter greet him when we walk in. I guess that means he's a regular. He has a big, stupid grin on his face.

"This," he says triumphantly, "is a *real* deli. Lox, bagels, everything you could want." When I don't answer, he dials it back. "Hey, thanks for coming. I mean it."

Manny's is a cafeteria, just like at school, with trays and everything. It's huge. We go through line and some old grandpa waves him over, so he heads to the tables up front. No thank you. I grab a high top under the TVs. He talks to Gramps for a minute and then joins me.

He seems nervous, like he's ready to pop. He keeps rubbing his forehead, right between his heavy brows.

The bagel is good. Really good. Damnit.

"So this is different," he says. "A Monday. Did your block schedule change?"

"Pulaski Day. No school."

"Only in Chicago." He chuckles, shaking his head. "Did I ever tell you I used to work here?"

"No." Big surprise. He never told me anything.

"Every summer through college, starting about your age."

"Yeah?"

"Yeah," he says, ripping his napkin into little pieces. "They threatened to fire me all the time, but my dad was a regular and we lived so close that I could come in whenever they needed me. When I graduated from U of I, the manager, Pauly, gave me a whole salami and wished me luck in my next career." He's chuckling again.

I can't imagine him being bad at anything. He always seemed so confident, cocky almost. Or maybe I was just little and didn't notice this side of him. Today he's kind of—I don't know—like a regular person.

"Why did you quit band?" he asks.

"Too many rules. You had to be in symphony band *and* marching band to do jazz. It took a ton of time. Plus, the new band director is an asshole."

"Watch your language," he says seriously, but then winks and it makes me smile. "I'm glad you stuck with the sax."

"I love it," I say. "I'm saving up to get a bari. I even tried Ellie's clarinet. I'd like to be proficient at all the woodwinds." I'm leaning toward him over the table and we're looking at each other eye to eye. It's weird because it doesn't feel weird.

"That's really great," he says, and I think he might mean it. "I had no clue what I wanted to do in high school, other than play basketball and date girls. I wanted to do that a *lot*." He stops and turns ketchup red. Gotta admit, I'm kinda loving his discomfort. But I decide to give him a break and let it slide.

"I don't really date," I say. "We have a good group and all kind of just hang out."

"That's really great," he says again. "Did you, ah… " he clears his throat. "Did you get a chance to listen to that album?"

183

"I did. It took me a while to order a new needle and then get the turntable hooked up to some speakers."

"And?" he asks. All casual.

I make him wait a tick. "It's pretty great." I grin and he grins back. We talk about the record a bit. He really doesn't know much about jazz, but he's listening, like he's interested in what I know about it. He's looking at me kind of soft and funny and now it feels really weird. "Hey, can we get going?" I ask. "I've got the whole day off and the guys want to get in a good jam session."

He drives me to Joey Z's, and I'm about to get out when he asks if we can meet again a week from Wednesday. I reach for my wallet and flash my shiny new permit. "Only if I can drive the 'Vette."

He puts his head in his hands and says, "Oh, no." It feels good when we both laugh.

## APRIL 13 — **Ross**
*KAUFMAN'S BAGEL & DELICATESSEN*
SKOKIE

We're up in Skokie and the forsythia is already in bloom. Nathan chose Kaufman's because he is meeting his buddies nearby. *He* called *me*. This bagel thing seems to be working.

I watch Nathan as he comes back to the table with more food. "You're so skinny."

"I'm skinny. I'm tall. I'm hungry. Any other brilliant observations?"

It's warm out, so he's not wearing his ubiquitous beanie and I do observe something. "When did you start wearing a yarmulke?"

"When that guy attacked the Tree of Life Synagogue in Pittsburgh."

"I think that would make me *less* likely to advertise my Jewishness," I say, "not that it's such a big part of my life anyway."

"You're Ross Jacob Lieberman," says my son Nathan Adam Lieberman. "You can't hide who you are. I won't."

"What makes you so wise?"

"Not you." He's smiling, but he means it.

"No, not me," I sigh. We eat in companionable silence.

I pick at my potato salad, screwing up my courage.

"I'm sorry, Nathan," I finally say. "For all of it. I'm sorry I hurt your mom. I'm most sorry for how I treated you and Ellie. You didn't deserve that."

He's serious now. "You're right. We didn't. Mom says she forgives you."

"Your mom's a really good person. I know, because she raised really good kids."

"Are you expecting my forgiveness?"

"I don't have the right to expect anything from you."

He raises his brows and challenges: "You could ask."

I'm a coward, I know. But I can't ask him that. Not yet, anyway. And maybe I don't want to. Not because I don't want forgiveness. I do. But if he forgives me, that may be all I get.

And I want more. More of this. More of him. More of us.

"All I'm asking—for now—is that we keep trying."

"I'm here," he says.

# Rage Room

by Mary Nelligan

Allie gripped the dinner plate's wide rim and heaved it at the nearest wall. It splintered and cracked with a satisfying crunch, stippling the rubber floor with shards of glass.

"You can throw harder than that." Faye's disembodied voice burst from a speaker mounted in the corner and bounced off the room's concrete walls.

Instead of release, an outcome all but guaranteed on the Rage Room's website, Allie's anger intensified at her boss's intrusion, like water on a grease fire.

Faye knocked hard on the spectator window. "Go again."

Allie grabbed a second plate and flung it against the dirty cement, imagining the disk smashing Faye's pointy chin.

"Better," Faye said.

"Condescending witch," Allie whispered to the scraps of glass gathered at her feet. Raging shouldn't be a spectator sport, even in blood-thirsty Chicago.

"You should see Hannah beating up an old stereo next door." Faye's voice swelled with glee as if she'd reared Hannah's aggression from infancy. "She's killing it."

What had started as a team-building outing at a downtown rage room had devolved into yet another demeaning competition. Faye had said she wanted her five-person public affairs team to work well together, but routinely pitted them against each other. Twenty bucks said Hannah was picturing Faye's face on that stereo.

"Time's almost up. Finish strong," Faye said.

Allie considered heaving the remaining plates at the window but couldn't risk alienating Faye. Not if she wanted to stave off moving back to her father's dank suburban basement.

Instead, she hurled the last five plates at the wall in quick succession, grunting at the effort. She likely was the only person who left a rage room angrier than when she came in.

186

Allie yanked off the mandatory safety helmet and stormed into the colorless reception area. Harsh overhead spotlights drilled into her scalp. Bad lighting would factor into the already low Yelp rating she'd give the place.

"I'm Joe, one of the owners. All good?"

Allie looked up at a good-looking man not much older than she, maybe late twenties. "Yeah, all good." She wished he hadn't seen her scowl or that she'd at least stopped in the bathroom and picked any stray nacho bits from her teeth.

"Has anyone told you how much you look like that *Star Wars* actress, Padme, what's her name?"

"Natalie Portman? No never, I mean—never when I'm this sweaty, but thanks."

He was cute, in a leading-man's-scruffy-best-friend sort of way. The kind of guy who could drag your broken window air conditioner to the alley garbage can without breaking a sweat but didn't spend all day throwing tires at Orange Theory. Could maybe see past a too-long nose and unwhitened smile.

"This was your first time, right? What did you think?"

"Fun, loved it." She couldn't be expected to tell him the truth. Not with those dimples. She could learn to like public raging. She pointed to a chalkboard on the wall behind Joe's head. "Tell me about the Deluxe Rage Package."

"Good choice. One month of unlimited visits and all the plates you can smash."

"It's not that I'm angry," Allie said. "I'd come for fun and you know, stress relief. Not that I'm overly stressed or anything." She willed herself to shut up. One day she'd learn to flirt like a normal human.

"I meant," Joe said, "good choice because we'd see a lot of you this month."

Sold. Allie fumbled in her purse and handed him her Mastercard. She would not calculate the interest charges she'd rack up with this splurge. Maybe Joe was her reward for putting up with Faye.

❋ ❋ ❋

At work the next morning, Allie sat behind her computer writing a client's news release. She'd spent hours rereading the same four sentences, distracted by thoughts of Joe and by her coworkers' muddled voices circulating through the lofted, open-air office.

"Where's Mara?" Faye's voice flooded the space. She peered around the office as if Mara's colleagues were harboring a fugitive under one of the pod-shaped desks.

"In the bathroom," Hannah said.

"Again? Is she incontinent as well as incompetent?"

Someone gasped, the sound as small as a hyphen. Allie focused on her computer screen. Faye's rampages usually only lasted a minute or two, but no one knew who she'd lash out at next.

Poor Mara. Sitting on a toilet seat, unaware of the hurricane awaiting her once she flushed.

When Mara arrived at her desk, Faye tossed her a file. "I need my remarks for tomorrow's award breakfast."

"But, I thought I had more time," Mara said. "I thought you wanted me to—"

"To what? Spend the day affirming yourself in the bathroom mirror?"

Allie willed Mara to bare her teeth and hand over an impeccable, finished speech.

"I have a rough draft right here," Mara said.

The muscles in Allie's throat tightened. It was as if Mara had a death wish and messed up at least once a week to engender Faye's wrath and keep both feeling important.

"A rough draft? Do you have any idea what it's like to accept an award for communication excellence and mumble through a speech because of your useless speechwriter?"

Allie typed "shut up, shut up, shut up," wanting both the courage to intervene and the safety invisibility afforded. Her survival strategy at work was the same as it had been in her home growing up: avoid mistakes and stay the hell out of her father's way.

Mara clicked on her keyboard as if faster fingers would ease the beast at her back. She looked like an erased version of herself, see-through and vulnerable.

"I'm trying to run a business here." Faye tapped on Allie's desk.

Allie had watched Faye eviscerate coworker after coworker the past five years and could predict the next words out of Faye's mouth.

"I need you to write my remarks."

Bingo.

"You're the only one I trust to not fuck it up."

There it was. The familiar singling out for praise at someone else's expense. Allie longed for and dreaded the elevation, the dynamic a reminder of her family where Allie's perfectionism had won her father's approval and her younger sister's carelessness had earned his wrath. Both drove a wedge between sisters. And somehow always resulted in more pressure for Allie.

"But I have to finish all of Advocate's shareholder materials by end of day." Allie couldn't write a speech now. She'd be at the office all night.

"Do this first." Faye shouldered her oversized purse and clicked toward the front door.

This was the fifth time in three weeks Allie would have to work late doing someone else's damn job.

Hannah wheeled her office chair toward Allie's desk. "You're lucky, you know. She doesn't criticize or scream at you."

"Not yet," Allie said.

"Oh please, you're her favorite. She essentially called me a greasy cow for eating a bag of chips at my desk. Apparently, I'm supposed to choose more virtuous snacks."

"That's low, even for her."

Allie spent the rest of the afternoon avoiding her coworkers and writing and rewriting Faye's speech. She finished at 4:30 pm and spent the next three hours editing news releases and Q & A documents and munching a left-over turkey sandwich. She almost ignored a call from her sister until she remembered their planned run along Lake Michigan, an undiscussed effort on Allie's part to rebuild their strained relationship.

"Ugh, I'm sorry I forgot to call," Allie said. "I've got a deadline and can't run tonight."

"You can't just bail on me," Becca said. "You're not the only one with a demanding job."

"No, of course not. It's not that. Someone messed up, and I need to help."

"Right, you 'need to.' What you need is to value other people's time."

Becca was rightly peeved, but without a properly calibrated apology this would escalate. "You're right. I'm really sorry."

"You know you're going to keep getting shit on unless you tell your boss to fuck off and walk out."

Too bad Allie needed to pay rent, not to mention cover their post-run beer tabs. "Maybe, but I can't. Not today."

"I would've done it years ago."

Of course, Becca would. But her audacity had cost her more jobs in her three years out of college than she could afford. At least Allie's timidity kept her employed.

Allie sat with the silence as long as she could. "I went to that rage room on Clark Street—"

"Rage room? What do they do, steal your money and give you pillows to hit?" Becca laughed and told Allie to hold on a minute.

Allie imagined herself standing up to her opinionated sister. She'd tell Becca to lay off the unsolicited advice. She'd tell Becca to shove her arrogant tone. She'd tell Becca to get her own damn rage room. But not today.

"I've got to go. Rick took my car again and left me on empty," Becca said. "Boyfriends are worthless." As if Allie would know. Her romantic dry spell stretched back farther than her student loan payments. But maybe Joe would break the drought.


Two hours later, Allie walked into the Rage Room. A tall, lean-limbed woman named Rena staffed the front desk. Rena looked like an upbeat, energetic yoga teacher who never sweat or reeked of garlic after eating red curry chicken. No sign of Joe. Maybe for the best. Allie wasn't up to pretending she was the carefree woman the men she knew seemed to prefer.

Rena handed Allie a helmet and a stack of mismatched plates and asked if she wanted anything else, like a computer monitor or printer. "People seem to really like hitting printers."

"Plates are fine."

After hurling upwards of 20 dishes and screaming obscenities at dinged concrete, Allie struggled to catch her breath. Instead of feeling calm and relaxed, she wanted to tear down the walls and rip the world into tiny pieces.

She tracked down Rena at the front desk. "I may be doing this wrong, but I'm angrier now than when I went in—I want to break everything in the place."

"Happens a lot," Rena said. "Some people get release, others get jacked. There's no right way."

Allie itched to rip the knowing smile off Rena's perfectly-proportioned face. "Give me a printer. And a monitor. All of it."

The next morning, Allie's workload for the day doubled before she'd taken off her coat—Mara and another coworker had called in sick. Allie spent hours scrambling to meet other people's deadlines and fantasized about throwing office chairs and filing cabinets out the fourth-floor window.

When Faye arrived, she waved Allie into her office. "Nice work on those remarks. I can count on you, unlike most of the damaged goods I employ."

Allie flashed on the printer she'd mangled the night before. "Stop talking about your people like that. You're killing morale." She froze. She'd said that out loud. Faye's left eyebrow hiked the tiniest bit. Allie could nearly taste the familiar sour tang of mold in her father's water-logged basement.

Faye tilted her chin high, like an irate ostrich. Allie leaned back, out of reach of the homicidal bird's beak.

"Let me get this straight. You're uncomfortable with my behavior?" Faye said.

After years of avoiding confrontations, Allie had picked her boss for an inaugural run. Brilliant.

"You thought your—outburst—was a good idea? And other people have told you they feel the same?" The sharp beak inched closer.

"No, but it's obvious everyone's—"

"You're now everyone's spokesperson?"

"No, no, but everyone's work—my work—is impacted by, by—"

"Seems to me you're the one with the problem. I do what it takes to run this firm. If you can't hack it, there's the door."

Maybe this was her problem. No one had asked for her help. Maybe she was Becca in this equation.

"If you choose to stay, I will not tolerate you telling me how to behave. I've gotten this far, exactly as I am."

Allie avoided Faye's gaze and sloped out of the office, down the elevator and out into the icy air. She doubled over and gulped breaths. Only a special kind of idiot would call her boss a bully to her face. She should have swallowed, stuffed and shoved her self-righteous impulses. Focused on her work. What a mess.

She walked among Wabash Avenue's towering office buildings and stately cathedrals. The intermittent rumble of a nearby jackhammer mimicked the roar in Allie's head. Day or night, this city pounded with noise. An unrelenting din no one could escape.

Walking the aisles of Trader Joe's would calm her. Maybe she'd grab a box of Joe's O's and drown herself in sugar. Instead, she turned west and headed toward the Rage Room.

Joe and his dimples had to be manning the front desk. Couldn't be Rena or some distracted receptionist Allie could ignore.

"Welcome back." Joe ducked into the equipment room, and Allie raced to the bathroom. She pressed wet paper towels to her eyes and spackled concealer around her reddened nose.

Back at the counter, Joe handed her a helmet. "You're becoming a regular."

"Oh, I'm only coming for fun."

"That works. Plates or bowls?"

"Just a few plates, not many." Allie willed herself to keep it together, to project an attractive mix of enthusiasm and restraint.

But once in the rage room, she grabbed a crowbar and swung mercilessly at an old Xerox printer left in the corner. She wanted to brutalize something outside of herself for once. Out of breath, she leaned over, hands on knees. A series of deep coughs erupted from her chest like mini-explosions.

"Be sure to take a break if you feel lightheaded." Joe's voice crackled over the wall speaker.

Shit. She hadn't meant for him to see her like this. Allie waved him away.

"You'll want to bend your knees so you don't hurt your back."

She waved him off a second time.

"If you want, I can—"

Allie whipped around and hurled the crowbar at the spectator window. "Leave me alone!" The metal bar crashed against the glass and bounced off without doing damage.

Allie backed into a corner, expecting Joe to charge in, maybe kick her out. "I'm so sorry. I don't know what came over me."

"No apologies needed," Joe said through the speaker. "That's what you're here for. Let me know if I can help."

Allie slumped to the ground. Now she'd done it. Ruined her career and a potential relationship in less than an hour. Tears and snot streamed down her chin, and she cupped her face in her hands. Images of her father edged out thoughts of Faye. He'd been violent when they were kids, pushing Becca up against walls, berating her mercilessly whenever she made a mistake. Allie never said anything, never intervened. She wanted Becca to stop being bad so their dad wouldn't get angry. It was like she was beating Becca up too.

She rubbed her leaky nose on her sweater sleeve. "Hey, Joe. If you're still there, I need Kleenex." She'd already blown it with him. Hiding wouldn't help.

Moments later, Joe stood in the doorway holding out a box of tissues.

"I don't want to be like this, this angry."

"I get it, but there's nothing wrong with your anger. Maybe it's trying to tell you something."

Allie grabbed at the tissues. "It's trying to get me fired. And unfortunately, I like to eat."

■ ◆ ▨

Faye was waiting next to Allie's desk when she returned to work. "I need the PowerPoint deck for Feed America."

Allie gripped her purse strap. "I haven't started it yet. Their conference isn't until next month, and I've been working on—"

"I don't need excuses. I need that deck."

She couldn't be serious. The client hadn't even approved messaging and other projects had priority. "Of course, I'll work on it tomorrow once we hear back from Gary."

Faye rested her hand on her slim hip and leaned in. "I want that deck before you leave tonight."

"No." The word slipped out before Allie could consider the consequences.

"Excuse me?"

"I'll get it done tomorrow, but I'm not staying late again."

"Do you understand—?"

Hannah cleared her throat and called across the room. "Faye, sorry to interrupt, but Matt Beam is on the phone."

193

"Damnit, are you blind? Can't you see I'm in the middle of something?" Faye yelled.

"Please don't talk to me that way." Hannah's eyes shone. "You told me to find you if Mr. Beam called. Do you want to talk with him or not?"

Allie stifled a gasp. Courage must be contagious.

Faye smoothed the front of her skirt and appeared to reconfigure herself, a split-second reboot to human. "I'll take his call in my office." Her tone reflected the brief pause and she turned back to Allie, a scared baby ostrich peeking through her strong features. "Tomorrow's fine."

Allie acknowledged the shift with a nod. "I'll get it done."

Allie's phone buzzed. A text from Joe. "Thanks for being vulnerable today. Grab a drink later?" She sat at her desk and laughed. And she cried. Fat, juicy tears of release she both understood and didn't that smeared the last drops of concealer she'd applied an hour before.

# You Did Good

by Jason Lavicky

Teddy opened the packet of M&M's just as footsteps over creaking floor-boards advanced closer to his office. He dumped the colorful confections into his mouth, crumpled the empty packet, and tossed it into the trash bin, covering it with the toner cartridge already in there. Then he started pecking away at his keyboard.

Sheri opened the door, walked into the small room, pushed aside a pile of papers, and sat down on the oak desk.

"Hey," Sheri said.

Teddy smiled.

"It's bedtime. Will you be working late?"

Teddy nodded.

Sheri chuckled. "Do you plan to swallow, or are you just going to let them sit in your mouth as long as I'm in here?"

Teddy chewed, swallowed, and swiveled around in his chair to look at her. "I'm just a little stressed."

"Don't let Edgar see you eating them, or he'll want some. The last thing we need is a thirteen-year-old getting a sugar high before bed. So, what's going on that you need chocolate this late?"

Teddy took a deep breath and turned his chair around, facing the computer screen. "I wonder if I ruined Dad's death."

"Well, considering what he went through, I can't imagine you did anything that could've made it worse. Besides, that was eight years ago. Where did this come from?"

"In this script I'm working on," Teddy said, motioning to the iMac in front of him. "The protagonist is talking to his dying father, and he tells him he doesn't need to suffer anymore—that he can finally let go knowing he was the best husband and father anyone could ask for."

"That sounds nice."

195

"It's basically what I said to Dad before he died, but my agent said I need to rewrite that scene. His wife is a hospice nurse and she said she'd never tell someone to just 'let go.' Instead, I should've—I mean, the protagonist should comfort his father and tell him that everything will be fine. He should tell him to be strong and that he'll get through it."

"Really? Is this Marc, the same agent who wants you to add that ridiculous car chase in Venice?"

"But what if he's right?"

"About the car chase?"

"No. That's…whatever," Teddy said, waving his hand as if to brush that topic aside. "I mean what if Dad's final moments were spent listening to a blabbering idiot telling him to go ahead and die?"

"Teddy," Sheri said, "you know that's not true. What you said was very sweet." She rubbed his back and rested her head atop his. "He knew you better than anyone. He knew exactly what you meant." She walked to the door. "What the hell does this Marc or his wife know about you or your father anyway? Screw 'em. I'm going to bed. Don't stay up too late."

Teddy stared at the email on his screen. One word kept drawing his attention. The word Marc's wife used to describe someone who would say "let go" to a dying man—insensitive. Teddy wondered if she'd think differently if she had been there.

� ⊛ ☒

*When Teddy got the call about his father's accident, he told Sheri to start packing while he checked the air pressure on the car tires.*

*"We're driving to Branson?"*

*"It's faster than flying."*

*"Don't you need to sleep first?" she asked. "It's a nine-hour drive!"*

*Teddy didn't think about sleeping before leaving. The rush of everything going through his head didn't make him tired, just anxious. It was him against time. He felt the need to drive—to do something where he was in control.*

*"It's better this way," he said. "Edgar can sleep through the night, and by the time he wakes up, we'll be there."*

*They arrived at the hospital close to nine o'clock the following morning. The doctor gave Teddy the rundown, and his aunt and uncle let him know that hospice was his father's choice and, honestly, the only option he had. Friends and family who were there offered their sincerest thoughts and prayers. They told Teddy the situation was beyond anyone's control, everything happens for a reason, and it's all part of a bigger plan by a higher power that no one is meant to understand. None of this brought him comfort. And his own anxiety increased as he wondered what he would say when he walked into that hospital room.*

Teddy couldn't help but think Marc's email occupied more space in his mind than it deserved, and it angered him. He wasn't angry that his agent would challenge something so well-written. He got notes all the time telling him to rewrite something, and he did it without protest, as any professional would. This was different. This was personal. He was angry someone had told him what he said to his own father on his deathbed was insensitive.

At the same time, what if they were right?

"Dad! Go!"

It took Teddy a few seconds to realize everyone was honking to remind him green meant go. He snapped out of his trance, took his foot off the brake, and continued on to Walter Junior High. Edgar was in the passenger seat, backpack in his lap.

"What've you been doing in school, Ed?"

"I dunno. Stuff."

After all the times Teddy had said this to his own father, he silently admitted he deserved it from his son.

"I noticed your light was still on in the middle of the night," Teddy said.

"That's because of this stupid group project that's due today in Social Studies. Brad and Teresa didn't even do their part. I had to do all the work!"

Teddy took that last line with a grain of salt, but he was willing to believe Edgar.

Teddy pulled up in front of the school and unlocked the car doors.

"Group projects suck!" Edgar said. "Don't blame me if we get an F. I did my best." He turned to get out of the car, and Teddy reached over to squeeze his son's shoulder—something his own father used to do to him while saying, "You did good." Despite the cringe-worthy grammar, Teddy always found comfort in that squeeze, so he continued the tradition with Edgar, who always reacted with a scrunch of the shoulders and an annoyed grunt.

As Edgar disappeared into the crowd of students Teddy exited onto Main Street. He decided to call Marc.

"Teddy, good to hear from you," Marc said. "Did you see—"

"I want to talk about the deathbed scene."

"Yeah," Marc said. "It's beautifully written, but like I said in my notes, my wife said no one should say those things to someone who's dying. Just take—"

"Marc. I think that scene is powerful. We really get into the head of our hero, and I can't imagine him telling some comforting lies to someone he cares about so much."

The sigh from the other end of the line didn't give Teddy much hope. "I don't know, Teddy. I don't want him to come off as some insensitive jerk during such an emotional scene."

Teddy ended the call. Maybe Marc's wife was right. Maybe he was insensitive, telling his father to just give up and welcome death. Maybe he should have lied to his father despite what he and everyone else knew about his prognosis.

※ ◆ ※

*The weather that autumn day was cold, but the hospital room felt even colder. When Teddy, Sheri, and Edgar walked in, it was hard to find his father at first. The bed sat in the center of the room, but there were so many tubes and wires around it that Teddy had almost mistaken it for another piece of equipment. He wasn't pre-pared to see the old man shaking and convulsing so much. The nurses had warned him, but nothing could've prepared him. His father's hand was warm. Oddly enough, Teddy thought, this dying*

198

*man's hand was warmer than any of the "comforting" words his relatives had to offer. He squeezed the hand, but his father was too weak to squeeze back. Teddy wanted to say something, but the lump in his throat prevented it.*

*He didn't know what the old man was thinking or if he'd even be able to hear anything. Teddy didn't know what to say. A writer without words is like a knight without a sword. He felt weak and vulnerable. He turned to Sheri, hoping she'd know what to do, but she looked just as lost as he felt.*

*"I'm here, Dad. And Sheri's here," Teddy said. "Edgar's here, too." His father, still shaking, moved his eyes and turned his head slightly. Teddy was relieved that his father could at least hear him. He pulled Edgar over so his dad could see him better.*

*"Edgar just had a violin recital last week." Teddy brought his phone out and played the video of the recital. "He played* Perpetual Motion. *He may be perpetually off-key, but he still sounded better than the other kids." Anywhere else, that joke would've gotten a groan at best, but Teddy knew that his dad was cracking up inside. He ruffled Edgar's hair and encouraged him to say something.*

*"Hi, Grandpa," Edgar finally said. It saddened Teddy to realize Edgar wouldn't grow up knowing his grandfather. Edgar rolled his toy car along the mattress and asked, "Do you wanna eat pizza with us?"*

*Teddy shared a look with Sheri, who was wiping away tears. He pulled Edgar closer and squeezed his shoulder.*

As the kids poured out of the school's front entrance, one student stood out from the rest. With his shoulders slouched and his head down, Edgar eventually got in the car. Teddy kept the car in park as his son lamented the grade his group got for their project.

"It's not fair! It sucks!" he said, punching his backpack. "I did my part!"

"What kind of feedback did the teacher give you?"

"None. Just a big, fat F. Why do we even have to do these stupid group projects anyway?"

"Well, Eddy, you have to do them because..." Teddy thought about what to say. Should he tell his son that group projects are a necessary part of learning? Should he tell him it's the foundation of building trust with others? Should he tell him everything he was told growing up when he complained about group projects, or should he tell him the truth?

"I agree." Teddy decided to go with the truth. "They do suck, and they are pointless. But if it really bothers you and if your partners really were as bad as you say, talk to the teacher."

"What's the use? He won't change the grade."

"This is about more than grades. Come on," Teddy said. "I'll go in with you."

Teddy followed his son to the Social Studies classroom. He introduced himself to the teacher and stood aside while Edgar pleaded with the teacher to reconsider his grade.

"I understand your frustration, Edgar," Mr. Kowalski said. "But the whole point of this project was to learn to work together as a group."

Edgar sighed.

"I see group projects haven't changed since I was in school," Teddy said.

"Can you just grade my part?" Edgar asked.

"I can't," said Mr. Kowalski. "I have to grade the group as a whole. It's part of the learning experience. Grading an individual student defeats the purpose."

Teddy cleared his throat and said, "I understand it was supposed to be a learning experience, but based on the grade they got, it doesn't look like they learned anything." He turned to Edgar and asked, "What are you hoping to get from this?"

Edgar addressed Mr. Kowalski. "Can you just give me some feedback on my part so I'd at least know how I did?"

"Well, the point of the assignment was to assess the group—"

"I think that's fair," Teddy said, interrupting. "He isn't asking for a different grade, just feedback. How often does that happen?"

Mr. Kowalski reluctantly agreed and gave Edgar an assessment of his work on the project. Edgar, relieved to know he did his part correctly, thanked his teacher for his time.

"That was a good call settling for feedback rather than a grade change," Teddy said as they walked to the car. "See, you won't always get what you want, but never be afraid to stand up for what you think is fair or right." Teddy opened the door for Edgar and squeezed his shoulder as he got in the car.

*Perpetual Motion echoed off the walls of the stale hospital room, but Teddy knew he couldn't just keep playing videos of little Edgar. Hoping to find closure, he asked Sheri if he could have a few minutes alone with his dad. She left with Edgar and closed the door behind her. Teddy battled with himself on what to say. He didn't want to just regurgitate the cold comforts his relatives were spewing. Nothing about this was comforting. If he'd learned anything from his father, it was that pragmatism never failed.*

*Truth was the answer, and Teddy decided to pour his heart out. He kneeled and leaned closer to his father's ear. Teddy waited, not for his father to stop convulsing, but for his own racing heart to slow down.*

*"Dad, I'm sorry this happened to you. I don't like it either, but you can still be proud knowing you lived a good life. You were the best father, grandfather, and husband anyone could ask for. I know you were holding out so you could see Edgar again. I'll make sure he grows up knowing how much you loved him. You're one of the strongest, most stubborn men I've ever met. But you don't have to fight this. Let go of the pain, Dad. Find your peace. We'll miss you, and it hurts losing you. But you don't need to suffer any more. Thank you. You taught me well." Teddy took a moment to catch his breath.*

*"You did... You did good, Dad." He managed to get it out. Grammar be damned.*

*He tightened his grip around the wrinkled hand knowing it wouldn't heal him, but it was all he could think to do. Perhaps he was holding on to something else—hope. Hope that one day they will meet again.*

*The trip back to the hotel was a quiet one. The rest of the evening was uneventful. He got the call he was expecting from the hospital the next morning.*

*⬛ ⬛ ⬛*

Back in his office and satisfied with how Edgar handled the meeting earlier at school, Teddy decided to take his own advice. Sheri was right. He knew his father better than anyone, and he trusted himself to know what was right. So he picked up his phone.

"Marc, it's Teddy." He continued talking before Marc could squeeze in his thoughts on that night's Bulls game. "With all due respect to your wife, and with what I know about this character after writing him for the past five years, I have to disagree." Teddy could hear Marc struggling to take the phone off speaker and popping in earbuds so his wife wouldn't overhear what was about to be said.

"Look," Teddy said, "after my father's accident, I got countless visits, emails, and phone calls from family members and friends—his and mine—telling me that everything would be fine. There's a higher power that's in control, and while we might not understand how it works, we have to put our faith in it. I got no comfort from any of that.

"And in the hospital, his body convulsed and shook. He was unable to talk or even move. I was supposed to just tell him everything would be fine? I understand what your wife said and why she said it, but she didn't know my father, and she doesn't know my character. Neither would find comfort in that."

For once, Marc was speechless, so Teddy continued. "Look, I'm willing to compromise. We'll keep the deathbed scene as I wrote it, and I'll throw in that ridiculous car chase you want so much."

"Fine," Marc said. "You win. Finish the script, and I'll start making calls."

Teddy hung up knowing Marc couldn't hear the smile on his face. He turned around and realized Sheri had been standing at the door the whole time.

"You did good," Sheri said.

Teddy smiled. "Thanks. I figured if my advice about standing up for yourself worked for Edgar, then I should try it myself."

"Yeah, I heard it. You did good."

Teddy stood up and made his way out the office with Sheri behind him. Before they got to the kitchen, Teddy, startled, turned around and looked at her. "Was that you?" he asked.

"Was what me?" she said, looking at her phone.

"Oh," Teddy said. "For a second there it felt like something was squeezing my shoulder."

# A Promise Kept

by Fred Fitzsimmons

Dismay and seething anger washed over Becky upon reading the article in *Publisher's Weekly* about the soon-to-be-released novel *The Unveiling*. The piece heralded the re-emergence of the award-winning author, June Tunney, who had not published a book in fifteen years. Reading the story rekindled a guilt Becky had borne for two years for failing to fulfill her promise to her friend Madeline "Maddie" Fisher. Conscience consumed her, and shame drove her to rectify the brazen insult to her friend.

She immediately contacted Edith Monroe, the editor who worked on the new book, requesting a personal meeting between herself, Monroe, and June Tunney. Edith granted Becky's request because of Becky's reputation as a short story writer and her stature as a manuscript editor, much sought-after by accomplished authors.

■ ◙ ▨

Exiting the taxi, Becky stood a moment to admire the magnificence of the publisher's fifty-story LaSalle Street headquarters building—intimidating, she thought. The meeting's potential consequences made Becky's nerves jangle as the elevator sped to Edith's fiftieth-floor office. Finally, she compelled herself to relax—breathe deeply—focus—two objectives—rectify the wrong—clear a conscience.

Not having met *the* June Tunney of fiction fame and recalling only fifteen and twenty-year-old photos from her book covers, Becky envisioned June as a rod-straight, full-bodied, energized woman with dark hair and attractive features. But when the door to the editor's office opened, Becky saw a tired, frail, gray-haired wisp of a woman with gnarled hands sitting at the small conference table. The seventy-five-year-old's decline unsettled Becky, giving her pause for thought about how she would conduct herself in the meeting. She would need to be polite but firm. Not angry, resolute. Most of all, she had to right the wrong and salve her conscience.

As she approached the famous author, Becky saw that June had to strain forward to greet her, offering a quick nod, limp handshake, and practiced smile. Edith Monroe also stood to greet her; she was a slim woman with graying hair, maybe in her fifties.

Becky took a deep breath to quell her pounding heart. The success of this meeting was essential to relieving her two-year regret.

Edith offered coffee, tea, or bottled water before Becky could get seated. Everyone declined. That pleased Becky. It helped assure the focus would remain on the topic. After all, she thought, this gathering was serious business, not a coffee klatch or tea party.

Becky slipped into a chair across the table from June and offered an icebreaker, saying, "I can't tell you how impressed I am with your novels. I reference them often in my classroom and in workshops."

June eased forward in her chair. "Please call me June, dear. I'm delighted you found them useful, Ms.—Oh, forgive me, my memory. But, please, your name again?"

"Hastings, Rebecca Hastings, call me Becky."

"Have we met before, dear?"

"No," said Becky. "We do, however, share a link of which you're likely unaware. Our mutual acquaintance, Madeline Fisher. Maddie and I were close friends until her passing two years ago."

June snapped back in her chair, bolt upright, then shifted forward to listen.

"How did you come to know her?" June asked.

"We met years ago at one of my lectures and became friends," Becky said. "I'm a free-lance manuscript editor and an instructor at the University of Missouri's Summer Writers' Workshops. Maddie attended one of my manuscript revision sessions and returned year after year."

June told Becky the workshop was also where she and Maddie met, and they had both graduated from Missouri's creative writing program. It grated on Becky that June then spoke so glowingly about how they had hit it off, even though she and Maddie were years apart in age. "We stayed in touch for the next thirty years," said June.

June shifted in her chair, arched her back, half-smiled, and continued, "Both of us yearned to be novelists. But short stories turned out to be her calling. So tell me, dear, were you and Maddie friends, too?"

"We were, and we became confidantes. She often shared her frustrations about the novel she was writing."

"But she was such a respected short-story writer!" said June. "I never understood how her failure to write a novel could make her so miserable. There were times when I thought she might give up on writing the book altogether."

"However, she never stopped trying," said Becky. "Even after her short stories appeared in the most respected literary journals and awards poured in, she felt unsatisfied. Frankly, she yearned to be a celebrated novelist like you—who she called her best friend."

June labored to sit erect, her thin, large-knuckled fingers beginning to tap the table. She looked away from Becky and, in a whispered, remorseful tone, said, "Yes, I know. Poor thing. Maddie was only sixty-two when she died. So young. A shame. A splendid writer. I miss her."

Edith leaned forward in her chair and cleared her throat. "I don't mean to be impolite," she said, "but where is this conversation going?"

Becky had fumed while listening to June's sodden portrayal of Maddie. Now she fixed her gaze on June, leaned in, and struck. "Ms. Tunney, you wrote many excellent novels over the years, but they stopped about fifteen years ago. And now, suddenly, this remarkable book. Why such a long gap? Was it by choice or circumstance? How did this story idea come to you after all these years?"

June fidgeted in her chair. Left elbow planted, she raised her hand to her forehead, shielding her eyes and part of her face from Becky's view. The hand slid lower, covering her upper lip, mouth, and chin. Becky noted June's hand and fingers quivering and her eyelids closing halfway as she stared at the table. She spoke in a muffled monotone behind her cupped hand.

"You're an author," June said. "You understand what can happen to a writer—unable to grasp a theme, drawing a blank. After eight bestsellers, I couldn't repeat success. I had tried and tried, but I couldn't muster the energy to try anymore. I despaired. Finally, all these years later, I found the means, the message, and the spirit I coveted. I couldn't resist seizing the opportunity to reap success again."

Becky felt her patience nearing breakpoint. Even though June's explanation contained some truth, it was a terrible lie. Becky felt her fury rising as she realized that June's profound self-absorption had driven her to behave in the deplorable manner she did.

Becky took a deep breath. "I read the *PW* piece on *The Unveiling*. It stunned me. A marvelous story, obviously headed for acclaim and big sales."

"Thank you, my dear," June said, her voice faltering.

June cocked her head to the side and, with a quizzical eye glance, said, "But why would you travel to Chicago to meet me?"

Becky flashed a cold smile. "June, meeting with you means everything to Maddie—and me. I would have flown twice the distance to share my story with you and Edith. It's about Maddie's last months, and I knew you'd want to hear it because you've always been her editor and mentor."

June's eyes widened, and her lips pursed. "Of course," she said.

"Over the past few years, Maddie turned to me for editing help because she just couldn't finish the novel working only with you," said Becky.

June's eyes squinted, and her head tilted quizzically.

"She asked me not to tell anyone," said Becky. "She didn't want to offend you."

June stared, jaw now taut, mouth open, eyes hard set.

Becky continued, "I helped her complete the manuscript, and when done, I told her it was worthy of awards. But we kept her work with me a secret. For your sake."

June's eyes fixed on Becky, her blue eyes shrouded by gray cataracts. Her shoulders shivered, and her words came hesitantly. "I didn't realize you also worked with Maddie."

"We collaborated until the last. Then, in Maddie's final days, when the book was ready to take to an agent, her health failed. So, I promised to take it the rest of the way. You beat me to it."

"What do you mean by that?"

"I write short stories, teach, and edit for a living, and I got a late start on marketing Maddie's book. I don't have many contacts with agents, and finding one was involved and time-consuming. But, you, on the other hand, with your agent already in place and a very marketable name, could easily navigate the publication of her book much faster. So, when I read the announcement of your new novel, I knew I had to come to see you. I think you now understand why."

Becky removed a thick manuscript fastened by a large metal clip and two copies of the first chapter from her backpack. She methodically laid the manuscript on the table, then gave June and Edith each a copy of the first chapter. She said, "I think you will find that the copy in this chapter is virtually identical to the first chapter of *The Unveiling*."

June's eyes focused on the manuscript, squinting hard to read the title: *The Unveiling* by Madeline Fisher and the red stamp—DRAFT. A look of dread swept her wrinkled face.

"You even stole the title," said Becky. "I'm sure you plagiarized all the other chapters too."

June's hands trembled as she saw her theft laid bare. Her eyes welled as she peered at Becky. Then, slump-shouldered, her tears fell upon the manuscript pages in her hand.

Wide-eyed, mouth agape, Edith scrambled to the phone and direct-dialed Robert, the publisher. Becky heard the out-of-breath-sounding editor say, "Oh, my God! Robert, we've got a May Day—stop *The Unveiling* launch." She then left her office to speak tensely to Robert.

Tears ran down June's cheeks as she mouthed remorse in a hoarse whisper. "I'm sorry, so very sorry, for what I did." Her body shook. "I didn't mean to hurt anyone."

■ ◆ ■

Robert's jaw clenched as he fingered the manuscript and looked at June scornfully.

June turned from his glare, curling sideways in her chair.

Becky reached across the table and rested her hand with tenderness upon June's. She packed the manuscript in her backpack and rose to leave. "I'd best take my leave. You all now understand what you have to do."

Lightness enveloped Becky on her elevator descent, a sensation she hadn't experienced in two years. Then, bursting out of the building, she sucked in a deep breath and thrust her fist in the air. "*Yes!*" she exalted. Guilt relieved. Her promise—kept.

■ ◆ ■

Four months later, Becky received an express mail package containing an Advanced Reader Copy of *The Unveiling* by Madeline Fisher. A letter from the publisher and editor thanked her for saving them and their company from great embarrassment and assuring Maddie Fisher received proper credit for her work. Becky grasped the ARC, kissed its cover, and clasped it close. She noted two changes when thumbing through the book: a warmly written foreword penned by June Tunney crediting the brilliant writing of her deceased friend, and a heartwarming acknowledgment of Becky's vital editing contribution.

The foreword was June's last piece of writing for publication.

# Arctic Addy and the Grizzly Bear

by Alan Souter

## DEADHORSE, ALASKA, USA, 1975

Wrench in hand, I was deeply into the dark mechanical innards of a two-seater Cessna when some fool shouted, "Excuse me?"

I straightened up and conked my head on the airplane's half-open cowling. Seeing stars, I backed out of the greasy cavern. The shout came again.

"Excuse me?"

Not feeling hospitable, I piped out, "Sure, what did you do?"

Ignoring the sarcasm, the voice answered, "I'm looking for someone to fly me to the caribou herds."

Standing on the Cessna's wing, rubbing my head's conk spot, I replied, "The regular drilling crew will be here in three days. Fly for free with them."

He shouted, "Too late, I've got to get back to the lower 48 for another job."

Slowly, as the cosmos of stars, planets and comets faded away, I climbed down from the Cessna, a feminine vision in my work boots, Levis, plaid shirt, and backwards baseball cap. I paused a moment to assay my visitor: leather jacket, denims, ice-and-snow-boots—well worn, about 30 or so, clean-shaven and quirky good looks wrapped around a tentative smile. Decision made.

"I can fly you there," I said, wiping my hands on a rag.

My potential customer, laden with camera cases replied, "…Um."

"No, really, I am a pilot. I got a certificate and my book of hours to prove it."

I endured his stare as I moved into the light and shook loose a mop of black hair that uncurled down onto my shoulders. I was taller and slimmer than most Innuit women. My Caucasian Dad had seen to that. I had high cheekbones, brown eyes and no lack of proper curves. Or maybe just because I was a woman pilot. My camera jockey seemed confused.

I said, "I'm Inuit—that's a Native American—we can fly planes, drive Ski-doos, Jeeps, trucks; we're very versatile."

210

He shook his head. "Sorry; I'm a new boy in town. Can we start over?"

"Sure, I can take you. I've flown a lot of photographers. We'd better take the Jeep. My chopper is in the hangar at the end of the row." I pointed toward a smallish Quonset hut way down at the end of the taxi way.

I led him to my bright red Jeep—the WWII design. I helped him load his gear into the rear seat.

"I'm Jim Brady."

"I'm Addy. It's short for *Adlartok*. That means 'Clear sky.'"

"My name just means 'Jim Brady.'"

I laughed, shifted gears and popped the clutch. The Jeep spun its rear wheels and we were off.

He stared. I was used to being stared at. My body was a gift from the Inuit gods.

"What brings you up from the 48?" I asked.

"Caribou, I have to get some shots of caribou bumping their snoots on the new oil pipeline."

My eye roll was deafening.

I took my foot off the gas. "Who sent you," I asked, "the tree huggers, or the wild-catters?"

He struggled to keep the mood light, "I'd hardly call Atlantic Richfield a 'wild-catter.' Weren't they one of the first lease holders up here?"

"Sure, we got their airplane crashed somewhere on the tundra with the others—didn't even bother to use the bulldozed airstrip, just crashed into the ground and claimed the lease. It was like the gold rush when the crude oil bubbled. Then the shooters making a thousand a day and the media made big bucks flying in to show the investors with pockets full of money what they were buying, courtesy of Big Oil."

"Jesus!" Jim sprawled in his metal-frame seat. "How did I get to be the bad guy? We still going to the caribou, or are you dumping me here?"

I growled, "I need the cash for a new fuel injector." The Jeep resumed its travel.

I suddenly braked again. Jim skidded down to the floor. I shouted down at him. "Do you know how many clowns we get from the 48 asking stupid questions?"

"Lady, this ride ain't worth the price of the ticket! Can you get what's eatin' you off your…chest, or let me out and I'll hitch a ride."

"Get back in the seat and I'll take you to my baby."

Jim scrambled up, but this time braced his boot against the dashboard. Five silent minutes later I stopped in front of my hangar; it needed a paint job. I dismounted and after a struggle, wheeled out "Baby."

"Oh, hell!" Brady gave the blue sky an exasperated sigh.

My relic of the Korean War crunched to a stop. It was a Bell helicopter—and not the latest model, but the war-time type with the outrigger pods to carry wounded soldiers—one on each side of the cockpit. The pods had been converted to haul freight or supplies. The enclosing plexiglass bubble beneath the blades offered a great view, as well as great noise and vibration from the engine right behind it.

I scowled. "Her name's 'White Hawk.' I got her for $500, but had to build her from boxes of parts. I can carry your gear in the pods and you can shoot from a steady platform—if it's not real windy."

"Christ," Jim scratched his blond head. "I just finished flitting from peak to peak in the Brooks mountains in one of these bouncy bubble-tops—and a newer model than this museum piece."

I was getting pissed and showed him one mad Inuit. "Well, no wonder, there's all kinds of updrafts and downdrafts, and them peaks are 10,000 feet or higher. My baby bumps her head at 9,000 feet. From the ground up to 5,000 feet, she's sweet—and that's loaded! This is flat country down here with the caribou herds. You should get great shots—if you know your business!"

"I'm going to have to land," Jim rounded on me. "I need shots of the calves and moms, and to avoid getting the daddy caribous pissed off at me. I don't need them to decide their hat rack of horns needs me for a decoration."

I folded my arms. "The oil companies bulldozed gravel roads across the tundra that I can land on. Better yet, there's a big herd not far from the Richfield camp. We could drive there with the Jeep, Mister Sharp Shooter. I didn't just fall off the turnip truck."

Thoroughly thrashed, he capitulated and slapped a mosquito on his neck. Then he slapped a mosquito on his exposed wrist.

"Oh yeah," I nodded and got out quarts of mosquito repellent. "I'll sell it to you for $10 a pint. Mosquitos are thick out there. As the tundra loses its freeze, the retreatin' ice leaves small hexagonal lakes all over the place—perfect for breedin' skeeters."

Jim thrust his hands into his pockets. "I been goin' all day. Any place I can bunk for a couple hours before we begin this odyssey?"

"I got a cot in the back of the hangar I use to catch some Zs. You're welcome to it—for a couple of bucks."

"You got a price for everything," he said as he appraised the iron-legged, gut-sprung bunk at the rear of the hangar.

I grinned. "Livin' out here, ya gotta keep sharp, or get et by bears."

"Bears?" Jim asked.

"Yeah, with the sunshine, the Barren Ground Grizzlies come down to eat everything in sight—including know-it-all photographers. Just remember, them big bears can haul freight as fast as a racehorse in short sprints. Are you packin'?"

It took a couple of beats for Jim to realize I'd just asked him if he was carrying a gun.

"Uh, no, I don't have a gun. Too much hassle with permits."

"Well, keep a sharp lookout then. You go get some sleep while I finish puttin' new plugs in Baby and check her out. I'll be back in a couple of hours and we can head for the herd.

"By the way, I keep my distance from them randy oil crews, them bein' away from civilization for months at a time and I'm the only available female for miles around. One night they cornered me. Next thing they knew, they were lookin' down the barrels of two .45 caliber derringers I always carry in my hip pockets. They're part of a survival kit in case my Hawk goes down sudden. A .45 caliber round in the balls slows down any lonesome urges real fast."

Jim shrugged, "Hey lady, all I want is a ride." He tossed me a salute and began unloading his gear into the hangar. Without comment, I turned the Jeep around and drove off.

Half-awake later, Jim readied himself for his sortie into mosquito land. He'd sloshed on a pint of my repellent, and when he emerged from the hangar, he was a new creature: thick socks, leather jacket, elastic-tape sleeve closures. His stiff denim "mosquito pants" could stand alone after enduring mosquito repellent and native soil over the years. His hands were protected by thick leather gloves. He was, in theory, mosquito-proof.

I couldn't help staring at him when he emerged.

"You plannin' a trip to Mars?" I asked.

He grumped at me, "I've met clouds of mosquitos before."

I sniffed at him and wrinkled my nose. "Love your aftershave."

He arched an eyebrow, "You're no bed of roses."

"Meanin' we both stink. Nobody out here to offend. Shall we?"

"Drive on," he gestured.

My Jeep topped a hill above a large herd of caribou: males with giant horn racks, females less endowed, yearlings from last year's rut, and calves staying close by their mommas' sides spilled across acres of tundra.

I stepped out of the Jeep. "That enough for you?"

"Plenty," Jim answered, reaching into the back seat and hefting his big lens from its case. He slung his canvas gadget bag over his shoulder. His collapsed tripod draped over his head to hang down his back. "All set."

I pulled a pair of binoculars from the Jeep's dashboard compartment and surveyed the herd for stalking bears. Next, I buckled on a gun belt with my large revolver in its holster. It rode easy on my hip like a third leg. I noticed his interest.

"If a bear shows up, the noise of the shot should spook him."

Jim nodded. "And if the bear doesn't spook?"

I gently stroked the holster. "This here's a .44 Magnum, most powerful handgun in the world."

Jim closed his eyes, gritted his teeth and stepped off. "Come on, Clint." He couldn't resist the *Dirty Harry* reference.

We walked, then stooped, and finally crawled to a place where he photographed a roll of film, reloaded and shot some more. Elegant portraits, family groups, shaky-leg calves, males who trotted around the edge of the herd looking squinty-eyed pissed off at any bachelor male. Noting the wind shift, Jim moved along a tundra depression to catch a mom feeding her very new baby. He moved slowly so as not to spook the herd. Smart.

After three hours, he whispered to me, "That's about it."

Back at the Jeep, he repacked his gear, slipped the exposed film into a waterproof pouch and leaned against the fender, rubbing his strained eyes.

Over his shoulder, he said, "Whoa!" as I reached out to him.

I'd watched him work and figured he'd earned some relaxation. I offered him a hand-rolled marijuana joint the diameter of his index finger and at least as long.

Lighting up, Jim asked, "They let you have weed up here?"

I gave him a resigned look. "Richfield won't allow alcohol on the slope. Nobody ever said anything about weed. It's the only way anybody stays sane up here, especially when the sun disappears November to January."

I flicked a cheap plastic cigarette lighter. Together, we sat in the parked Jeep, quietly getting stoned watching the caribou graze.

This was the silence I loved: time out from chasing a dollar. I had been this way since I was little: always on my toes, wondering what lay beyond the next hill. Silence is a palpable thing in the arctic. No trees rustled. No birds sang. No traffic rumbled past on the road. Even the caribou seemed to walk softly in the wet lichen.

I couldn't help watching Jim as he sat on the Jeep's hood, quietly puffing on his huge joint. He fit the lonely landscape: a watcher and listener like me.

I looked at my wristwatch. "We'd better get going. They might send someone looking for us."

Without a word, the caribou safari was over. Jim looked exhausted from the physical effort, the weed, and the tension.

"One more place to look," I said. We rounded a hill and there was the pipeline—and crossing under the shiny steel was a small herd of running caribou. Jim hoisted up his camera and blazed away until the last caribou passed under and disappeared.

He shouted into the silence. "The money shot! That was the money shot! It tells the whole story in one picture." His face lit up like a penny arcade. "Oh, man! Thanks, Addy! I owe you big time."

"Hotshot, you don't owe me anything except gas for the Jeep. Tell you what, I'm tired of eating alone. Come over to my place at the airport. I got a caribou steak that's been marinating for a week and should be fit to eat. I'll throw in some spuds and such. How about it?"

Jim screwed a cover on his lens. "I'll help you eat your steak."

I winked and keyed the ignition. "Our secret: I got a bottle of Jack Daniels I've been itching to open. Strictly illegal, but that makes it taste better."

"Deal." Jim climbed up into the front passenger seat and we were off.

My small white house is deceptive from the outside. The inside is fully furnished. Sanitary facilities are at the end of a short hall leading to a rare—for the Arctic—flush toilet.

"Well?" I asked after Jim's reconnoiter of his surroundings. I poured him an iced glass of Jack Daniels and offered a short Cuban cigar. I took one myself.

"Quite a nest," he grinned and toasted the warm and welcoming interior. Two wing-back chairs faced an electric fire. I felt him watching me while I put my caribou steak, potatoes, celery and onions into the kitchenette's iron frying pan.

"If you don't mind," I said, "I'm going to change out of this mosquito armor into Lower 48 civvies. After I'm done, you can use the shower. Sound okay?"

"Uh…" he managed. "Sure. Do you have many dinner guests?"

I drew a curtain along a curved ceiling rail around the tub and now undressing area. "No. I have some Inuit neighbors who come over on holidays, or I go to their digs." I paused. "But not many gentlemen callers."

I couldn't help chuckling as he grilled me through the shower stall's sliding curtain. It took a while for the warm water to come, but when it did, I luxuriated in its spray.

He called out, "For your information, tree-huggers—they're footing my bill— friends of the caribou, not Big Oil."

Ablutions concluded, robed and barefoot, I glided past collapsed Jim's chair to tinker with the steak dinner. I felt his eyes on my transformation from greasy-thumbed mechanic/pistol-packing caribou guide to tall, slim, warm beauty in a sheer, clingy robe and bikini panties—I loved this other me. He tried his best to blink occasionally.

"I like you, Brady, you're the real deal. All this time and not one pass at me. Am I losing my touch?"

Jim untied my robe. "How often do you practice with those .45 derringers you carry around?"

"*Touché*," I exhaled, "Our steak has at least another half hour to cook." I stood in front of him. My lips brushed his.

I breathed "You taste of whisky and tobacco. You taste like a man."

"I can't let my gender down," he whispered.

A half hour later, the steak didn't disappoint, nor did the rest of the evening.

I felt Jim wake up around six. Our dinner plates and garbage sat in two buckets ready to be taken to the dumpster and the wash pump out back. Being a thoughtful guest, Jim hefted the two buckets and, wrapped in an old army blanket, padded out the back door into the perpetual twilight. Apparently, according to the deep grumbling roar, my house guest had arrived just as Momma Grizzly and her two cubs sat down to their dinner. Seven-foot Momma bear took immediate umbrage. Jim Brady crouched down to four feet and scurried to the dumpster's far corner. The cubs climbed atop the dumpster waiting for dinner amid Mom's savage roars.

Bam! Bam! Bam! Three explosions shattered the Arctic night. Bears fled the tundra. Jim shouldered past me; cloaked in pale blue gun smoke, my magnum revolver still pointed at the sky. He snatched fresh underwear from his open suitcase and dashed down the toilet hall.

## MONROVIA, LIBERIA, WEST AFRICA
## ROYAL GRAND HOTEL

I sent Jim Brady a letter. It chased him through three countries until it landed in his Monrovian hotel mailbox. I was in Amsterdam with some college friends and his name came up from a free-lance photographer. I asked Brady if he had seen any bears or smart-ass Innuits in his travels. He said no, but he still carried those three .44 magnum brass cases on his key ring from the shots I fired to scare away Momma Grizzly and her cubs. His reply was James Brady through and through:

> I'll be in Amsterdam in a month shooting for a drug story. If you can find a real steak, I'll help you eat it if you show me around town. Oh, one thing; nix the bear.

# Into the Beast

by Kirk Landers

## FEBRUARY, 1968

They were nearly a block away, maybe twenty of them, defying the icy winds of winter. They were young, long-haired, exuberant. Even from that distance, he could hear their shouts and see their arms wave antiwar signs every time a car drove by or some poor guy walked into the Armed Forces Induction Center and out of his civilian life.

Jackson groaned. His mother didn't need this. She was already fighting back tears. He had her drop him off at the far end of the block, a goodly distance from the protesters. She didn't need to hear a bunch of slogan-shouters reminding her that her college grad son was now going off to war. She cried when he said goodbye. He felt guilty for going, not that he wanted to go, but still, she'd been through too much already. He wondered what his father might have said to make her feel better, but nothing came to him, so he just hugged her and reminded her that he had enlisted as a clerk. "You'll be in more danger driving home," he said.

She forced a smile and he stepped out of the car. He took his bag from the back seat and waved as she pulled away, then set off for the entrance. He tried not to dwell on her fears and sorrow, just like he tried not to think about what might come next for him.

The protesters stirred to life as other inductees made their way to the doors. He watched them wave their signs and chant and yell, knowing they would soon direct their judgments at him. The hell of it was, he had once hoped the raucous demonstrations flaring up all over the country might force the government to end the draft and set him free to have a career and a girlfriend and do the things young American men used to do before Vietnam began devouring them. Now, not only was it too late for the protesters to save him, he was going to incur their scorn and jeers for doing something he was being forced to do. The last choice he had been given was whether to get drafted and almost certainly become an infantry grunt, or enlist to get training in something that might keep him out of the jungles and rice paddies.

"Life's a bitch and then you die." The words of Bess, his long-ago high school girlfriend, echoed in his mind, the perfect benediction for his current situation. Bess, a willowy girl with a mischievous smile and a kind heart, had spouted the line many times and it always made him smile, even now. He was probably the only one on the street smiling. He wondered what Bess was doing now, and he thought he'd made a bad choice to pursue college girls instead of her.

Halfway down the block, Jackson neared a panhandler sitting on the sidewalk, his back to the induction center's wall, a dirty cup in front of his crossed legs. He was insulated against the February cold by a faded army fatigue jacket, a soiled blanket over his lap, and a ratty stocking cap on his head. There was a nametag on the jacket—Gibson—and the faint outline of the three chevrons of a buck sergeant's stripes on his sleeve. The guy could have bought the jacket at a surplus store, but there was something about him that made Jackson think he had acquired the jacket the hard way. His face was thin and haggard, like an old man's face, but he wasn't old. He was just a few years older than Jackson. A junkie maybe, or a crazy person with no place to go.

They established eye contact as Jackson drew close. The man's eyes were as dead as rocks and they made Jackson shiver inside. His lips moved and Jackson startled at the sound of the man's voice, like when the tree in the Enchanted Forest talked to Dorothy in the *Wizard of Oz*. Except this was no yellow brick road and he sure as hell wasn't going to end up in the Emerald City.

The panhandler gestured for Jackson to stop. Jackson did. He didn't believe in God, but he figured if there was one, this was the kind of stuff a deity would want to talk about at the pearly gates. The panhandler said something in a raspy voice that Jackson couldn't hear. He bent lower and the man repeated himself.

"Don't let them turn you into a frog," said the panhandler. He smiled a ghoulish smile with missing teeth, but Jackson sensed he meant it in a friendly way.

"Okay," said Jackson. "Thanks." He couldn't think of anything else to say. He couldn't really think of anything except how wasted the guy was and how he smelled like rotting teeth and body odor. He wondered if he would be like this in a few years, but slammed the door on that thought. Whatever was going to happen to him, it was too late to worry about it now.

The guy kept staring at Jackson and Jackson stared back until he realized what the guy wanted. He dug in his pocket, pulled out a dollar bill and stuffed it in the collection cup. The guy nodded, not a thank-you nod, but an acknowledgment—yeah, you gave me something, and I gave you something first.

The guy closed his eyes and Jackson walked on, wondering if the frog thing meant anything or if it was just the guy's hallucination of the day. A few steps later he reached the protesters, who greeted him with a full chorus of anti-war crap. *Baby killers. Hell no, don't go. Make love, not war. Resist. Hey, hey, USA, how many kids did you kill today?*

One of the protesters stepped in front of Jackson and held up a hand for him to stop. The guy had a belligerent expression on his face and a voice as loud as a bullhorn. A group of his pals gathered with him, their voices showering him in babble, their faces red with cold, streams of vapor flowing from their mouths as their hot air hit the icy winter breeze.

"They're going to make you kill other human beings!" the guy yelled. "Have you thought about that?"

He posed the question as if it was an answer, like a Bible-thumping street preacher filling the air with rhetorical questions to which the answers were always subservient to whatever bullshit he was selling. The guy was taller than Jackson, and about the same age, with a reddish beard. He wore a wool stocking cap, jeans, and a puffy winter coat. His eyes were blue and his skin was chapped from the winter wind. Jackson could see he was someone who was sure about things. He was the absolute, unquestioned authority on right and wrong, and he was there to save everyone else.

"Yes," said Jackson, "I've thought about that."

"You can live with that?" asked the guy.

"Only if I get him before he gets me," said Jackson. He meant it like a fuck-you, but it was also how he felt about the war. It wasn't a moral imperative, not for him. He had tried to get out of it, but he wasn't rich enough or smart enough and he wasn't willing to run away to Canada or Sweden. So he was in it, and now it was just about surviving.

"You're okay with killing babies and women?"

"I don't think I said that." Jackson pushed past the protester, thinking if the guy laid a hand on him, he'd smash the fucker's teeth down his throat. It was almost funny, the thought of fighting his way into the induction center so he could be part of an army he didn't want to be part of and join a war he didn't want to die in. It was crazy, but it would make a good story to tell his grandchildren. If he survived.

But the guy didn't touch him.

"It's the big green killing machine," the guy yelled. "They'll make you a murderer!"

Jackson glanced back at the protesters when he got to the door.

"You could die there," another guy yelled. He was shorter than the loud mouth guy, but just as righteous. "Nothing's worth dying for."

Jackson smiled to himself and nodded and rolled that thought around in his mind. *Nothing's worth dying for.* Couldn't argue with that. But you die anyway, everyone does.

Jackson tried to turn off his mind when he entered the building, but he couldn't shake the feeling that he was stepping into a nightmare, the one where he was passing into the belly of a huge beast, where he would be digested, slowly and painfully, and die in agony.

The induction center wasn't exactly a nightmare. It was more like one of those weird dreams filled with white noise and bodies drifting by in slow motion, people floating along oblivious to one another. He was part of a throng of young males being herded to various stations to be poked and prodded and fill out forms. At each stop, a uniformed enlisted man would call out instructions, and then the room returned to a low buzz as the inductees responded. There was no harassment, no shoving, not even any cursing. The military people were just doing their jobs and the inductees were too nervous to engage in much banter. Jackson wondered if the stories about troop hazing were just inflated war stories, or if maybe the military had cleaned up its practices to avoid heat from the public, especially the protesters.

After hours of processing, and sitting and waiting, and being segregated into different areas, a staff sergeant lined up the Army inductees in alphabetical order. That process brought a higher buzz to the room because it seemed like they'd be moving out soon, and because guys now knew the names of the people lined up near them.

Jackson found himself in between two other Jacksons, cousins who had enlisted on the buddy system so they could go through training together. Aaron Jackson stood in front of him, and Charles Jackson was just behind him. His

221

first name was Alan, not that anyone ever used it. The three got a good laugh out of it.

The cousins were from a white, working-class neighborhood in Chicago, both eighteen years old and filled with bravado. They had completed a good Catholic school education, so they were smart enough even as teenagers to enlist for clerk school. But they were still eighteen and full of testosterone and they'd grown up listening to friends and relatives tell stories about the glories of combat, so they signed up for Airborne training, too.

Jackson, who'd done lots of research before he enlisted, was aghast. "As soon as you jump, you're infantry," he said.

"Yeah." The cousins laughed, like they knew it was crazy, but it was all going to work out. Jackson once had that feeling, too—like dying or getting his legs blown off couldn't happen to him, that he was special that way. But what he felt now was doom, and his weird vision of people floating by in silence had morphed into a posse of dead soldiers coming to welcome him to the not-so-great beyond.

He scoffed at himself. He was just being stupid. There were no ghosts. He wasn't going to die. He was enlisting as a clerk. The worst thing that could happen to him was someone dropping a typewriter on his foot.

Jackson wondered if maybe the cousins had the right attitude and he was just a coward. Or maybe a college degree made him older and wiser, though he didn't feel that way. He was as clueless as anybody else in the room, other than knowing better than to go Airborne.

After they lined up, the staff sergeant gave them a facts-of-army-life talk. They would be bused to Fort Leonard Wood, Missouri. "And you're going to love old Fort Lost-in-the-Woods in the winter," he quipped. He talked about their eight-week basic training cycle, in which they would get in the best shape of their lives and learn to shoot the Army way, and get trained in hand-to-hand combat and bayonet fighting. After that, they'd move on to Advanced Individual Training or Officer Candidate School, and then they'd be ready to "be all they could be." His play on the Army's oft-mocked advertising slogan elicited a smattering of nervous laughs.

When he opened it up to questions, someone asked why some guys had RA serial numbers and others had a US prefix. "RA stands for Regular Army," he said. "That means you enlisted. If you enlisted hoping to avoid Vietnam, I have some bad news for you. No matter what your recruiter said, you're going to do a tour in Vietnam. So just get used to the idea."

He paused and scanned the faces watching him. "And if you enlisted for some kind of pussy training, like a technician or a clerk or something, don't feel like you've got it made. The Big Green Machine can make you an infantry grunt any damn time it wants to."

Jackson tensed. The recruiter had made it sound a lot less scary. You could end up a grunt if you flunked out of clerk school, or if you didn't perform well as a clerk, or if you were assigned to an infantry unit and they needed another rifle on the perimeter. The recruiter said it like it was something that would never happen. But now that Jackson was signed up and at the Army's mercy, he felt doomed to die slogging through a rice paddy, falling face-first in water, snakes crawling over his dead body. He had never felt so fucked.

"You draftees," the sergeant continued, "have a 'US' in front of your serial number. You're going to Vietnam, too. It's a big party and everyone's invited. So, all of you, shed your tears now. When you get to Basic, pay attention, work hard, learn everything you can. It's your best chance."

The sergeant didn't finish the thought. He didn't have to. The room was filled with stony faces and furrowed brows. Aaron and Charles Jackson exchanged nervous glances with each other, then with Jackson.

"Life's a bitch and then you die," said Jackson.

The cousins smirked. "That's good!" said Aaron. Charles nodded with a grin. It was a funny quip because it didn't apply to them. Jackson thought it would be nice to feel that way. A little euphoria wouldn't change whatever was going to happen in the end, but it would make getting there more fun.

An hour later, the buses that were scheduled to transport them to Fort Leonard Wood didn't show up. An hour after that, a sergeant announced that the buses were late. He didn't say why and he didn't say when they'd arrive. A murmur of indignation rose from the group, but Jackson didn't join the voices. He realized that this is what it meant to be a soldier. He hadn't understood it before, but now he did. He was no longer someone who had a right to an explanation. He was an expendable part of a machine, the Big Green Machine, and the machine could do anything it wanted with him.

The buses arrived in the dark. They were handed box meals as they stepped aboard—bologna sandwiches, potato chips, an apple, and a can of warm soda.

The sergeant informed them merrily that they were going to pull their first all-nighter in the Army, but there'd be more, lots more, so enjoy the ride.

When they drove into the dark streets, Jackson got that feeling again. He was in the digestive tract of the big green machine, and he was being propelled along by a force he couldn't resist, like a frog being swallowed by a snake.

*Don't let them turn you into a frog.* He finally understood what the panhandler was saying: they can dress you like a frog, and they can treat you like a frog, and they can even kill you, but they can't turn you into a frog unless you let them.

He clenched his fists and promised himself that no matter what, there'd be no mewling or begging. He'd take whatever they had to give—the Army, the Viet Cong, the fucking protesters. And if any of them got to thinking he was a frog, he'd tell them all to go fuck themselves, and when he got out of this shitstorm—if he got out of this shitstorm—he'd walk tall on two legs and he'd still be a man.

# POETRY

Kelly Q. Anderson

# Upon Being Asked Where I Get My Ideas

When the fog rolls in, wildflowers sprout on my arms. My hands become feathers and I fill them with ink. When the fog rolls in and hides the children's bicycles, anything can happen. I don't recognize the faces. Who is walking? Who is running away? Who is staring at me? I'm intrigued by the darkness. Which clowns will crawl out of the storm drains? Who will walk the wooden fence? What will curl around my ankle and trace its hand up my leg? When the fog rolls in, I become a dark, dark crow. In blackest blue feathers I hide the blackest blue plans for tales that creep around while you sleep. I open my wings and go.

Thomas Tepper

# Bird's Eye View

I possess the seat by the window.
I am seeing clouds and earth as if from heaven.

Including before calendars existed
birds cause people to wonder.
how the world looks through birds' eyes.

How can you not want it enough to fight for it?
I do not understand you.
You can read that magazine any time.

I'm disconcerted you do not understand what I value.
I will continue to look for whoever
possesses the missing part of my soul.

## Laura Joyce-Hubbard

# Precession

We were peacekeepers. We were heading to war.
I called for Combat Entry Checklist.

I called for helmet, chin-strap, flak vests,
waiting for compass: spinning, steady.

I waited for gyros' spinning, heading
to Bosnia, black kevlar in kick window.

Kevlar blocked vestibular, the tilt of war.
I remember a farmer pushing a till,

below. A farmer slipping into a hill.
He looked up at us as he cleared his land.

I looked at him, cinched harness, *Cleared to land.*
I flare, touch ground, reverse torque, remember:

His plow and stare—a torque, ushers precession.
Like a flare in reverse. We were peace: keepers.

[previously published online in *Ninth Letter*, Summer 2021]

Kathy Mirkin

# On Seeing Pablo Neruda's Isla Negra Home in the In-flight Magazine

What strange world is this, the poet's ship-shaped home so near the sea?
His abode, crammed with collectibles, beguiles me as I fly above the sea.

Why did he fill his rooms with tiny ships sailing only in bottles?
Why collections of shells and ship wreckage, these shrines to the sea?

Masthead maidens on his walls stare with sea-mirror icy eyes.
How could those busty barnacled babes protect against the monstrous sea?

The angel statues gaze with eyes as sad as the poet's own dark moons
as if about to sing or cry, lost in their taunts and lullabies to the sea.

Schooner paintings voyaged across my father's office walls. As a child, I
played with a whale's tooth, sailing alone into my fantasy of the sea.

Now I soar in a craft so quiet, as if on a ship inside a bottle
floating away from earth, above the whale-skin black, wild sea.

Lisa Sukenic

# She will imagine it away

Like doves in a song,
a war with words, a feather pen,
syllables light like wind but bold.

When they ban books,
they wrap the words, send them downstream
to be caught in cattails and lily pads.

Caged words, wings clipped,
syllables stopped without expression.
Banned, banished and burned.

*First they came for the socialists*
*and I was not a socialist so I did not speak out.*
We will be silent no more.

The pink triangle, the yellow star patch,
your father had numbers tattooed on
his arm, wore long sleeves and cuff links.

They will use barbwire to snag the words,
but syllables float in the breeze
and land on laundry lines.

Slicing syllables, mangling meter, ruining rhymes
We tip tap the type, the tone, the time, our time
Engage, enrage, imagine it away.

Marcia Pradzinski

# Today you come to me

(a Cento)

when I close my eyes.
>Only ghosts live between us.
>>Still I see you there bright as the sharp blue sky,
>>>>smiling.


You occupy a little apartment in the corner of my head—
>just up and over the rung of consciousness—
of my happiness this is the key.


>What word, what act
tumbling through space
>>>illuminated
>>>>>a memory
gave it a shape and a name
>>>>to speak a life back into being
>>>as if it could be your body
>>>>again—
I crochet my heart back together.

**Cento Sources, starting with the title:**
John Paul O'Connor, Heather Bartlett, Jenene Ravesloot,
Michael Lee Johnson, Donna O'Shaughnessy, Maya Angelou, Chloe Bausano,
Rachel Jamison Webster, Keya Fowler, Jane Hirshfield, Susan Stewart,
Reginald Gibbons, Isidore Schneider, Chelsea Wagenaar, Tanya Runyan,
Rachel Jamison Webster, Connie Post, Jill Angel Langlois

Beth Bower

# Mosaic

How should I grieve?
No map, no compass,
no sky of stars or sextant
points the way.

My true north died on a Monday,
and I'm awake—alive, mid-week, mid-year,
midnight—afraid to open my eyes
and see he's not here today.

Lay out the *ofrenda,* marigold petals, beer cans,
lyrics, guitar picks, pencils, sketchbooks,
pictures of a middle child, tow-headed curls
turned grey, and bald, somber looks.

There is no celebration,
no collective honoring of his soul
all speaking the same language of loss,
all is left untold.

I score and smash pieces of green glass
into sharp, angled shards. I choose a tree.
I work a long time, get cut and bleed,
lose patience with the work, with myself.

When I finish I stand back and
I see boughs of shattered multitudes,
a mosaic of green glass reflecting my grief.

Nora Orschel

# Buy the Flowers

You were always so busy, he said
when his dementia took his filters.
You never sat down, he said.

But there were kids and dinners to make,
laundry to do, homework,
A big house to clean.

I even gardened in the backyard
at night with spotlights.
I wanted to grow some flowers

I didn't know he'd be gone so soon.
I could have sat down with him—
I could have bought the flowers.

## Sherry Kromer-Shapiro

# Migraine

Anemone-supple, mussel-crusted woman lying on her bed,
Legs wide. In her water-seeking form resides
Soft arms enfold the orb that is her head.

She-creature explores the sun-pierced red
Of caves. Sings porpoise songs. All senses tried.
Anemone-supple, mussel-crusted woman lying on her bed.

Rising, her sun-set face of day presented,
Snarled tangles of salty hair, her life denied.
Soft arms enfold the orb that is her head.

Awake, migraines couldn't be prevented. Doctor said,
Here's more codeine. She wishes she had died.
Anemone-supple, mussel-crusted woman lying on her bed.

As leaves reach up to the light, from roots indented
She, diving deeply, upsweeps into the advancing tide;
Soft arms enfold the orb that is her head.

At last, afloat on rainbow reef she, newly dead,
Like jellyfish, smooth currents she does ride.
Anemone-supple, mussel-crusted woman lying on her bed.
Soft arms enfold the orb that is her head.

Toni Louise Diol

# The Hermit Crab

Alone at the water's edge,
a small, determined hermit crab
pays me no heed, runs, perhaps, to a lover.
I search Carolina steel-grey skies.
I speak to the heavens.
I sing a word, a sentence,
recite a poem, test my sound
on this bitter November morning.

Wind carries intonations and breath.
The skyscape waits,
creates hilarious, misshapen clouds
resembling dolphins
that collapse before my eyes.
Do those formations study me
before they dissipate into nothing?
They laugh, knowing they will collect again,
always closer to that place
where the sun and moon live, but I cannot reach.

The sea nears my feet. I back away.
Abandoned, the hermit crab
watches roaring waves chase me.
When heavy dark masses fill the atmosphere,
I shout at the heavens.
I whisper a plea and promise to write
a poem about the sandy crab
as whale-sized raindrops speak to me.

Nora Naughton

# Firefly

Once again, I find myself at this park,

In a garden in this city,

A calm center amid the bloody hustle.

I let my thoughts wander in the scrappy verdancy.

I shimmer to the rhythms of hidden cicadas.

I listen to the profound breathing

of ancient oak trees, among their roots,

sheltered in the shade beneath their branches,

at arm's length from the screeching traffic.

This city park has become the world to me—

Or have I been caught,

like a firefly in a glass jar,

by the gentleness of its breath?

Belinda Copeland

# Losing Myself, Finding Myself

I lose myself on the trails

a woodchip of infinite possibilities

nestled in the midst of car horns and smog

I lose myself

to the songs of the blackbirds

red spotted marked in despair

to the buzz of the bees

the sun's warmth hits my face

the rays play tag with the leaves

in and out the shadows go

in a game of hide and seek

the caw of the crow sounds from the belltower

brings me back to the now

I'm no longer hiding within the shadows

the brook bubbles with life

I lose myself in its calm

in my newfound hope

I am one with it all

I find myself at home

on the trails.

Margot McMahon

# Street Cred

Canopy of light green leaves
clean the soiled city breeze
monopoly of sun-showered young trees
Tripoli, Chicago, New York city's
remedy condemned and dying trees
with saplings, transplanted Street Kids
makes their lonesome way
standing tall along parkways among
cousins, neighbors, a few new friends.
on its own it must contend
not a brother, sister, mother, father
to web its roots, share its fodder
streets kids die young
the demise of carbon consumption,
street kids untethered, oxygen exhaling
street kid roots; burlapped, balled, trimmed,
extending tendrils in search of kin
street kids gulp sun with abandon
stretched tall fast, no shade thrown
gobble carbon from its hood
spew oxygen as it should
tired young without shared trees
screams withered of lonesome plea
street Kids, don't grow with abandon
slow your bravado, calm your exhaustion
slow your mien that spent your cred
store your reserve, elude the dread.

Fred Fitzsimmons

# Regrets

Regrets, I've had a few, in business,
and in my home life, too.
I most regret speaking harshly to my spouse.
In year five of my decade of hubris,
when self-esteem ran overly strong in me.

As I headed out the door to the airport,
she asked me an important question.
I was impatient, preoccupied, short on time
and my hurried response was harsh,
ill-advised, intemperate, irretrievable.

They were fiery words,
not meant to hurt but cutting still,
my position defended but at a steep cost.
I regret those words, the hurt, and the memory scarred.
My Love, forgive me, please.

Moira Sullivan

# Dream Child

Dark hair and eyes, unlike my own,
she holds me with a friendly stare.
I feel as if I'm far from home—
Adrift in space, I know not where.

She dances in her muddy clothes,
a fallen angel, full of grace,
with tangled hair and broken soles,
a phantom girl from inner space.

Called to life, then vanishing, she
flees me in my waking dreams.
I run to where I think she'll be,
down winding pathways, dark ravines.

I feel forlorn when she's not there,
this wily, impish gypsy child.
Is she the answer to my prayer?
A buried hope, unreconciled?

Peter Hoppock

# The Broken Plate

A plate slipped from my hand,
My helplessness compounded by gravity.
Neither you nor I anticipated
This occurrence, or the shattering.

There's always a tiny shard you cannot find,
the urge to repair is as embedded as the urge
to replace what's broken. The plate pieced together
and back on the shelf, we prepare another meal.

Beneath the eggs and bacon, a crack meanders
like a fault line and reveals the unhealed wound,
I wash the plate and return it to the shelf,
to its hiding place among the others.

Habit diverts us from our unhappiness.
The earth, with all its scars, still supports us.
Repairing, again and again, is our daily work.
Perhaps in heaven we will find the pieces we have lost.

Elizabeth DeSchryver

# Seasons

A cherry blossom
Cradles unexpected snow:
A hope born too soon.

Magnolia trees:
Porcelain cups of perfume,
Thick with summer sleep.

Autumn jeweler
Dips leaves in molten sunshine:
Transient beauty.

Arthritic fingers
Strain to reach the steel gray sky:
Branches in winter.

R. James

# Monet World

Crosswords once dispatched
in the first minutes of a lunch break
now consume entire days.
The most common words can disappear
for hours at a time.

Past events, large and small,
distort in mists of time, or disappear:
the depth of my childhood valley;
the names of comrades in Vietnam;
those witty essays for Modern American Authors
the best college course ever.
I'm a camera that can't quite focus,
a witness, but to what?

I no longer stroll in your sensate world
with its sharp contrasts and precise colors.
I live in a world painted by Monet,
a canvas of maybe water lilies in a maybe pond,
the light always soft and just so, a picture
with sunbeams and shadows and a beautiful haze,
and crossword puzzles from here to the horizon.

Sarah Malone

# Desk Clock

I never noticed it before.
Beating like the heart in my chest.
For twenty years, ticking here on the desk.
What brought the passing of time to mind?

Did my fear of time slipping away
Muffle the sound of passing time?
Is it that time is fleeting and now
I resonate with the passing of it?

Is it that time, the tick-tocking of time
Laid in wait right here, every day for me to see,
To reference, to measure, the vanishing away of it?
What brought it now to mind, this sound of time?

Paco Aramburu

# Deadline

The clock says six o'clock
the spectral parade of lingering sleep
arrives at the call of duty.

The clock says ten o five.
ignoring River Time and its obstinate stream of hours.
The clock says five thirty
Sarah lies a hand away. The rhythm of her breath
hosts hundreds of crepuscular falls.

The clock says seven o seven
Sarah's snores cut by the ringing.

The clock says five and two zeroes
The light phantoms in my closed eyelids
sketch a face in smokey lines.
Prone to disappear, your smile has a tinge of goodbyes
You were always generous in your opinions of me
Perhaps you never cared enough.

The clock says four thirty-seven
I anticipate the surrender to death rehearsal,
navigating near the ultimate waterfall
I dwell in foggy parlors busy with old dreams.

My eyes open, a machine shows my heartbeat,
only my body is now my clock
ultimate door leads into a darkened room
filled with smoke-drawn denizens of the…

Nancy Hepner Goodman

# Small-Town Intensive Care

My patient's eyes communicate trust
as if in some uncanny way she knows
my attention to details
could save her life.

She tells me the taco recipe she knows by heart.
Minutes later my steady hands are on
her pale white sternum, counting
in full resuscitation mode.

The bed is too high so I jump up onto it
kneeling over her portly body in this intimate space.
Whiffs of vegetable soup, her lunch half eaten on the tray.
Alarms, adrenaline, a musky odor, rubbing alcohol,

the rhythm of bagged breath, and compressions,
breathing, compressions again and again, then
the order to clear and paddles shock her heart,
the slippery gel, the sting of sweat in my eyes.

Only minutes ago, with cheerful optimism
she explained her rub of smoked paprika, garlic, cumin,
believing she'd be back in her kitchen soon.
It's time for fresh arms to spell me, but I don't give up

until the time of death is called.
The room falls into stunned defeat, then silence.
I remove IVs and monitoring leads, wash her ashen body,
dress her in a clean gown, wishing for an open window.

Joyce Burns Zeiss

# The Sheepherder

Under the Idaho sun a farm boy turned sheepherder
When the Grimm alfalfa seed refused to grow
in the dead land of the Dust Bowl.
Alone, he talked to sheep and stars, and yearned for more.

He escaped, returning to the sweet Illinois prairie
where his parents had met before heading west to homestead.
He wore a tattered sweater and carried a battered suitcase.
He studied engineering to make something of himself.

After a stroke when he was eighty, he liked to talk
Of sheepherding and raising alfalfa seed.
He longed for the mountains of Idaho as he stared out
at the flatlands of Chicago where he lived with his daughter.

He still worked hard, studying letters that, like stray sheep,
Wandered into the sagebrush, refusing to listen.
He tried to herd them back together into words,
But they scattered into the foothills of his mind.

He pored over paper, pen in hand, struggling to find the words.
When he closed his eyes, he saw sheep on the hills
and slender alfalfa stalks, and he wept for a farm boy,
A sheepherder who yearned for more under the Idaho sun.

Alan Souter

# On Top of the World

I step down from the aircraft
that brought me to the top of the world,
I take that first breath. A chill sails down my spine.
White corsairs course overhead,
I walk, leaving tracks behind that disappear
in the wind that is freezing my hands and face.
When the aircraft takes off, I am alone,
like no loneliness I've ever known.
Each breath is empty of scent.
A speck appears in the distance.
A bear sensing an easy meal?
I squint into the swirling snow.
The speck appears and disappears
growing larger in the white maelstrom.
There is no place to hide, no trench or tree.
I crouch down before the approaching shadow
and the clanking sound stops.
*Wait,* I think. *Bears don't clank.*
A shout comes from the steel-tracked creature—
*Sorry we're late, professor!*
I stand on shaking legs and climb inside the beast.
Which smells of wet wool. My face warms and
the vehicle turns toward our destination
at the top of the world.

Barbara Chiprin

# My Hill

The first time I saw you, I left without saying hello.

The second time we met, I flirted with you.

The third time, you spoke and took my breath away.

You derailed me the fourth time we met; my knees buckled.

Yet I came back to you a fifth time.

And the sixth time I wobbled when I stood before you.

The seventh time, I braked and you caught me.

You chained me the eighth time.

The ninth time you met me halfway.

Finally, the tenth time, I became your Queen.

# CREATIVE
# NONFICTION

## OVERCOMING

# Borders of Being

by Anna Carvlin

## NOVEMBER 2019:
## TWO MONTHS ALONG

Eight weeks after we'd transferred the embryo, I sat in Dr. Daria's River North office at the fertility clinic. A photo of him and his family sat prominently on a shelf behind him. Unsmiling, he folded his hands. "The embryo isn't measuring at the size we want to see for its gestational age."

We knew that. Sussan, my wife, was on the phone, her presence distant and soft.

"There is a chance it may not make it," he added.

I nodded to show I understood, but I didn't, really. Yes, the techs had told me the embryo was measuring a week behind at three appointments in a row. But they smiled and seemed at least neutral while relaying the information. A few days before, I'd become nauseous before work, as a real pregnant lady might; proof I carried a growing baby.

Then I asked, "If you had to put a number on it, what percent chance do we have?"

I could have spent the following week in blissful denial until he stamped our fate with his answer. "I'd say about fifteen to twenty percent."

Stunned, I swallowed hard, then followed up with more questions to subdue a swell of sorrow and shame. How embarrassing to have wanted something so badly, and to have believed in it so thoroughly. Hadn't I already learned? Yearning and desire lead to disappointment. I had allowed myself to love and dared to hope; now the heaviest disappointment loomed. Tamping the emotion down in my throat, I asked what I'd need to do to get the embryo out if things "went south."

"If things 'go south,' there is a possibility you'll need a D&C, but it depends on whether your body expels the embryo on its own," he replied.

253

My mind and heart iced over. It seemed certain I'd need to have my uterus scraped out. In my rudimentary understanding, I imagined a dead embryo hanging on like an empty chrysalis well past its welcome. I wasn't about to wait for it to leave "on its own"—I needed to continue trying to have a baby, and soon.

I thanked him and walked out with barely a goodbye.

Sussan messaged me: "Are you done? I don't understand. My heart is breaking."

"Me too."

The most likely outcome, in my mind, had been this negative outcome all along. The doctor's prediction confirmed my deeply held belief: I didn't deserve a baby. My fault. I waited too long. Advanced maternal age. When this terrible news came, I understood it as the normal course of events. Success would have been out of the ordinary—extraordinary; beyond my grasp.

"But it's not over, Anna."

Sussan had sent me a message a week earlier: "Honey, I'm getting attached to the name Morla. Is that bad? Or should I let my heart love? I want to kiss her nose so, so bad."

I'd been getting attached, too.

I walked out of the clinic down the outdoor corridor along the canal, toward a job I now dreaded. The prospect of a new baby had formed a translucent soft pearl around me, protecting me from work woes, buoying my mood despite first-trimester fatigue. In a team where mansplainers called the shots and my authority was nil, being pregnant felt like a secret superpower. They didn't care what I had to say, but I could create humans. But now shame thoroughly depleted the oxygen from its sister emotion, pride.

I would have taken off the afternoon, but I needed all my paid time off for fertility treatment and, maybe, maternity leave.

Throughout the morning, I sat at my desk staring at the computer. My phone vibrated with messages from Sussan as I sipped coffee. She still had questions. When were we going to lose her if we were going to lose her? When would we be safe if we were not going to lose her?

I suggested we mourn and grieve and move on, rushing to the acceptance phase of the new reality.

She asked: "Do we act like it's over and then be happy if it isn't?"

"Yes, basically."

Alongside my bitterness and resignation, a frustrating, niggling hope inside me blossomed at unexpected moments despite my best intentions to snuff it out. I knew logically we had a tiny chance our little Morla could survive. (We'd nicknamed her after the wise, tough turtle in *The NeverEnding Story*.) I hadn't completely given up, even though everything I said to Sussan was to the contrary.

That evening, I went straight home and up to bed. Without taking off my work clothes, I lay down until sunlight vanished and darkness surrounded me.

When Sussan finally came home, I was still in the same position. She tried comforting me, but I thought her voice sounded too regular, not sad enough, as though the imminent miscarriage were happening only to me.

The impending loss felt like a cruel lesson. I had not really heard when people mentioned an early miscarriage. Losing a nonviable embryo so early clocked as barely a blip in the master plan to have a family. Right? Now I understood in a new way the loss of joy, the attachment to this particular potential person at a specific point in time.

Still seated on the edge of the bed, Sussan asked, "Do you need a cup of water?"

I finally lifted my head and yelled, "Why are you asking me questions? I don't understand why you're asking me anything. Stop. There's nothing to say!"

She left me alone without barking back.

Sussan and I proceeded with our weekend plans: a drive with her mom to Albion, Indiana, to meet her aunt. We cried in bed together in our few moments alone. We sauntered down unpaved roads and through a cemetery. On a return walk to the lake house, we moved in close and said "hello" to a small herd of black and white Holstein cows. Some drank water out of a trough while others observed us. Minutes dripped by like the long, viscous snot hanging out of their nostrils.

An unwelcome realization surfaced repeatedly: I'd be okay. My resilient spirit stayed lit, a little. Even though continuing without Morla sounded bleak and flatline, the propulsion to reinvent, reignite, redo, superseded my depressive mode.

I rush-walked to the clinic the Thursday after our trip—week nine and, I was certain, the end of my pregnancy—entered the exam room, pulled off my pants, and lay on the exam table. I had to get to work for a meeting and warned the OB tech before she inserted the probe, "Prepare for bad news."

"Really? Why?"

As I explained Dr. Daria's dire prognosis, the tech was already looking at the screen and typing notes.

Still shaking my head, I bemoaned my fate and the possibility of a D&C. Then the tech angled the screen toward me. Morla emerged into view in iridescent greens and black shadows, like a misshapen seahorse from the depths of a cold ocean.

"I mean, the baby's measuring on the small end," the tech said, "but I definitely see a heartbeat."

*Get comfortable.*

*Make yourself at home.*

## JANUARY 2020:
## FOUR MONTHS ALONG

At my routine twenty-week anomaly ultrasound, we drove to my gynecologist's exurb office; the sun shone brilliantly on a cold, late-January day. My confidence soared. We were about to check this obligatory box, one of many on the already long and arduous road to baby cheeks.

The young ultrasound tech had me lie down on the medical table and gelled up the probe. Our baby's hands wrapped around her head as if doing a duck-and-cover drill. *Damn!* We wanted to see her face.

"Move, Baby," the tech encouraged in a cutesy voice. The probe rolled efficiently around my belly at different angles to capture everything: heart, brain, spinal cord, head, bones. Flashes of my child's ribs floated onto the screen; her vertebrae, feet, hands. We'd catch glimpses of her small face, but not in its entirety. I couldn't look away, soaking up every view.

"She's snoozing away," the tech said, putting the probe away. She handed me a tissue and a printout of our baby's perfect foot. "I'll check with the doctor and make sure we don't need anything else," she said and walked out.

Sussan and I looked at each other. Was this standard?

I wiped off the gel. We waited. She returned and said, "The doctor can't get a read on the kidneys and she wants a redo."

"A redo?" Why was this tech relaying the message without a hint of recognition she was delivering a punishing message? Didn't she know? We'd been on this baby journey for so long. "Can't we do a redo now?" I could try waking the baby by moving it around.

"Unfortunately, no."

"Listen," I said, "Are you being straight with me? Is something wrong?"

"Even if something was wrong," she replied, "I can't tell you by law."

She agreed to get the doctor.

Dr. Lugosi came in a few minutes later. "I really can't see the kidneys, so I'd like you to get a higher-level scan."

I waited for reassurance. I wanted: "It's fine. Don't worry. This is routine, very common. No big deal. People get second scans all the time." But she didn't budge. Kind, but clinical.

Sussan and I walked out of the building with slumped shoulders to my Honda, which was streaked in gray from late winter salt accumulation. "I hate everything," I said.

I called the hospital later. The earliest available appointment wasn't for another week and a half.

I paced around and researched fetal kidney pathologies. Fetuses can live without kidneys in the womb. I had no idea!

At the redo anatomy scan, Sussan and I sat while a doctor assessed the results. We needed to make it over this hump, then I'd sail through the next five months of pregnancy, heavy and happy.

But when the doctor entered the room, her face drooped with what looked like so much anguish. She remained standing, took a long deep breath, and started talking.

I only heard explanatory, preparatory mumbo jumbo, and stopped her mid-sentence. "Can you tell us if she's okay, please?"

"Oh." Her eyebrows went into a "surprised" position. "Yes. Everything looks fine!"

Finally, I could exhale. Why didn't she just say so?

Our baby would not need dialysis or a kidney donor. Nor would we have to abort her for bilateral renal agenesis (no kidneys is not compatible with life). With the scan behind us, now we would feel *even better* after reaching "viability" phase in a month.

# MAY 2020:
# EIGHT MONTHS ALONG

I focused on the fluorescent lights above as my breathing became more strained and audible with every passing moment. The ultrasound tech seemed not to notice as she rolled the probe over my abdomen, studying the screen and clicking notes onto her keyboard. I tapped my Fitbit with two fingers. Only *three minutes* had passed since the appointment started.

My body felt wrong. I had to tell her. "I'm about to faint."

Lying supine with a heavy belly had caused inferior vena cava compression, she explained; the baby's weight squashed the big vein that carries blood to the heart from lower extremities. I readjusted my cumbersome body, crinkling the paper sheet beneath me, to lie sideways facing a white wall. My cloth mask stifled my breathing, but now at least I wasn't about to pass out.

Sussan sat nearby. She came to support me but *needed* to see the baby. A month before, Sussan had cried when the clinic requested patients attend appointments unaccompanied because of COVID. When I reread the clinic's reminder text, I noticed they *preferred* patients not bring a guest; we preferred Sussan be there.

The previous September, during a voice journal Sussan and I recorded after the transfer, I'd told the embryo, "Your little home is inside my belly."

I vowed to make my body a comfortable spot.

Sussan and I begged our little embryo to stay.

*Burrow in.*

*We hope you like it in there.*

*We know you're working hard.*

*Can't wait to meet you.*

Now, thirty-five weeks into the pregnancy, I felt confident and relaxed at checkups. But sixteen minutes in at this examination, I realized with a trace of alarm, appointments had never lasted this long.

The tech asked, "Are you peeing a lot lately?

"No. Why? Is something wrong?" She remained silent and rolled the ultrasound transducer on my gelled-up belly.

My heart started racing and my palms were sweaty. Above her mask, Sussan's eyes betrayed no emotion. Was I alone in thinking the worst-case scenario was materializing?

*Stick with us.*

*Join us.*

Barely two more minutes passed. I asked our ultrasound tech again, "Can you please tell me what is going on?" She revealed nothing. I ripped the cloth mask off my face, threw it down, and yelled, "What is *wrong*?"

"Put your mask back on, please," she said.

Sussan picked up the mask and handed it to me. "Put it back on," she said. I complied. "We don't know if there's anything to worry about." But behind her words, she revealed later, lay an ocean of worry.

The tech vaguely affirmed what Sussan said with a nod, and I clung to that, but tears streamed down my face, my chest racked with muted sobs.

*Stay here.*

*Stay with us.*


"Just a few more minutes till the half-hour is up," the tech assured me. Until that instant, I hadn't known they allotted the baby a maximum time window to do something. But do *what*? I still didn't know. During prior appointments, the baby passed the test well before the half-hour ended.

I had questioned the extensive monitoring since I was so healthy but attended the tests with little complaint; fitting appointments into my schedule as a newly laid-off person was easy. Besides, with the pandemic in full swing, doctor's office trips provided a welcome diversion from monotonous walks in the forest preserves, parks, and cemeteries.

When I told my aunts and mom over group text about all the tests, one aunt replied: "BS. It just scares mom." I agreed with her then. But later, after my experience, countless times I would think, *Why wasn't I monitored more?*


Twenty-seven weeks after the miscarriage scare, and twenty-seven minutes into the ultrasound, my baby still hadn't accomplished the mystery task to pass the biophysical test. As I understood later, my baby would have passed the test had she made at least three "gross body movements" during the half-hour, along with several other parameters.

Tears trickled sideways down my face. I wondered if I should be in an ambulance getting to a hospital. As the tech scanned my belly and looked at images of my baby, I wanted to see. What if it was the last time? But the back of my head faced the screen. Sussan held my hand.

The longest half-hour stopped. The tech handed me a tissue and left the office to call the doctor. I wiped the gel off my stomach, then gathered my coat and bag. Time lasted forever. I needed to leave the room and fly to the hospital.

The tech returned and handed me a cell phone with Dr. Lugosi on the line. "Anna, your baby wasn't making any major movements," she said, "and your fluid is low. I need you to go directly to triage at Christ Hospital."

"Okay," I said. I handed the phone back to the tech and started walking out the door. The doctor's urgency seemed to validate my worst fear: my baby's heart could stop beating any minute.

"Wait!" Sussan said. "Where are we going?" She took the cell phone.

I inched my way backward toward the exit while Dr. Lugosi gave Sussan instructions.

"Go directly to triage at labor and delivery, second floor," she said. "Not the emergency room. Tell them your doctor sent you. Don't go home first and don't stop anywhere."

Sussan caught up with me in the hallway. We ran to my Honda in the lot. She insisted on driving after I screeched the tires reversing out, but I had no intention of sitting with nothing to do in the passenger's seat. I drove thirty-five in a heavily-policed thirty-mile-an-hour zone the two miles to the hospital, parked in an upper-level spot in the pavilion, and ran down the stairs holding my stomach—the elevator was too slow. Sussan shouted, "Walk!" afraid I might trip and fall on the concrete steps. But I needed to be where doctors could get my baby out *now*.

We arrived at triage.

I recognized the location from an earlier group tour of labor and delivery. Christ Hospital had a new level-three neonatal intensive care unit (NICU) center, the highest level possible in Illinois, which provided another layer of reassurance to an already strenuous journey. We never thought we'd need sophisticated care for our baby.

I handed the lady my insurance card. She buzzed me through. A nurse led me to a room and had me put on a hospital gown. Five seconds to strip down and another five to get my gown on. I called the nurse, still catching my breath, before situating myself on the hospital bed. She put the leads on my belly and turned on the monitor. I exhaled. Proof my baby existed right on the screen: green dips and valleys, spikes up and down, steady beeping.

Alive.

For now.

*Please, choose us.*

# Mother Knows Best

by Nancy Hepner Goodman

My seventy-two-year-old mother yelled like a mob boss, "Pull over and we'll throw the dog in the trunk." Her voice had a terse, determined edge to it. I had just run over the neighbor's cocker spaniel puppy. It started chasing the car and got pulled under the wheels. My mother (aka Grandma Fran) was best known for her kindness and fresh-baked cowboy cookies. Her words stunned me. *I was the one driving. Why was Mom acting like she was in charge?*

I swerved over to the curb in front of the neighbor's house and bolted out of the car. My 110-pound mother jumped out too. Mom blurted, "It's dead," but I saw the dog gasp for air. *No, you're wrong,* I thought, *She's alive. She has to be alive.* Her wavy, auburn fur had a healthy shine. I saw no blood or broken bones. Her floppy ears lay soft against her head.

I glanced at the neighbor's front porch. A black plastic mat sat worn and rippled on the block of cement below the plain white door. The house had a generic square patch of mown lawn and a blacktop driveway, but no flower pots, wind chimes, or touches that transform a house into a home. I stared, laser-focused at the house—white with gray trim—hoping the neighbors would appear. I pictured telling them what happened while we called their veterinarian.

"Better not mess with them!" Mom said as she saw me eyeing the front door. Did she know these neighbors or was she being paranoid? The neighborhood had changed in the last twenty years; some yards had gotten rundown with grass the color of straw, houses begging for a new coat of paint, teetering gutters full of leaves. "Riffraff," Mom had muttered at the sad looking houses.

I glanced over at the dog and realized within those few seconds that she had died, her neck slack, her body limp, her lax tongue jutting out of her mouth like a freakish dragon. I stood outside the car door, silent. I needed time to think, to gain control of the situation; to gain control of my mother.

She lifted the dog. It was all floppy legs and neck like Mutsy, the life-sized stuffed animal Nicole, my four-year-old daughter, slept with. The muscles in my neck and shoulders tensed. My hands shook. *What the hell is Mom doing?*

I wished I could put my head in my hands for a crying jag, but neither my stoic German heritage nor my image of how a good mother should behave in front of her children would allow it. I steeled myself, glancing back at Nicole, innocently sitting in her car seat. Her little face was soft, framed by her wavy red hair.

We had just flown in from Chicago for our semi-annual trip to visit Grandma Fran in Portland. When we rolled into the driveway, the daffodils were in full bloom, lining the path to the front door of my childhood home. A "WELCOME TO THE PORCH" sign hung above two Adirondack chairs perched on Mom's veranda, a perfect spot for relaxing and people watching, with a bird's eye view of the neighborhood. I was looking forward to tall glasses of cold lemonade, digging into a book that had languished on my nightstand, Dairy Queen drive-throughs with Nicole, and porch sitting with my mom.

But first on our list was Shetland pony rides and snow cones at the local grade school's fair.

We had tumbled into the rental car at Grandma Fran's house while I made sure Nicole was secured in the back seat, Mom had her purse and house keys, and everyone had made a trip to the bathroom.

We'd only made it halfway down the block when a streak of brown fur appeared, running along the passenger side of the rental car, and within seconds I felt the uneven bump of the dog in the road. It could have happened to anyone. It was an accident. I wanted to confess to the dog's owners and accept the consequences as a totally capable adult.

But in that moment, I did as my mother commanded. Previous conflicts with my mother had ended with "I told you so," the silent treatment, or worst of all, my mom enlisting my older brother (the man in the family since my father passed away more than a decade ago) to join her side in our arguments. Although I was calm and obedient on the outside, my anger and frustration bundled up tight on the inside.

I pictured the Ten Commandments framed in pink metal still hanging in my childhood bedroom. *Thou shalt honor your mother and father* is still seared into my soul.

Watching my mother throw the dead dog in the trunk seemed wrong to me, but I obediently went along with her plan. I said nothing and popped the trunk.

"Get in the car. Let's go," Mom said in a no-nonsense manner. She scurried towards the front of the car and jumped in the passenger seat as if nothing had happened.

The same dog—energetic, fun-loving, darting around the lawn, escaping outstretched hands—had run into my mother's yard earlier that morning. I had given her a drink of water and a hug before killing her later in the day. She had panted from the heat and excitement, a blur of merriment as she dashed around. Mom said the owners let the dog run all over the neighborhood. I should have checked for an ID tag with a phone number. That's what I would have done in my own neighborhood, but this was Mom's turf with neighbors I no longer knew. I let it slide, muzzled myself to keep the peace.

We drove a few miles to the fair, set up in a grassy field in the back of a grade school, a perfect image of three generations enjoying a beautiful spring day together. We petted the lambs and found the snow cone truck while I imagined the dog in the trunk of the rental car; the stench of death mixed with urine and feces, the hot sun, rigor mortis. Mom waved at Nicole on the pony rides, as she slurped down a cherry snow cone, red syrup dripping down her fingers. *Had she forgotten about the dog?* I forced myself to smile and laugh, not a care in the world, while I envisioned the neighbor's children whistling, then yelling, "Chasy, *Chasy*, **Chasy**," the name I gave to their dead dog earlier in the day as it ran across my mother's lawn.

After a few pony rides around in circles, Nicole tired of the fair. An hour later we drove back to Grandma Fran's house. Time for a nap, I closed the shades. The sparrows chirped through an open window. I lay down next to Nicole to encourage her to sleep. The curtains moved in a peaceful breeze. My lips stuck to my teeth, my mouth turned dry with anxiety, and my head and ears pounded out a silent scream I held within me. Just a few hours ago, the vacation was off to a good start and then in a second it wasn't.

Mom cooked up a plan to put the twenty-five-pound puppy in a cardboard box, drive it down to the neighbor's house, and knock on the door. They wouldn't get angry or give *her* any trouble, being an old woman, she told me. So that's what she did.

I had given up trying to argue with my mother years ago. She held grudges. She saved letters I had written her, reading specific sections back to me, disputing my words. After I moved to Chicago, according to Mom, I had gotten smarter and more sophisticated with my graduate degree in Nursing from Northwestern University. From her perspective, our fights weren't fair. I struggled for my independence from her, my own voice, my freedom. In Chicago, it was easy to be my own person. Back in my childhood home and staying under Mom's roof, I regressed to my younger self, while Mom dug in her aging heels to maintain control.

She slipped out of the house and into her car. I imagined the dog laying on a blanket in a large fruit box retrieved from the garage as my mother drove slowly down the street. I pictured the dog's limbs stiff, with urine soaking its hindquarters and a pungent smell of musty fur, mixed with the odor of decaying fruit.

I stayed home with my napping child while Mom took the blame. She wouldn't elaborate on the conversation, only saying the neighbors weren't surprised. I imagined her confession; a dash of dementia here, a pinch of fabrication there, stirred together for a good story. I'm sure she slumped her osteoporotic shoulders and gazed at the neighbors with her faraway look and wrinkles that would settle on her face when she was tired. Her voice might have cracked and faded out with feigned exhaustion, an effective trick she used from time to time to elicit sympathy.

On subsequent visits to Grandma Fran's, I never saw the neighbors at the end of the street. Maybe they moved. But when I drove by that house, I always paused in my mind to remember their fun-loving puppy. The one I named Chasy.

Seventeen years later, at her memorial service, the Lutheran minister described my mother as "the character who had character." He had never met her but coined this phrase after talking to friends and family. A colorful storyteller, my mother had a propensity for exaggeration and a cackling laugh which often left me wondering if the stories she spun were true. As she entered her eighties, what started as a mild cognitive impairment progressed to Alzheimer's disease. Over those eight years of decline, I tried to check a second source before believing many things Mom told me.

As I remember this visit, my husband says he never heard this story. He wasn't there and it was so long ago he questions whether it happened. Perhaps I have confabulated the details, a family trait on my mother's side. But I know married couples can reflect back on their lives, each with very different cataloged memories of a life together.

I asked my now twenty-eight-year-old Nicole if she remembered when I killed a dog while visiting Grandma Fran. She told me no. "I'm so glad you didn't see it," I said.

This visit, of all the many Oregon visits, came back to me recently in the memory box of items my brain tries to bury. A tinge of guilt is mixed with a transgenerational understanding of my mother and her actions to protect me. As a nurse, a mother, and a people pleaser, I have comforted and helped many people. I am sorry to say I killed a dog once and went along with putting it in the trunk of a rental car thinking mother knew best, but feeling in my bones that's not always the case.

# Conviction

by Barbara Chiprin

*To my son: Never give up on your dreams.*
*They can happen despite life's curve balls.*

*Love: Your ordinary, pragmatic Mother.*
*To the Moon, around Mars, back to Earth.*

I fasten the race monitor around my ankle as the mantra repeats in my head, "This is it. I'm here. I'm doing this. For real." And double-check that the gear for three disciplines—swim, bike, run—is properly placed in the transition area.

It's August 2018 and promises to be a clear, hot, humid day in Wisconsin. I always wanted to compete in a triathlon, ever since the 1980s when I was in high school and the sport was in its infancy. But I never had the conviction to do the training until a year ago. I was in-between jobs, a single, overweight, asthmatic parent of a fourteen-year-old, reflecting on life's accomplishments, hurdles and blunders when I decided to undertake this rigorous, seemingly impossible dream.

Last October, I sent an innocent text to a couple of high school friends. "Who wants to do a triathlon with me?"

Kris responded, "I'm in." That didn't surprise me. Kris did a triathlon the past summer and is an avid runner. Unfortunately, she injured herself and dropped out of this race. Lisa, however, shocked me when she responded, "I'm in." Like me, she spent the past thirty years with family obligations and pursuing a career, our health taking a back seat.

As Lisa and I walk from the transition area to the start, my heart accelerates. Her expression mirrors mine. Nervous. Overwhelmed. Excited. That lake looks longer than the practice swims.

I recall an early morning, weekend, open-water swim practice. I only made it because Lisa persisted. It was an overcast day and the clouds itched to open. But we went. The lake was large and crystal clear with water above our heads and no lines to steer us straight. Seaweed lived everywhere. We entered the water and stopped when it hit our knees. We didn't make it to the middle of the lake where all the swimmers were circling in a large loop or past the creepy seaweed that morning. The 5:00 a.m. alarm was not welcome, until today.

Our mantra continues under our breath as we arrive at the start area and leave our flip-flops by the fence. "We can do this. Cross the finish line on two feet. Don't care about the time. Finishing is the goal." When the National Anthem finishes, we line up.

I watch the first wave of competitors run into the lake. In no time they're halfway through. They're fast and look like they're hydroplaning. My heart quickens. I double-check the snugness of my gold swim cap, the color indicating my 50-54 age group. I lose sight of the swimmers as the sun rises above the horizon, blinding my view. I am in awe that the first group will finish the swim before we start. I take a puff of my inhaler, place it in a plastic bag and tuck it inside my bra, then lower the goggles over my eyes and pull the straps tight.

Our wave is at the start line. It's go-live time, the familiar phrase from thirty years in technology implementation. I shake my arms, roll my shoulders forward and back. The pre-race jitters dissipate as survival mode kicks in.

I break our trance and say to Lisa, "Good luck. See ya at the finish line." And off we go for our half-mile swim. There's no turning back.

*Just like—My divorce several years earlier.*

*Keep Moving Forward.*

※ ※ ※

The water is murky. I can barely see my hand in front of me as I swim into the beaming sun. Within ten strokes, I am smack-dab behind three women who are doing the side stroke while having a friendly chat as they inch their way across the lake.

"Are you kidding me?" I yell to myself. I slow down and shift to a breast-stroke. I don't want to be stuck behind them.

What to do? Swim through them or over them? I'm not a strong enough swimmer to do either.

Realization dawns: Swim around them. Here goes. I switch to freestyle, pick up the pace, swim around them and keep on going. WOW! I did it.

Panic strikes. I'm swimming in open water. I have very far to go. People keep crashing into me. A few grab my foot and pull me under. Others, who are in front of me, suddenly stop, causing me to bump into them.

People. Are. Everywhere.

I stop. Tread water. Look around. There's no open space for me to swim. It's like the *Twilight Zone* or a Stephen King book; the more I swim, the longer the lake gets.

NO! I will not be rescued by the lifeguard. Where's a raft?

I look around to grab onto one. I'm on the left side where the buoys are. How'd I get here? I swam diagonally? I'll be stuck in the water. I'm never getting out!

I swim: freestyle, breast, side, doggie paddle. Finally, I flip over onto my back, catch my breath and reset. I think I even invented a couple of strokes.

I hear my coach whisper in my head, "Go to your happy place." Her happy place is singing Happy Birthday.

The first song that enters my mind, "Twinkle, twinkle little star. How I wonder what you are? Up above the…" whatever the words are. Humming, I flip back onto my stomach and start swimming. My breathing back to normal.

Where am I?

I'm back on the right side. I went diagonal again?

I sigh. Figure this out. Think. Think. Think.

I want to be on the right. This is good. What did I do in the pool? Got it! Count strokes and breathe.

One, two, three, four, breathe.
One, two, three, four, breathe.

A few more rotations pass. Time to spot. I'm in the middle of the swim area. Diagonal again. Crap! At least I moved forward some.

My head screams. I am halfway through the swim in the middle of the lake. I can do this. And there's no seaweed.

269

I forgot to set my watch. The thought pops in my head. I'll set it in T1 before the bike.

Back to the swim. I find a new rhythm.

> One, two, three, breathe.
> One, two, three, four, five, breathe.
> Spot.
> Adjust course.

Thank you, coach, for forcing me to learn bilateral breathing.
Repeat.

> One, two, three, breathe.
> Twinkle, twinkle…
> One, two, three, four, five, breathe.
> Spot.
> Adjust.

Eventually, I eye the last buoy. Almost there. Longest swim EVER!

I make it to the shore, gasp for air, struggle up the sand and into the transition area. I pass Lisa's area and see her bike is still on the rack. She must still be swimming. Pulling my goggles, earplugs and swim cap off, I recall the past year where I barely swam twenty-five yards in a pool, and revel in my accomplishment of completing a half-mile swim in open water.

Reaching my bike, I go through my T1 mantra.

> Swim stuff on the ground.
> Sunglasses, headband on.
> Adjust ponytail.
> Helmet on.
> Wipe feet.
> Socks on. (Yes, I wear socks.)
> Shoes on.

Why won't my left foot fit in my shoe? It fit last night. Loosen the laces. Shove my foot in. It's a little tight. I'll loosen it more in T2 if needed.

Right shoe on. No problem.
Set my watch. Note time.
Unrack bike.
Walk it out the transition exit, past the line.
Hop on bike.
Time to ride.

*Just like—When I moved 2,500 miles across the country from San Francisco to Chicago as a single parent with my eight-year-old son to be closer to family. Keep moving forward.*

At first, I'm wobbly as I start riding the eleven-mile bike segment. My coach and I discussed the transition. "Take it slow for the first mile. Get used to the bike. You'll be in seventh heaven knowing you finished the swim. Get your mind on the bike for the first mile." We practiced the motions of going from the swim to the bike in the gym parking lot several afternoons.

She's absolutely right. I can do this!

About a mile into the ride, I need water but am terrified I'll either drop the bottle or fail to put it back in the cage without crashing. I've practiced for months pulling the bottle out, sipping, putting it back in the cage. Most of the time, I either drop it or come to a crawl, or outright stop riding to get a drink. It's now or never. Why didn't I put a second bottle on the bike in case I drop it?

I reach down, grab the water bottle, take a sip. All is good. Now, to get it back in the cage.

Oh no. There's a curve ahead. Can I do this before I reach it? I need both hands on the handlebars for the curve.

Too late. I have to hold the water bottle through the curve.

Here goes.

Crap. Potholes. Now I remember when Lisa and I drove the route a couple of weeks ago. All right, hold the water bottle while navigating the curves and the potholes. This will be tricky. Don't bump into the other 650 women in this race. If someone stops in front of me, I'll crash, altering my race.

*Just like—When I suffered a concussion, impacting and limiting my physical and mental stamina, and altering my balance; one that many years later I am still recovering from. The Tri training advancing the recovery leaps and bounds.*

*Keep Moving Forward.*


I make it past the curve and the potholes with the water bottle in my hand without crashing. Yippie for me!

I settle into the straightaway; it's about two miles until the next turn. People are passing me, I'm passing people. All in all, it's a beautiful Sunday morning. I'm only missing Kris and Lisa. Where is Lisa? I hope she is out of the lake by now and on the bike. On our weekend morning rides, Lisa usually led, then Kris in the middle, and I brought up the rear. It's awkward to be in front. But triathlons are a solitary sport.

To pass the time, I calculate my swim time. I entered the lake at approximately 7:20 am. The time on my watch said 7:47, or was that 7:57? I quickly do the math. But math in my head is tricky since the concussion.

Stupid head.

Think. An under-thirty-minute swim? That can't be. There's no way. I zigzagged too much. It must have been 7:57. I quickly check the time again.

Nope. It was 7:47.

AN UNDER THIRTY MINUTE SWIM!

I was so busy calculating the swim time, a couple of turns flew by, and I see mile marker four. This ride is going fast.

The turnaround is coming up. I take another swig of water, my overconfidence oozing. Then suddenly, I feel like I'm riding into a headwind.

Where did this come from?

My legs can barely push the pedals. I've slowed down to almost a crawl. Maybe I'm running out of gas? I open my bento box and grab a couple of chews. Then navigate around the turn and head back the way I came. The wind seems to die, or my legs grabbed the chews' energy.

A group of women in front of me are waving to their friends on the other side of the road. It seems everyone is out for a joyride.

I keep riding and feel like I'm going fast. But I know there's a hill at the end. I set my mind to become its Queen and chuckle as I recall training to conquer the hill by my house.

A few more miles and there's the hill. I start the climb and instantly come to a crawl—almost a stop—leaving me breathless.

*Just like—One night the phone rang. My ex, unexpectedly, dropped dead. My son was ten at the time.*

*Keep Moving Forward.*

I make it to the top of the hill, panting and gasping for air. I take a deep breath and descend the other side while picking up speed to the bottom.

Around a curve. Up the hill again.

Down the hill for the second time and around a group of women—having a chat.

Let's finish this ride.

One final turn and the dismount line is in view. I brake and the volunteer says, "Only the 5K run left."

He's right. That eleven-mile bike ride was fast. Definitely under an hour. I walk the bike at sloth pace with legs feeling like bricks. The transition from bike to run is torture, and my foot is killing me. The Tri-suit is now partially dry, mixed with sweat, and sticking to my body.

Reaching my transition area, I start my T2 mantra.

Rack bike.

Remove helmet.

Put on visor.

Switch watch from bike to run. Note time.

Loosen shoe.

Grab water bottle.

Head out.

The path is crowded. Women praise each other. Spectators cheer on both sides of the path. Where did all these people come from? The sun is bright and warm. Sweat streaks down my face and back. I hope I applied enough Bag Balm and don't chafe. There's no shade with a paved path around the lake and a gravel offshoot at mile two.

I head down the path. It's the same path we walked earlier to the start of the swim.

*Just like—My son was entering his teen years; we moved from the city to the suburbs, where I spent my youth. Within the year, my role was eliminated. Having devoted the past thirty years to working, I decide to take time off from Corporate America, determine what I want to do with the rest of my life, who I want to be in my golden years.*

*Keep Moving Forward.*


Surprisingly, I pass several groups of women in this first half-mile. All those practices where we went from the bike to the run are paying off.

I finish the first mile. I can't believe I've almost finished my first Triathlon.

I enter the offshoot for mile two and am overwhelmed by the heat. I take a few sips of water and try to keep my brisk walking pace, but my foot throbs. Mile two is all uneven gravel. I am forced to slow my pace, and now the same women I passed earlier are passing me. There must have been something in the lake. Maybe seaweed and I scraped it. Or something bit or stung me. As I exit the gravel offshoot, I see Lisa entering it. We give each other two thumbs up.

One mile to go. I've got this.

I see the chute and the finish line. I can run the last bit. It's now or never. So, I do. I run down the chute and cross the finish line. Spectators are still around cheering everyone who crosses. The medal is placed over my head, around my neck as I grab a cold bottle of water.

*Just like—The past several years have been especially hard for my son and me. We started over, and I went back to Corporate America.*

*Keep Moving Forward.*

I'm speechless, excited and in awe of my accomplishment not only in this race, but life up to this moment. Emotions reach the sky, and I want to party like it's 1999. But my lungs still gasp for air as if I'm in the middle of the lake trying to outswim an eel. My legs feel like spaghetti and say not another step. And in the back of my mind, there's a nagging, if only I could run.

As Lisa comes through the chute, I scream, "You did it!"

We exchange hugs, pats on the back, grab our after-race meal and find a couple of chairs to sit down. Neither of us can believe it.

We schmooze for a while and regain some energy. Pull out our phones, check our official times and rehash our race. We are winners. We lapped everyone still in bed or sitting on the couch. It doesn't matter that we finished in the bottom ten percent. We met our goals and crossed the finish line on two feet. Triumph!

Eventually, we head back to the transition area, pack our gear and load it into our cars, then swing by the start area and claim our flip-flops.

The throbbing in my foot intensifies. A few days later, my ankle will break out in a rash. And, a week later, I will realize I'm having an allergic reaction to the rubber-backed race monitor around my ankle, causing my foot to swell.

Lisa and I gaze across the lake, where we stood a few hours earlier. My smile widens as I congratulate myself. Not only for the past few hours for completing my first triathlon, but how life's challenges prepared me for the race.

I utter, "We did it."

"We did it," Lisa confirms.

"Let's do it again," I state. "Next year. All three of us."

*The Future awaits.*

*Keep Moving Forward.*

# When I Grow Up

by Kitty Malik

n the early 1970s, when I was about seven years old, my mom spent certain special Saturdays getting her hair done at *The Golden Lady*. There was a lovely woman there who cut her hair and created elaborate up-dos for holiday parties. Her name was Marsha. She was petite and pretty and had ash-blonde highlights, which were youthful and flattering and went well with her perennially tanned skin.

*The Golden Lady* was exotic. Upon entering the salon, visitors descended a small set of stairs making a grand entrance as they swept in from outside. Inside, a large tropical pond was the starring attraction, placed in the center of the room, with stylists' chairs arranged strategically around the perimeter. Every seat had a view! At one end of the pond, a mini waterfall gurgled and flowed gently down into faux tropical greenery and among a handful of brightly colored koi—the pond's sole inhabitants. I was delighted to be a guest in their beautiful home, if only on occasion.

My favorite part of visiting *The Golden Lady* was the access to one of my all-time favorite foods: donuts! Yes, they had donuts. Cinnamon-sugar donuts, powdered-sugar donuts, choc-o-late-iced donuts. While my mom was getting all Gibson-girly pretty for a holiday party she'd attend with my dad, I'd be sitting high up in a stylist's chair watching big, fat, fancy fish swim around in a luxurious pool while I ate white powdered-sugar donuts presented to me on a silver tray. I was in small-child heaven.

Right around this age, when I would have preferred to daydream about shiny golden fish, my parents asked me the question that every kid must eventually contend with: "What do you want to be when you grow up?"

I knew my answer, and provided it enthusiastically, without hesitation.

"A hairdresser! Like Marsha!"

I can still see the quizzical look on my dad's face, and the one of bemusement on my mom's. I remember the feeling of "Uh-oh. Did I say something wrong?" that arose inside of me.

"What's wrong with being a hairdresser?" I wondered.

In my head, I ran through all the reasons I liked my idea. Marsha's pretty. She's nice. Mom likes her. *And* she gets to work at The Golden Lady, making everyone look glamorous, all the while surrounded by glittering fish in a beautiful pond. (Not to mention the donuts!)

I just didn't get it.

I knew that my mom was determined to see her eldest child—my brother—become a doctor, the first in our family. According to family lore, he'd been apprised of his destiny from the time he was about four years old, though in all honesty, the message may have been transmitted earlier, possibly *in utero*. I'm not sure what caused this intense desire for a "son who is a doctor" in my mom. Perhaps she believed this would increase her social prestige, via a very specific form of socially accepted currency: a son with an MD. Or maybe it was because she had thought of becoming a physician herself, but was unable to continue her studies after she got married, had kids, and life filled up with other responsibilities.

I hadn't thought much about a career path for myself after that initial exchange. I hoped for some guidance from my parents, though there was very little. I knew they expected me to go to college, but to study what? I was the middle child and the only girl.

What's the *girl* supposed to do, I kept asking myself.

Be a nurse?

I mulled this over, concerned that I might once again provide the wrong answer.

I remember hearing "dentist" mentioned quite a bit, though I had somehow acquired the disturbing knowledge that dentists had the highest suicide rate of any profession at the time. This information was almost certainly passed on to me by my mother, the person who most wanted me to be one. She had worked briefly as a dental hygienist when I was growing up and had loved her job. But from an early age, the smell of the dentist's office made me queasy. I refused to even think about going to dental school. There was no way in hell I was going to be a suicidal dentist, gagging over rubber dams that weren't even in my own mouth. No, thank you.

The next time my parents posed "the question," I was starting high school and my brother, Jack, was just finishing. He was about to enter college where he would, naturally, focus on pre-medical studies. There were numerous discussions about his medical school aspirations—clearly a point of pride for my parents. I had become keenly aware of the fact that there were certain more or less acceptable careers from my parents' point of view, and realized I needed an option that would meet or exceed their expectations. Since dentistry was out, I offered up a job that seemed professional and intellectual, yet not physically revolting.

"A lawyer."

Long pause as parents pondered this new-and-improved career choice.

Then? Smiles all around. Yes! A *loy-yer*! This was apparently a good thing.

Was it? I mean, I wasn't exactly sure what a lawyer did. I thought it had something to do with a lot of papers, a judge, and dressing up nicely to go to court. I could do that, I thought. Having secured parental approval, I didn't care what it entailed, exactly. I shrugged off this future concern and told myself I'd figure out the details later.

Except that later came sooner than expected. Shortly after the school year started, my dad was diagnosed with stage IV cancer. It had started in his colon and migrated to his liver. The doctors also said he had a dime-sized tumor on one of his lungs. I was 14, Jack was 18, and our little brother, Peter, was only 7.

The surgery took place almost immediately. Afterward, a doctor came into my dad's hospital room and delivered his blunt prognosis to my mom.

"Your husband has 6 months to live," he stated, his voice devoid of emotion or empathy.

My dad was forty at the time. He left this doctor's practice and enrolled in a clinical trial at a nearby academic research hospital. He continued to work full time throughout my high school years, just like before his diagnosis. I was impressed with his medical team and was sure that with the right care, my dad would live a long time. Suddenly, I became a lot more interested in helping people who were sick get better and began to think about becoming a doctor myself.

My brother started college that same year. It was hard not to notice the aura of reverence that surrounded him whenever my parents announced to anyone (a relative, neighbor, doctors in the hospital, someone in line at the grocery store) that he was going to be a *doc-tor*. It seemed this was the ultimate achievement—to my parents, anyway. I decided to abandon my lawyerly ambitions and become a doctor, like my brother.

In the same way that I didn't know exactly how to become a lawyer, I wasn't completely sure what was required to become a doctor. I knew that it was quite competitive and required lots of difficult coursework, including calculus and organic chemistry. I also knew it required constant studying so that after college, you could go on to medical school and eventually become a bona fide doctor, with the letters M.D. after your name.

I probably should have had second thoughts about this plan at some point during my high school years. This was the timeframe when my dad was undergoing chemotherapy and other cancer treatments. He rarely complained, but on occasion, had to be readmitted to the hospital to help manage his side effects. One day, when I was about 15, our family went to visit him in the hospital.

When he went to work, my dad always wore a suit, or a blazer with a dress shirt and tie. But now, he was sitting up in white-sheeted hospital bed, dressed in a pale blue hospital gown with those inept string-ties that never quite hold the back together properly. It was disorienting to see him looking so much smaller than I pictured him in my mind, and so vulnerable. I had brought him a blueberry muffin to help supplement his hospital-food diet and (hopefully) improve his appetite, which had been dulled by the chemotherapy. As I leaned over the bed railing to offer him the muffin, and he reached to accept it, a thin line of blood crept up inside the plastic IV tubing toward his hand. I passed out cold, from a standing position.

Face? Meet floor. Floor? Face.

My black eye radiated various, evolving shades of purple—from eggplant to a deep purplish burgundy to light lavender—and varying tints of green for weeks on end. I was in the 10th grade and extremely self-conscious. A black eye was the last thing I needed! I tried to match my eyeshadow to it on the other eye in a desperate attempt to disguise it. I'm pretty sure some of the teachers wondered what happened to me. No one ever mentioned it, though.

Maybe they didn't see it, because I had also developed a penchant for hiding behind my hair whenever I felt awkward, which was pretty much every single day of high school. This had started back in the 9th grade in Ms. Stein's English class, when I wrote an essay that so impressed her, she wanted to read it out loud to the class. Even though I loved to write, I was mortified at the thought of personal exposure. So when Ms. Stein turned toward the chalkboard to write something down, I snuck up to her desk and snatched it back to safety. From that moment on, I avoided her gaze by allowing my straight, side-parted hair to fall across my right eye. I figured if she couldn't quite see me, I wouldn't get called on. It didn't always work, but the habit persisted.

Fast-forward to about 8 years later when I was 22 and ready to graduate college. I had completed a biology major and all the required pre-med courses, though it hadn't been an easy road. I struggled with physics and organic chemistry, and the symbols used in calculus looked like squiggly lines to me. (Ironically, I excelled in the elective classes I chose, all of which required a fair amount of reading and writing.)

My dad passed away on Memorial Day weekend in 1984, three weeks after my freshman year ended. The cancer that had spent the last 5 years traveling throughout the inner recesses of his body had left no territory unexplored. Toward the end, it found its way to his brain and spine and lodged there, inaccessible to any doctors' interventions.

I turned 19 the month after our dad died. Peter was only 11. Jack was already out of the house and on his way to medical school. My mom was falling apart and so was I, and we counted on each other to help care for Peter and to get through the long days that defined our new reality.

It was hard going back to college only four months later to start my sophomore year. I could manage to get myself to class and take notes, but doing homework was next to impossible. Nothing felt important, and I was failing most of my classes. I decided to request permission to take the rest of the term off and finish my classes the following semester. With my mom's help, I set up a meeting with the proper officials. She came along to offer moral support.

The university administrators had no sympathy. They strongly suggested I withdraw from school: permanently. This was quite a surprise to me. I'd been accepted to the university only two weeks after applying and had tested out of a required freshman English course, which I'd been told was quite unusual. So instead of kicking me out of school entirely, the administrators compromised by allowing me to *withdraw* for the semester. This meant my instructors assigned me failing grades in every single class, while the school simultaneously required me to pay the entire semester's tuition. I had been so preoccupied with sadness that I had missed the deadline to receive an "Incomplete" by about a week. My grade point average was shattered.

I eventually returned to college. But after my less-than-exemplary sophomore year it was difficult, if not impossible, to raise my grade point average enough to reach the expected standard for medical school admission. I was rejected from every single one to which I applied. Undeterred, I decided to pursue a Master of Public Health in Epidemiology, to further my education and raise my GPA so that I could apply to medical school once again.

It worked! I mean, the GPA part of the plan worked. My graduate school grades were stellar, and my letters of recommendations were from a world-class scientist and the dean of the school of public health. Still, I received one medical school rejection letter after the next. I was only wait-listed at one university: the same one where I was completing my master's degree.

When I found out I was on the wait list, I bunched up all my courage and requested a face-to-face meeting with the Dean of the medical school. I was nervous but confident, right up until the time of our meeting. I dressed up in heels and a wool skirt and sweater, a smart choice considering that the Dean—a large, imposing man who seemed irritated by my presence and the intrusion on his important schedule—was wearing a suit and tie. I remember him towering over me and gruffly waving me toward a chair opposite his own.

I was hoping for a pleasant and collegial conversation, like those I'd had with my professors in graduate school. I sat down and smiled as best I could, under the circumstances.

"Thank you so much for accepting my meeting request," I began, as genuinely as possible. My parents had raised me to be polite and cordial with all adults, and this was one important adult.

The words he spat out in reply let me know immediately that he had no interest in me as a person, in my story, or in why I was there.

"*Everyone* does that. You'd be stupid not to!" he scoffed, literally laughing in my face.

I was stunned into silence, not knowing if I should defend my intelligence or walk out and apologize for wasting his time. While I don't remember how our meeting ended, it goes without saying that it did not result in my admission to "his" medical school.

Way back at the end of 9th grade, my English teacher, Ms. Stein, asked if she could keep one of my creative writing projects to use as an example for the next year's class. The assignment had been to examine headlines and images from magazine ads for subliminal messaging intended to subconsciously influence the consumer. I loved this! I still remember the ad for a perfume brand that read: *Sensual...but not too far from innocence* as a voluptuous young woman rode a horse along the beach at sunset, gently led by a gorgeous dark man in a billowing white shirt. I laughed out loud at the obvious wordplay, which read to me as: *Sexual...but not too far from intercourse.* Another ad featured a glass of whiskey with the not-so-subtle silhouette of naked woman stretching her voluptuous body within the contours of an ice cube. She seemed to beckon provocatively from her amorphous perch within the drink. I thought it was absurd.

I'm not sure if Ms. Stein wanted to keep my project because it was good, or simply because it was unexpectedly funny from the girl who hid behind her hair. We finally brokered a deal, whereby I allowed her to keep the project in exchange for an A+ (instead of just a regular A) that semester. I mean, I knew the importance of a good GPA, even then.

Ms. Stein's glimpse of talent sparked a tiny flame of hope inside me that perhaps one day I'd be a "real" writer. I had loved to read and write since the 3rd grade, and English was now my favorite class. Her acknowledgment of this potential was the highlight of my year.

Accepting this bit of talent as a possible career direction was difficult for me, though. I'd convinced myself that the only worthy calling for me was medicine. But after multiple research jobs, and while I was working at a clinical research site, I began freelance writing on the side. A few years later, I landed a job as a medical/pharmaceutical copywriter. I've been writing almost every day for over 20 years now. And while I've never been brave enough to submit any creative work for publication, I've written and edited websites, ads, manuscripts, emails, promotional and educational materials, and even a newsletter or two. For doctors, no less!

It took half my lifetime to finally accept that what I enjoy the most is writing. It clears my mind and allows ideas, hopes, and dreams to unwind and expand. Writing eases the pain of disappointment and diminishes my anger. It calms my fears and helps me focus in on next steps. I write in journals, on the computer or my phone, on random scraps of paper, or on my hand if I don't have any paper. I write at all hours of the day and night, sometimes until my wrists ache. Even as I wrestle with imposter syndrome, I force myself to keep moving forward.

Looking back, I sincerely believe that my failure to be admitted to medical school was the result of the Universe looking out for me. Considering the fainting episode in my dad's hospital room, keeping me away from patients—and blood—is probably best for everyone, myself included. I took a detour or two on the way to get to where I am today, to becoming what I want to be in my best and worst moments: a Writer. And in retrospect, I'm pretty darned grateful for all those medical school rejections.

# Good Enough

by Sherry Kromer-Shapiro

Cindy, a thirty-five-year-old woman, sits on the floor in the darkness of the guest bedroom's walk-in closet, in her parents' snowbird home in Palm Springs, California. She has shut the bedroom and closet door so neither she, nor her children asleep in the room, will hear her mother screaming in the kitchen at the opposite end of the ranch house. Before exiting the kitchen, Cindy watched as her mother, Esther, bent over the ironing board, her ragged, plaid robe tied around her bulk, her eyes, pooled by mascara, like burnt-out sockets. She was sprinkling water on her grandchildren's clothes, before steamrolling the iron over the five-year-old boy's jeans and the eight-year-old girl's T-shirts. Rather than this sight, what wounds Cindy is her mother screaming; "You God damn bitch. I told you yesterday to wash their clothes. Now they'll never dry by morning." Caring more about others' opinions than her daughter's feelings, her mother needs the children to look perfect for the other grandparents, who place no importance on clothing. Tomorrow Cindy will take her children on a bus to Los Angeles, where they will meet up with their father, finished with year-end billing, at the airport, so they can visit their other set of grandparents.

Cindy stretches out on the closet's carpet in corpse pose. She will practice her yogic breathing until her parents' bedtime, when she can open the den's hide-a-bed couch. There is no reason for her mother to iron clothes that have been in the dryer so often that they are way beyond possible shrinkage, which is what she says will happen if they are put in her dryer. But her mother is way beyond reasoning. As a younger woman, her energy, like a forest fire, could become an explosion of self-feeding conflagrations. Perceived past betrayals added fuel to the present until, depleting her energy, her hysterics sometimes devolved into spending the night in a motel, or a debilitating migraine extinguished by her doctor's bedside injection, when the flames were banked until the next match dropped to rekindle the parched underbrush.

Longfellow's poem about a little girl with a curl in the middle of her forehead seems an uncanny description of Cindy's mother. "When she was good, she was very good indeed. But when she was bad she was horrid." Cindy presses her lips together and inhales through her nose. As a child, her mommy had fooled Cindy. She had eagerly accepted Mommy's gifts of cashmere sweaters and charms for her bracelet as proof of her mother's love. When Cindy had a problem, Mommy's advice calmed her. And Mommy's good-night, sleep-tight back rubs were better than Daddy's quick kiss.

"But," there was always that three-letter word. Lulled by the "good," believing Mommy would always protect her, Cindy was never prepared for her mother's turn to the "horrid." On a teeter-totter, with Mommy as anchor, Cindy, sitting high in the air, was thrilled by the view's potpourri of possibilities. It was when Cindy felt the safest that Mommy spewed insults that had to be true, because Mommy was always right. Suddenly abandoned, Cindy plunged to the ground. Depression, insecurity, distrust and latent anger became her bedrock.

Yet Cindy is her mother's daughter. As an adult with a family of her own, she had criticized and yelled at those she loved. She had indulged her impatience, anger and feelings of inadequacy until the evening her husband, David, returned home from work and said, "I never know what I'm going to find when I get home."

Hearing the anxiety in David's voice, a childhood memory flashed through Cindy's mind. Returning home from school, she would often hesitate at the front door, clutching books to her chest as protection, in case she had done something to make Mommy angry. Now an adult, David's words made Cindy blame herself for becoming the worst part of her mother. But instead of taking to her bed, Cindy did what her mother's generation had feared to do. She sought help, named her demons and—having created a new template—wondered how many past generations of mothers had unwittingly bequeathed such burdens onto their children.

Exhaling, Cindy counts to ten, then feels her hands, resting on her diaphragm, rise as she inhales. Suddenly she is aware that her usual knee-jerk reaction, of turning anger at her mother into punishing herself, has not happened this time. On past visits, she had mollified her mother by accepting the blame and apologizing. Or, after returning home from Palm Springs, she would wait a day or two, then phone, mother and daughter speaking as if nothing had happened. Or, if her mother remained angry, Cindy would send a present, thanking her mother for their wonderful visit. Cindy's mea culpas made life easier for her father, who coped by always siding with his wife. Forgetting to count, Cindy exhales. Admittedly, many fights lasted no longer and did no more harm than a dying ember. Once, waiting at the airport for their flight home, Cindy placed her arm around her mother's shoulders, kissed her cheek and said, "Yell at me so I won't mind leaving you."

The therapist had listed her strengths, "You are a college graduate, your children are healthy, you have a good marriage, you run your own house, you have begun a career in photography and you have close friends. What do you see as your problem?"

Remaining in corpse pose and sequestered in silence, Cindy concludes, I should not have to stay in a closet to avoid my mother's cruel words and irrational accusations. Neither my children nor I should be exposed to her hysterical behavior. This is the last time I will put myself in this vulnerable situation. I will never visit my parents in Palm Springs again.

By five-thirty the next morning, Cindy is awake and dressed in jeans for the bus ride to Los Angeles. Sitting at the breakfast-room table, she scoops raspberry yogurt from its plastic container, grateful for its smooth sweetness and this interlude of quiet, for her children and parents are still asleep. Gazing through the room's floor-to-ceiling sliding glass door, Cindy watches as the sun peeks, amethyst and egg-yolk orange, over the still-shadowed mountains. Oleander bushes, powdered with white flowers, separate the desert from the mowed grass of her parent home.

Her mother has decorated this new house in the sand shades of the desert as reflected in the sun's movement across the sky. She has embraced the area's history by choosing the Cahuilla Indian blankets and prints of these proud men on horseback. Geodes and crystal rocks glow in bowls and turquoise accents reflect her mother's appreciation of what lies beneath the desert's watered golf courses. She has walked with her daughter and grandchildren through Joshua Tree National Park and Palm Canyon's spring, after which the town was named. Cindy treasures her children's delight in being pampered by her mother and bonding with both grandparents. The children and she will have these memories long after her parents are gone. Though the town is too slow for her, with its early-to-bed golf days for her father, visits to Indian-themed souvenir shops and watching the children at the pool, where she must cover up to prevent sun poisoning, Cindy would prefer to keep visiting her parents, but she and David will have to find another warm place for the children's school vacations.

Still in her robe and slippers, Esther enters the kitchen quietly. Carrying her ubiquitous coffee mug, she turns away from the breakfast area and into the dark kitchen, where she puts up a fresh pot of coffee. Cindy's back straightens, her muscles tense and her eyes narrow. Will she get the silent treatment or a continuation of last night's fight? Her mother has never acknowledged her culpability or apologized for her aberrant behavior, and now she remains standing by the coffee pot. Good, maybe she will take her coffee back to her bedroom.

Without waiting for the coffee to finish percolating, her mother lifts the pot, stopping it in mid-stream, and pours coffee into her mug. That accomplished, she walks to the breakfast room table, places her mug and an ashtray, holding a freshly lit cigarette, across from Cindy, pulls a pack of Marlboros and a lighter from her robe's pocket, places them on the table and sits down. Asthmatic since childhood, Cindy does not allow smoking in her home, but here she has no choice. Her mother inhales the cigarette's smoke as if it were oxygen, she glances at her daughter then, putting the cigarette down, she looks past her. Cindy wants to shout, "Enough."

Her mother begins speaking in a slow, quiet voice drained of inflection. She speaks of an incident that occurred thirty-three years ago, in 1943, when her husband and her three brothers were overseas, fighting in World War II.

"I begged your father not to have my mother move into our apartment, but he wouldn't listen. He said you were a baby and had a cast on your leg and her living in the apartment would make things easier for me." Cindy knows about the cast, but not about her mother and Nanna's relationship. "There was no pleasing my mother. I gave her the maid's room off the kitchen because it had its own bath, and she accused me of wanting to separate her from us. She insisted a maid's room was for a maid and she should sleep on the back porch, which wasn't comfortable or private and was far away from the family bathroom."

Her mother's shoulders are hunched and both hands rest in her lap—for she has forgotten her burning cigarette. She appears disconnected from her story, for she continues speaking without emotion.

"In those days certain foods were scarce and you needed food stamps. I would save my stamps until I had enough to buy my mother whitefish. I invited a friend of hers over for dinner one night and when I served the fish, my mother said to her friend, 'I don't know what's the matter with Esther. Once I told her I liked whitefish and now that's all she ever makes. I'm sick to death of whitefish.' Her friend said, "Oh, Ada, Esther makes you whitefish because she knows you like it. She just wants to make you happy."

Is it the sunlight flooding through the wall of glass window, warming the room, or is it her mother's story that causes Cindy's eyes to tear? Her mother's story deflates Cindy's resolve, so that her once erect posture softens into the contours of the chair. As a child she believed Nanna's reason for not staying overnight at their house was because she had to go home and water her stupid plants, so Cindy determined never to have plants when she grew up. As a teen-ager, Cindy had dismissed the single time her mother complained to her: "I bought Nanna three dresses and had them altered. She won't take them. The store can keep them."

Recalling this story, Cindy pictures a Black Hole that obliterates the sur-rounding light. Her mother had left unspoken the incident that came between the dresses being fitted and Nanna's rejection of her daughter's gift. There must have been many ugly arguments, like this one, that lay hidden in the no-man's-land between what Cindy was told and what actually happened.

Cindy remembers her family arriving at the mortuary for Nanna's funeral before the other relatives. Bored, she had picked up the *Daily News* to read Nanna's obituary. It was the usual stuff, "Beloved mother of: Grandmother of:" White-hot rage had propelled Cindy into August's ninety-degree day. She had run, waving the paper, to where her mother stood under a tree, smoking a cigarette.

"You told me your father died when you were in high school. The paper says your parents were divorced. You lied to me."

Cindy's mother flicked her cigarette into the grass, ground it out with the toe of her high heel and, waving her hand as if to shoo away a fly, replied, "Oh damn, I told them not to put that in."

During the summer of 1960, the two sisters, first Cindy's great-aunt, Lena, whom she loved, and Nanna, who she was supposed to love more than her aunt, died two months apart. With these first experiences of death and packing to leave for her freshman year of college, Cindy asked nothing more about a grandfather she had never met.

Later, Daddy said, "When we were first married, your mother and her father tried to make up." He shook his head in disbelief. "They didn't make it from the door of the building to the curb before they had a fight and he drove away."

Cindy wonders why this once elegant and vain perfectionist, this woman who never spoke badly of her childhood, has chosen now to reveal Nanna's cruel indifference to her feelings. This story is like a glistening shell floating above an inscrutable sea of secrets. Was it pain or fear that prompted Esther to reveal how she had failed to make her mother happy? Cindy wants to make her mother happy. She wants to be good enough. Yet she seems as unable to help her mother as Esther was unable to help Ada.

Cindy's mother puts a fresh cigarette between her lips, lights it and pulls the smoke deep into her lungs, as if everything that needs saying has been said. This story is her mother's version of an apology for last night. But rather than the story, what startles Cindy is remembering a visit two years earlier, when her mother had hired a babysitter from an agency so Cindy and her parents could go out for dinner. The woman was her mother's age and, though the two had never met before that evening, Cindy saw them as interchangeable. One looks at Cindy and says, "Your skirt is too long. It looks sloppy." The other one concurs, "The blouse would look neater if you tucked it in."

As an overweight, awkward teenager, Cindy had believed her beautiful, thin mother's criticism of her appearance. Now an adult, Cindy responded to these old women with the self-assurance of a woman in her prime, "You're old and I'm young. You're fat and I'm thin. You're just jealous of me." Fearing an argument, for her words were insulting, Cindy left the room. But now, with her mother admitting to feelings of vulnerability, of never being good enough, Cindy finds a deeper meaning. What she had considered a statement of facts, has morphed into her realizing, for the first time, that she had challenged her mother's position of authority.

This morning, sitting across the table from her mother, Cindy accepts that she is not only responsible for her children, which she anticipated, but she is now responsible for her mother, which she had not expected. By sharing this story with her daughter, Esther had, whether consciously or not, allowed Cindy to become her anchor.

In the now sunbaked breakfast area, Cindy leans back in her chair and studies her mother, once declared beautiful by Cindy's summer-camp cabin mates in the fifties. Last night's sleep has not removed the bags from under her mother's eyes, nor has she dropped the weight gained in menopause. Cindy often heard her father tell her mother, "You can lose weight if you just used some will power." Her father has the daily luxury of playing golf and cards at his club. Coming home, he takes naps before early-bird dinners. But Cindy's mother, without her daughter and grandchildren nearby, wanders through stores or spends mornings in bed playing solitaire or reading the newspaper.

Cindy stands, stretches her arms toward the ceiling and feels the energy in her yoga-toned body. She walks behind her mother's chair and places her hands in the curves where her mother's neck meets her shoulders. From years of massaging her mother to help mitigate her migraines, Cindy knows the exact pressure needed to unknot the muscles. One time, when her father was in the room, Cindy wondered whether her mother meant to hurt his feelings when she said, "Only Cindy can make me feel better."

"We have to leave for the bus by eleven," Cindy says. "But the kids will want your famous M&M pancakes before we go."

Cindy's mother lifts her right hand from her lap and briefly places her fingers over Cindy's hand, her touch light as a butterfly, before she reaches for her coffee.

Esther's daughter turns away from her mother and opens the sliding glass door so she can inhale the cool morning air sweeping the oleander's perfume and the trill of birdsong into the room. Though saddened, Cindy is reconciled to her mother's inability to name her wounds so they can be exposed to the sunlight and healed. The best Cindy can do is to return to her parents' snowbird home with the children, for the three of them bring her mother happiness.

# Love and Loss in Buffalo

by Stanford Searl

*Love and Loss in Buffalo*

"We are all ultimately writing about the same four or five things: death, trauma, love, loss, recovery. Mostly death."
(Melissa Febos, *Body Work: The Radical Power of Personal Narrative*)

live on the edge of a small hill, the perfect spot for my roving mind and heart. It's a non-standard house, in a non-standard neighborhood, a large 1980s stucco home in the middle of mostly modest 1950s houses. This is the Baldwin Hills on the west side of the La Cienega cut, the northeastern edge of Culver City.

Designed by a local architect, nearly all of the house's rooms possess expansive views to the northeast and when it's clear enough, you can see the Hollywood sign to the northwest in the midst of the Santa Monica Mountains. In the winter, the snow pack reaches down from the top of Mount Baldy in the San Gabriel Mountains. From our perch about six miles to the west, there really is a downtown Los Angeles.

I'm living on the edge of things, yet open and expansive, a place for the imagination to roam. Sitting in the office in back of the house, the small backyard ringed by climbing pink roses and looking out at the green and lovely new fake grass, I relax and settle into the present moment. The house is sited on a steep, sharp hillside over three hundred feet high. Because of the late 1980s zoning, there are thirty-foot concrete foundational pylons anchored into bedrock. When the geologist survey guy walked through the house before the sale, he commented how one of the major earthquake fault lines happened to be five hundred feet down the hill and noted that every windowsill remained perfectly plumb.

Inner and outer meet here.

My story embraces a painful, difficult Quaker way of knowing that I have tried to resist. It's a way of knowing that originates out of waiting, listening and contemplative immersion in the Quaker silence. I need to submit to the Spirit, the Light, the Inner Teacher for guidance and direction. This knowing through deep listening matters. Too much of the time, I remain tethered to the ego and its discontents. I find myself turning that ego over to forms of Quaker love and tenderness. This lens of silent waiting for the Spirit's guidance brings vulnerability and possible humility.

The dying of our second child, Diana, started soon after her birth in April 1967. My wife Parnel and I were living in Syracuse and I was midway through finishing my Ph.D. in English at Syracuse University. Diana's six-week checkup got dramatic: Parnel took her to the pediatrician and he was shocked that Diana hadn't gained weight and she appeared to be malnourished. He insisted that Parnel take her to the Upstate Medical Center immediately. "*Don't go home first,*" he said.

Hospital doctors and staff learned that Diana didn't have the ability to suck, so they recommended a preemie nipple and that Parnel give up breastfeeding because it wasn't working. Diana wasn't getting enough to eat.

One morning not long afterwards, Diana trembled and shook uncontrollably so we took her back to the same hospital. As I stood around her hospital room, I overheard two doctors talking about her as they left her room. One said, "This is such an interesting case really…because we don't know how to stop the seizures." Eventually, phenobarbital got the seizures under control and Diana was put on that medication for years.

Three years later, we moved to Buffalo, fall of 1970. Diana's health hadn't improved. Numerous times she had some version of pneumonia and needed to be in the Children's Hospital. After renting for our first year, we bought a small but lovely four-bedroom Elam Place house in the Central Park area near the Zoo. We paid $13,600 for this house with its light oak woodwork and leaded glass cabinets and decorative windows. But it still felt like the city. On early fall evenings at night, with our back bedroom windows open for cooling, we heard the noisy, insistent chugging and wheezing mechanical sounds from the Windshield Wiper factory across Main Street behind us, letting off steam.

It's a wonder how I (we) could possibly have held onto any semblance of hope and renewal for Diana. She never grew or developed and lived with us as a critically ill, medically fragile child who happened to be off the charts completely, never hitting any of the key milestones—not for a six-month-old child, not even at seven years. She never walked. She never pulled herself into a sitting position. She couldn't crawl. She never moved in those fundamental developing ways. She didn't care about eating. She never spoke a word and never even babbled and never said *da-da or ma-ma*.

Diana was wracked by seizures, pneumonias, related respiratory blockages, malnutrition. To top it off, she was diagnosed, eventually, with ketotic hypoglycemia, a condition in which her metabolism was unable to access any of its stored sugar. Once we discovered this condition, we couldn't let her "sleep in" anymore: without external sugar (like orange juice), she might pass out and die.

In retrospect, my brief time as Diana's father was neither heroic nor a wonder. Sure, as her father, I hung in there. I organized and joined and even started a variety of parent support groups. And I loved Diana without any reservations or judgments or anything. She was simply part and parcel of our family. I helped a little with her feeding (or lack of such), diapers, emergency visits to the hospitals.

Even so, Parnel carried the cross and the burden. While we searched for family and health services in the wider Buffalo community, it was Parnel, accompanied by Julia, Diana's older sister by two years, who cared for Diana, as much as any caring was ever possible. Diana was in and out of Children's Hospital, with either seizures or pneumonia. She didn't care about eating. She cried constantly. She didn't develop and grow at all.

Looking back, the care for Diana was exhausting for all of us, and took its toll especially on Parnel and Julia. Soon after we moved into our Elam Place house, Parnel had significant fatigue and exhaustion. I recall that one diagnosis happened to be rheumatoid arthritis and the other was anxiety. She spent a lot of time in the back bedroom with Julia trundling up and down stairs, taking care of Mommy.

After graduate school, my first full-time teaching job was at Buffalo State College. Because of up-bringing and temperament, I threw myself into teaching as if my life depended on it. It felt like that July when I was fifteen years old and rode my bike about six miles up Route 100 from Ludlow, Vermont to "Red Bridge" on Lake Rescue. At the bridge, my friends and I climbed upon the foundational rocks to the side of the bridge, going back and back as far as we dared and then dove into the lake, over and over again. In fact, I dove so much that I got swimmer's ear and eventually had to have an operation to open up the bony growth in my left ear in my 60s.

The diving became a metaphor for my teaching: I dove into learning and classes and texts with my students. We swam underwater, immersed and floating and doing the butterfly strokes together. It was mutual exploration in an underwater submersion, pumping the body and its imagination, searching for secrets in the depths. This was teaching and learning by complete immersion. There would be no sprinkling of water in this baptism.

We lived a few blocks east of Delaware Park, maybe four miles from Buffalo State College on Elmwood Avenue. I had an old three-speed English bicycle and rode that bike to the College for years—even in the midst of Buffalo's icy and snowy winters. I rode around the north side of the park near the Zoo and then followed the Scajaquada Expressway for a few hundred yards and pedaled across a pedestrian bridge over to the grounds behind the Albright Knox Art Gallery.

Early in our time in Buffalo, Parnel took me to the Buffalo Quaker worship near the Science Museum. I became all-in with the Buffalo Quakers. For years, I played the piano before worship with Diana on my lap. I taught First Day School, including Julia as one of my students. We explored Quaker faith and practice by composing picture books about George Fox and other Quakers. We became members of the Buffalo Meeting and I joined various committees and became immersed in the life and death (through memorial worship events) of the community.

Together, we sang in the Buffalo Scholar Cantorum, the chorus of the Buffalo Philharmonic. We made numerous close friends in the singing group and had raucous times at Cole's on Elmwood Avenue, a local bar, after rehearsals.

I joined the Board of Directors of the Erie County chapter of the Association for Retarded Children. Eventually, I became President of the Board, and along the way, I participated in the Sunshine Committee of the Board. We brought Christmas sunshine gifts and monies to the various state institutions for retarded residents in Western New York, including West Seneca, where Diana lived for six months.

Since moving to Buffalo, it had taken over three years to "discover" that Diana was "too retarded" and there weren't any community school programs for her, even at the Association for Retarded Children where I was a Board member. The Cerebral Palsy Center, not that far from us, didn't offer a program for kids like Diana. The extended resources of the Children's Rehabilitation Center had done extensive and time-consuming evaluations of Diana, and their experts recommended that she be placed in the West Seneca State School for the Mentally

Retarded. *She will tear your family apart*, the research pediatrician said. He said we *weren't equipped to manage such a child* and that the institution was relatively new and had special programs.

From a fifty-year distance, it's not clear to me why we placed Diana there. We were young and inexperienced. And we were exhausted. We knew nothing about what sociologist Irving Goffman calls *total institutions*, systematically abusing the residents. There weren't any services for Diana in the community. She was labelled as too handicapped. In our naiveite, we decided, well, *let's give this apparent alternative a try*.

When we visited Diana in the institution, I entered a chamber of horrors. It was like a subterranean level of Dante's inferno. I had fallen into the great Johnny Cash's burning ring of fire. *And it burned, burned, burned, that ring of fire.* But this wasn't the fire of love and desire. These flames from hell threatened to consume me and all of our family, including Diana.

I never, ever acted out the disgust, anger and hatred that burned within my body. Well, that's not entirely so because these feelings did turn inward in the sense that—following in my father's footsteps that I vowed never to do—I drank too much beer. Became soused. Surprisingly, both Parnel and I discovered some hidden resilience or hope or what my Quakers call *Light and Love within us*.

It's not clear how this resilience was sustained. For all of my genuine disgust and anger, I uttered not one word or gesture of public blaming or shaming towards that institution. I started a parent chapter of the Association for Retarded Children at the institution instead. This required a number of meetings with the Director of the institution, a medical doctor from Hungary. This Director remained supportive of my attempts to contact other parents who had kids in the institution. Even so, I held him responsible for the institution's abuse of Diana and the other hundreds of residents. After meetings in his office, I often fantasized that I would return to his office to charge and gore him, seething spit and moisture like a raging bull. But I never complained or blamed.

Parnel's father insisted that I maintain my role as mature adult. Listening to our tale of woe and despair, he gave one piece of clear, strong advice: *don't burn your bridges.*

We hung in there with Diana, even though care in the institution was terrible and abusive. Somehow, we decided that we wouldn't immediately take her home and stiff the institution. As it happened, we attended a parent meeting at the

Association of Retarded Children where I was a Board member, and a social worker from the institution described a program for more capable adults who could return to the community on "community status." Even though the program wasn't meant for kids like Diana, we asked the Director for community status for Diana anyway. He agreed and we brought Diana home and started our own program for her and children like her. Today, this program thrives and serves more than fifty children and young adults and their families.

Diana died in early November of 1974, suddenly and unexpectedly. We were in the midst of moving out of the city and into a country rental. We had left Diana with two of her teachers and they took her to the emergency room where she was dead on arrival.

The circumstances of her death seemed to go on and on in that fall and over the winter. As it happened, we had decided—whatever possessed us—to rent a house thirty-five miles south of Buffalo in the Boston Hills. After Diana's death, we moved out there for the winter. It was as if her death followed us around and the snow and cold mirrored my frozen heart.

The house was a couple of miles up a long hill in the middle of the Lake Erie snow belt. When we drove back to this house from a week on Long Island's north fork in early April, the snow drifts were so high that we couldn't get into our driveway. The outer and inner freeze continued.

Diana's death sparked an inner shift for me. While I loved teaching and my students and colleagues, I got restless. I experienced a split or division in my heart and soul. A psychic wound festered, unable to be easily healed. I had an inner fissure. Soon after my birth, my mother had a massive schizophrenic breakdown and my father married again. From then on, I carried something unsettled and disruptive, a split in my psyche. This unsettled wound bubbled to the surface every ten to fifteen years. In my search for wholeness and healing, I felt compelled to move and change, mostly change jobs or places. I was unsatisfied, unhappy and not at peace.

Many years after Diana's death, we were living in Cutchogue, New York. After an August hurricane, when the lilacs bloomed again, we buried Diana's ashes next to her granite marker. We had an improvised ceremony and put her ashes and some of our memories to rest. Remembering, standing outside in the wind, I found myself singing the *Dona Nobis Pacem*, repeating this prayer for peace, praying that I might discover some of this peace for myself.

# CREATIVE
# NONFICTION

COMING OF AGE

# Bussed

by Ronit Bezalel

The beginning of the school year, usually a time of promise, deteriorated into chaos. Teachers went on strike. Parents took their children out of school and classes were half-empty. The remaining teachers doubled up their subjects: the music teacher taught math, the science teacher taught us how to paint. I crossed the picket line gripping my metal lunch box, sent to fourth grade by my mother who was emphatic that I still receive an education. She wasn't being political, she just wanted me out of her hair

My most vivid memory of that time period is of fists raining down on my back. These particular fists belonged to two Black girls who, with every punch, unleashed a dozen or so years of pent-up frustration on my white skin. I was ten, and caught in the crosshairs of desegregation. Years later, I realized I was simply a catalyst, a target for their rage.

It was 1978, and my family had just immigrated to Wilmington, Delaware, from London, England. Two years earlier, the United States District Court ordered in Evans v. Buchanan that the school districts in Delaware's New Castle County combine into a single district. The Court then ordered a desegregation plan in which children from predominantly white, suburban neighborhoods would be sent to schools in predominantly Black, urban neighborhoods and vice versa, to promote racial diversity.

Desegregation impacted my suburban Green Acres neighborhood with a bang. Instead of attending our local school, which was within walking distance, the kids from our neighborhood were now bussed to Martin Luther King, Jr. Elementary School on Wilmington's East Side. During the hour-long ride, I watched the suburbs turn into highways, factories, and public housing row homes. On that first day, I was given a classroom tour and shown the playground, but I don't remember the desegregation plan being explained to us at all.

My fourth-grade teacher, Mrs. Tomlinson, was also bussed in from a suburban school. She was a cranky and bewildered white, middle-aged woman with a craggy face and thick glasses. She muttered under her breath about the

299

urban Black students and constantly corrected their speech. "Not puncil... PEN-cil," she'd say to Walter, speaking slowly as if he couldn't understand. Walter would snap back that it didn't matter, and then refuse to do his work.

Back then, I didn't understand the deeper issues at play. I didn't know that segregation was legally mandated in Wilmington until 1954, when the Brown v. Board of Education decision ruled that segregation in public schools was unconstitutional. I didn't know that after that date, schools still remained woefully separate. I didn't even know about the legacy of the school's namesake, Martin Luther King, Jr.

I also wasn't aware of the difficult time that Wendy, one of my best friends, was experiencing. After school and during the summers, Wendy and I would bike around Green Acres for hours and catch crayfish in the creek. I would go over to her house for cool glasses of water and chat with her mother. Wendy was Black, lived in our suburban neighborhood and, like me, was bussed to Martin Luther King, Jr. School. Her mother was a vocal opponent of desegregation, saying that she worked hard for her daughter to go to a good, suburban school, and why should this be undone?

Years later, Wendy told me that she felt like she was straddling both worlds—that of the suburban community where she lived and the reality of being bussed to a low-income, urban neighborhood. One time, a bully with a red face and red hair screamed the n-word in her face, so Wendy threw her fist into his cheek. Another time, she punched a white girl who refused to drink from the same water fountain as she did. Wendy was also taunted and called an Oreo by the Black students. (Larry, a Black student, would constantly pull her braids, but she surmised it was because he had a crush on her.) Wendy had to be tougher in ways that I never imagined and faced things that I regrettably had no idea she was facing at the time.

For me, racial tensions simmered to a head the summer between fourth and fifth grades. My sisters and I squealed as we played outside Martin Luther King, Jr. Elementary School, the soles of our sneakers sinking into the hot asphalt, while my mother and her friend Mrs. Vestner volunteered inside. We were free to explore the playground close to school—the scorching aluminum slide, jungle gym, and sandlot replete with cigarette butts. Mrs. Vestner warned us to stay away from the playground down the hill, the one farther away from the school. She was afraid of "the neighborhood."

My sister Shira and I scaled the yellow rusted jungle gym. Shira was eight, all knobby knees and skinny legs. I was shorter and sturdier with a brand-new pair of tiny glasses. Our youngest sister Ilana, age five, played by herself in the adjacent sandbox, wearing a pink dress and matching barrettes.

Damp patches of sweat tickled our cotton T-shirts as Shira and I reached the top of the jungle gym and peered down at the landscape below. I saw the Purina Factory with its checkered red and white sign and the iconic Pepsi-Cola sign from the nearby bottling factory. During the school year, I was mesmerized by the Pepsi logo spinning slowly, an image of calm among chaos. I also noted the red, brick public housing row houses that had been built close together. People called these buildings the projects. We were told not to go near the area.

A group of Black kids, three girls and one younger boy, played on the swings in the playground further down the hill, the one that Mrs. Vestner had forbidden us to enter.

"You can't play over there, Mrs. Vestner said so!" Shira yelled over to them. She was a stickler for the rules.

I poked her in the elbow.

The kids ignored us.

"You can't be there," Shira yelled again.

We jumped down from the jungle gym and joined Ilana in the sandbox. Dirt rimmed our fingernails as we dug for treasures. Ilana found a penny and put it in her dress pocket.

"Why you honkeys telling us what to do?" The kids were walking towards us.

The previous year, I had learned that a honkey was a bad word for a white person. One of the boys kept repeating it loudly during class, until Mrs. Tomlinson ordered him to the principal's office.

Now, my stomach tensed as I heard the word again.

"My sister didn't mean anything," I said to the group approaching us. The girls were thin and taller than my sisters and me. The boy was shorter and much younger.

"Why you all talk so funny?" one girl asked, wrinkling up her nose. She wore her hair in tight cornrows, with neon beads on the ends.

"We're from England," my sister replied. Her accent was more pronounced than mine.

"I don't care where you from. You can't tell us where to play. Ya'll ain't my momma," said the tallest girl, her hands on her hips.

My mouth went dry as the kids surrounded the sandbox and glared at us.

Shira leapt up and ran like a gazelle into the distance. She was the fastest in the neighborhood. I was caught by the girls, one of whom who jumped on my back as they all repeatedly punched me. I took off running, but I was caught again. Curling inwards, I visualized that I was a snail, wishing for a shell as I felt their blows on my spine. I longed to be a braver Ronit, a superhero who could fix this, who could fix all of this. She'd somehow make friends with the group and we'd be off playing on the swings, or perhaps jumping Double Dutch.

But there was no braver Ronit. No quick thinking, no quick fix. There was only survival in the playground. I wriggled out of the girls' grasp once more and ran towards school, wheezing as my asthma flared up. The girls cornered me and were on me once again, their fists raining blows on my body. I tasted blood from biting my cheek in fear.

To my right, I saw my little sister Ilana, trying to outrun the boy. One of her barrettes had come loose and her hair was flying in the wind. The boy swung his fist at her and missed. He then grabbed her hand and asked, "Wanna be friends?"

I didn't understand this. I didn't understand any of this.

Two years ago, we had been living in London and enjoying tea and lady-fingers with my grandmother at her favorite café, The Almond Tree. We'd ride in the back of my grandfather's taxi and listen to him encourage us to pursue our creative talents. One afternoon, my parents asked us if we wanted to move to America. My sisters and I said no, but a month later, my father's company relocated us to Delaware and into one of the largest bussing programs in the United States.

I didn't feel American. I didn't know who George Washington or Abraham Lincoln were. In fourth grade, I didn't understand why we were being bussed to a faraway school. I remember there was a burglary in the neighborhood, and our school was on lockdown, for fear that the gunman was in the school. Life seemed unpredictable, and one couldn't trust the adults to explain things or make things safe.

As the girls chased me, I raced across the grass towards the school, panting in fear. I tasted blood in my cheek and felt rivulets of sweat sting my eyes. The worn leather strap of my right sandal snapped and my shoe fell off. I kept running, one foot feeling the earth.

Ilana and I stumbled into the school, where we saw Shira, unscathed, telling my mother what happened in a high-pitched voice. My mother gave us a long glance, decided we'd live, and started interrogating me about my lost shoe. I had no idea what happened to it, and Mom was furious.

My mom ventured outside, searching for the children and my sandal. I shuffled behind her. The thorns prickled my bare foot. We never found my shoe or the kids.

Several weeks after the beating, I heard the adults gossiping at the Green Acres' neighborhood pool, sitting on their lawn chairs as dusk fell and mosquitos feasted.

"Did you hear what happened in the high school?" one of the adults said.

"Yeah, the kids started fighting. I think one had to go to the hospital."

"I bet the Black kids started it. They always start things."

I sat silently on the edge of my chair, watching the shrinking glow of Mrs. Vestner's cigarette, which she handed me to extinguish, like she always did. I felt uneasy, like my world was narrowing in the face of their sentiments. I mashed the cigarette down into nothing.

We later learned that it was the white students who initiated the violence.

After the beating, I hyperventilated when I encountered groups of Black kids on the playground. My hands turned clammy, my mouth felt like sandpaper, and I'd take elaborate routes to avoid them. My friend Susan surmised that something was up. One day she put her arm around my shoulder and gently told me to me to "get over it."

In fifth grade, things shifted. Our teacher, Mr. Devlin, an elderly white man with a mop of white hair, treated the urban Black kids with respect. The administration reprimanded him because he let the local students lead a field trip in which we explored their neighborhood. I was happy to wander in the tall grass and vacant lots. I was concerned when we got lost and then relieved when we found our way back to school. Mr. Devlin also let the Black students play their favorite music on a gigantic boombox. We learned about the joys of hip-hop and break dancing. The classroom was electric for brief moments, as barriers fell and we briefly united.

Mr. Devlin showed us another way of being. In a way, he was my superhero. But he was not the only one. Our music teacher, Mrs. Pitts, a Black woman with large glasses and a rich singing voice, taught us Civil Rights songs. I remember a group of white kids, including myself, sitting in the lunchroom belting out 'We Shall Overcome.' One girl refused to sing. She said that it was a song for Black people, and her mother forbade her to sing it. My friends and I, sitting at the lunch table, argued with her that this shouldn't matter, but she refused to listen to us.

By the end of my three years at King, a curiosity broke through, like sun through clouds. I didn't fear the kids for beating me up once I was immersed in their world, walking through the same halls and sharing the same lunchroom. When I sang their songs, I wasn't just learning the words. I was wanting to know more about their lives. I became obsessed with the children's book, *JT*, by Jane Wagner with photos by Gordon Parks, Jr., which told the story of a ten-year-old Black boy living in a dilapidated neighborhood. After checking it out so often from the school library, the librarian finally asked me why I liked the book so much. I felt the sting of hot shame on my cheeks, as if I was caught red-handed doing something I wasn't supposed to be doing. I never asked for the book again.

Back then, I didn't have any tools to discuss race and class. I just felt the line dividing "us" from "them." The city and suburban kids shared the same space, but how much did we really connect? We suburban kids boarded the bus immediately after school and returned home to the familiarity of the suburbs. We may have been desegregated, but we didn't integrate beyond the school walls.

These experiences have long stayed with me and influenced my decision to become a documentary filmmaker. I've spent the past twenty years creating two films chronicling the demolition of Chicago's Cabrini Green public housing development and subsequent displacement of a Black community from the city center. Homes were torn down to pave the way for a gentrified, predominantly white replacement community consisting of modern high rises and town homes with shiny exteriors.

Would I have created these films if I wasn't bussed? It's hard to say, but one thing I do know is that I was changed forever.

# Summer Interlude

by Laurel M. Ross

t could have ended so badly.

The two of us, ages 15 and 16, used the old trick of each telling our parents that we were sleeping at the other's house one Saturday night in the summer of 1964. Instead, we boarded a Greyhound Bus with our bags packed. We were ready for an experience.

Youngstown to Cincinnati was to be the first leg of our journey. There was no particular reason to choose Cincinnati except that we could afford the bus ticket and neither of us had ever been there before. Eventually we wanted to go to New York or maybe Paris (both in the other direction!), but our wallets were thin and just getting out of Youngstown, we thought, was a start.

Janice and I were an unlikely pair: she a shy, dreamy, poet-type and me really good at math. The common denominator perhaps was our lack of social skills. We were both introverts and the opposite of popular.

We were not best friends. The only other crazy thing we had done together before this grand travel adventure was to pierce each other's ears in Janice's living room using thick sewing needles and ice cubes, as instructed by our expert teenage friends.

The needles made a creepy crunching sound as we pushed them through the cartilage of our ear lobes. It's hard to say which hurt more: to pierce or to be pierced. The ice only slightly dulled the pain. So we alternated roles. I did her right ear, finally getting the needle through after long minutes of effort. Then we took a break.

"Three more to go," we groaned. "This will take forever!"

Then Janice did my right ear with equal clumsiness and pain. It was miserable, but we couldn't turn back halfway through, so we forced ourselves to finish the grisly work between tears and giggles. Neither of us had ever drunk alcohol, but in retrospect this might have been a good time to start.

We also couldn't afford the 22-carat gold studs that were recommended, so we inserted cheap wires in the bloody holes. Months of seeping pus ensued.

I still have those holes in my earlobes, but I don't wear earrings these days because I am sporting more age-appropriate hearing aids.

The idea of an unsupervised road trip had been floating around in midnight conversations for months with Janice's cousin Patty, who was also my good friend. We shared fantasies of meeting famous people like Bob Dylan and J.D. Salinger and Allen Ginsberg.

"Greenwich Village is the coolest place to hang out," I suggested.

"Maybe, but what about Europe?" Janice countered.

"Yeah! Paris, France," Patty swooned.

To be clear, when Janice and I climbed onto the smelly Greyhound Bus that August night we were adventure seekers, not escapees from domestic or sexual abuse. Nor did either of us have a broken heart. Running away from home was a big romantic idea, a lark. We had only an inkling of how exciting the outside world was, but we wanted a taste.

My day-to-day existence was pretty dull. A voracious reader, my dreams were fed by such masterpieces as *Anna Karenina*, *The Catcher in the Rye* and *On the Road*. My family had no extra money for summer camp or vacations. Library books and television reruns were my main summer stimulation. Supervising younger siblings at the local pool and playing Stratego and chess on the front porch with neighborhood kids were the high points of my summer fun.

I can see now that I had no clue how to make my own excitement. My parents were coping with the daily problems of raising six kids—me being the oldest—so my little existential crisis was lost on them. I had never been a problem child and from their point of view, I should have been helping *them*!

Besides, we were not a family that talked to each other about our inner lives.

My best guess is that I was too frozen to act on constructive solutions like looking for a job, and incapable of pouring myself into a passion, the way I do now.

I do not know how I became so sheltered. So naïve. I do know that, at almost 16, with no available adult to notice my angst, I was dissatisfied, and my crazy solution was to go out into the world seeking something thrilling—at least that's what I think I was thinking. The idea of the two of us taking off unfolded with some kind of inexplicable internal teenage momentum.

We sat up talking for most of one night in July in Janice's bedroom.

"I want to go to New York City, Manhattan!" Janice was dreaming about Broadway shows like *West Side Story* and *My Fair Lady*, both of which she had practically memorized. "They have a subway that everyone takes—even famous people! It only costs a quarter and you can ride it all day."

I was thinking about the Beat poets who I had never actually read, but had read *about*—probably in something like *Life* Magazine. "There are coffee houses with live music. People sit there and write all day and then read their poems out loud at night. You click your fingers if you like the poem, instead of clapping." I think I saw that on Jack Paar.

"That is so cool!" Janice murmured under her breath.

My dad sometimes read poetry—Whitman, Emerson. He was different from the other dads I knew and I always wanted to impress him.

Poor Janice! I more or less dragged her along. She sensibly noted. "We don't have much money."

"But we could get jobs," I replied confidently.

Patty decided from the start that she was out of this plan, but that she would help us if she could. Janice and I were only casual friends, but somehow she was susceptible to the big idea. We spent some time thinking through the possibilities and hatched a truly foolish plan. "We'll just get out of here and figure the rest out as we go."

When we arrived in Cincinnati, we weren't sure what to do. We had departed late in the evening so we would get our first night's sleep on the bus. The Cincinnati Greyhound station became one of our hangouts because there were decent bathrooms and no one paid attention to anyone else.

"Looking for fun?" one fellow asked us. Even to our inexperienced eyes he looked like trouble. He seemed like an old creep—in his twenties at least—and way too dressed up for a bus station.

"No, thank you," I said and turned away. We were of course looking for fun, but not with him!

"We are traveling to see our sick grandma," Janice added, with fake sad eyes. He walked off.

How did we get by on the street for a week? Sheer good fortune, I guess. We could have been raped, robbed, or killed, but we were not thinking that way. Our euphoria receded slowly over the next few days as the reality of our situation sank in. We used the little money we arrived with to buy cheap food like apples, candy bars and cheese at grocery stores.

"Let's check the bulletin boards for jobs," Janice suggested. "Maybe we can do some babysitting." Nothing looked promising though, especially since the summer job season was over and we had no skills or experience.

We mostly slept in churches that we selected each day in our random wanderings. Their doors were always open and they were quiet and cool, with clean bathrooms. You could lie down on the pews instead of sitting up in the bus station seats. We wouldn't be able to get a job if we looked grimy and disheveled, so bathrooms were a priority. We did discover that others also sometimes used those facilities, so we learned to be careful not to assume we were alone and concocted outlandish stories in case someone asked why we were there.

"We could tell them we are doing research for a school project," I suggested.

"Okay, good. Or we could say that we are writing a book about Cincinnati," Janice added.

"That's a great idea! Maybe we *should* write a book," I crowed.

As our small nest egg shrank, we passed the time in long periods of gloom hoping for something good to happen. The church pews were hard and we longed for a comfy bed with pillows.

I do not remember whose idea it was, but we bought a cheap kit at Woolworth's and sat in the park and made potholders to sell to passersby. Janice had the great idea to claim it was for some animal charity to get a few extra coins. We had modest success before we decided to abandon the project.

"I once read about someone who spent the night in a department store. We could try that," I offered. We decided it was worth a try.

Wandering around in the very upscale H & S Pogue's near closing time, eying the gourmet food and the comfortable chairs, we noticed a hallway and followed it to a back room that looked like it was used for storage.

"This is perfect!" I grinned.

"They'll never find us here," Janice winked. She almost seemed like her old self.

We hid in a closet whispering about how we would soon be gorging on all the food.

Two burly security men found us in about two minutes and ejected us with a stern lecture.

"Do not ever, ever come back to Pogue's or you will be arrested," the short one warned

"You are lucky we are not calling the police right now!" added the fat one with the beard.

They did not touch us, but we could see their guns.

"We were just looking," I stammered.

I felt stupid and my stomach growled as we were escorted to the front door and ejected.

We plodded back to the bus station in silence.

Janice quietly confided, "I am kind of scared."

I do not remember being aware of being afraid. Maybe I lacked the experience to conjure any specific bad outcome. I went into big-sister mode and offered a soothing suggestion.

"We'll figure something out. Let's walk across the big bridge tomorrow and see what's in Kentucky."

We spoke very little for the rest of that night. I was worried, and only able to think about one day at a time.

The Ohio River was not the Seine and Covington, Kentucky was not Paris, but the next morning the idea of traveling to a new state brightened our spirits a little.

Across the river we found rows of shabby little houses with dirty windows and "Beware the Dog" signs. Hoping to find a church to crash in we headed away from the river, but were drawn to a hand-printed sign that read "Rooms to Let." A room with a bed sounded so good!

The fat man who answered the bell pointed us to a room on the third floor. We learned later that he was not able to walk up all those stairs—probably a lucky break for us.

"Ten dollars a week cash. It's pretty clean. No fan though." He didn't ask many questions.

We told him we were "visiting friends" nearby and gave him our last five dollars. "We'll give you the rest in a couple days when we get paid."

*Dear Patty,*

*Can you lend us a little cash? We got a room and need to pay the rest of the rent. We will pay you back when we get jobs.*

*We are having fun! Can't wait to tell you about it.*

We dropped this postcard with our new address into the corner letterbox and immediately fell into a deep sleep on the lumpy bed—the first real bed we had slept in for days

Exhausted and out of ideas for what to do next, we spent the next couple of days looking at newspaper want ads. We panhandled with modest success, shoplifted a little and survived on a diet of cheap snacks. The red-faced landlord was usually smoking and coughing on the front porch when we came and went from our new home base.

"Don't you think he's creepy?" Janice whispered. She was right. It gave me a bad feeling the way he looked at us. Besides, we owed him money.

As we lay in bed in silent misery our third morning in that stifling room, knowing the rent was due, a miracle happened.

"Police!"

Two uniformed cops announced themselves as they burst into our room shouting our names and issuing orders. "Janice! Laurel! Get dressed and find all your things! Right now! *Now!*"

They marched us noisily down the stairs, past the landlord's closed door, and to the back seat of a squad car parked with its engine running and its dome light blinking. There was no conversation in the car, but I found myself relaxing. It was both a relief and a shock to be back in the world of grown-up control.

We spent that day and one night in a juvenile facility nearby where we were served franks and beans on a tray in our room—our first real meal in many days. Protein tasted so delicious! The sheets on the bunk beds felt luxuriously clean.

Janice and I sat in silence in the gloomy room with the shades drawn, waiting for the next thing to happen. No one talked to us. No one told us what would come next.

That day was very long. No games and no tv. The only books were battered comics on the shelf above the desk. Not even a mystery novel. I was not exactly bored, but desperate for a distraction and this seemed outrageous to me. Thinking about it now, I am amazed that even in this extreme situation I was capable of being critical.

Our two sets of parents picked us up the next day in separate cars. My mother cried when she saw me, but she did not seem angry.

"We were so worried. We didn't know where to look for you. Are you okay?" She seemed to think everything was fine now that I was found.

"Thank heavens you sent that postcard," Dad said. "We were hoping you would get caught shoplifting, but this made it a lot easier—an address! The police said we were very lucky. Most kids are never found."

They had filed a missing persons report, but there was nothing to go on until our message arrived.

"Tell us everything that happened starting from the night you left," the stern social worker instructed back in Youngstown, where I sat across the desk from her between my parents. She wrote on a yellow legal pad as I breezily recounted the events of our trip.

"People in Cincinnati have southern accents," I observed, irrelevantly.

"You seem to find this humorous," she scolded when I tried to make the story more entertaining than it had actually felt at the time. She was not amused by the story of us trying to sleep at Pogue's.

"Do you realize how much trouble you caused?" Did I? I was starting to. My poor mother looked so worried.

Janice and I were interrogated separately by authorities who, along with our parents, kept asking the same questions, hoping for different answers:

"Whose idea was this?" "Did anyone touch you?" "Did anyone give you money?"

"Or ask for money?" "What were you planning to do? Quit school?"

Their questions were scarier than anything we had experienced on the trip. I flashed back to the guy who asked us if we were looking for fun, but did not mention him in my account. Nothing happened. Why upset them?

The adults didn't comprehend the idea of an adventure, a lark. There was no real payoff that they could see. No drugs or alcohol. No boyfriends. A little shoplifting to get staples like shampoo was about the extent of our transgressions. We were both good students with no "previous records."

"What did you do for money?" the social worker continued to probe, looking at me with what felt like disgust.

I tried to explain about the potholders. "...like we learned in Girl Scouts." It was the truth, but sounded foolish enough that my interrogator shook her head and seemed not to believe a word.

After the long interview and a severe scolding, the social worker pronounced, "You will not be allowed to see Janice for one year—no telephone calls either."

This felt like no big loss. We didn't really want to see each other anyway. Our failure was too embarrassing. Except for the occasional hello in the hallway, we went our separate ways in life.

Since no one at school except the discrete Patty knew about our crimes there was no stigma when we returned to our normal student world in September. I actually liked school and continued to excel as I looked ahead to college.

I learned in October that my mother had been pregnant with my youngest brother Peter at the time we pulled our stunt. He was born in January. I felt a little guilty about adding to her stress, but my level of teenage self-absorption was such that I gave it little real thought until many years later.

I had actually thought my father would be proud of our bold act. Dad was an unapologetic romantic who liked grand ideas. His favorite poet was Walt Whitman, who, at the time, I vaguely understood to be a radical non-conformist.

No one in my family spoke of this escapade again. When I mentioned it to Patty at our fiftieth high school reunion, she laughed it off as trivial. "You guys were so crazy!"

We foolish girls did not ultimately fail in our lives. I ended up as the 1965 Youngstown South High School valedictorian, though this episode would not have predicted that. Janice went on to a successful teaching career.

Sometimes when I read about an event that the media labels "senseless," I remember our summer trip.

# Cool Mom

by Rita Angelini

In the dressing room of Carson's Department Store, my fourteen-year-old daughter, Marina, twirled for me in a rose-colored satin mini dress, her choice for the homecoming dance. The florescent lights bounced off the sequins and flashed in the three-way mirror—six feet tall, waist-long amber hair, vivid cocoa eyes, looking like a cover girl for *Seventeen* magazine.

I reached to measure the length of the dress. She whirled and stepped back.

"Don't touch my crotch," Marina said.

"It's too short," I said.

"It is not." She placed her hand on the side where her legs joined her torso. "See."

"It looks too short," I said.

"I want this one." Her body stiffened. I expected to hear "I hate you" from my daughter but I held the wallet.

I was not a cool mom.

* * *

When Marina was young, she was my snuggle bunny, my entertainment, my shadow. She looked up to me with adoring eyes. Her sister—two years younger and born with extreme special needs—diverted my attention away from Marina. We adjusted to a new lifestyle, and though her sister's condition stabilized for a time, the threat of death still loomed.

Marina pitched in, expressing concern that her sister might feel excluded. When Marina went trick-or-treating, she asked for two pieces. She would drop the second piece in her sister's pumpkin and kiss her sister, who waited at the bottom of the stairs in her wheelchair.

Beginning at age four, Marina met with therapists and attended sibling support groups to cope with the challenges that having a sister who required around-the-clock care presented. The goal was to have an established relationship with a therapist in case something went wrong.

We camped, saw plays, and attended concerts. For Marina's eighth birthday, I threw the ultimate surprise bash. Having planned to raze our home and rebuild on the same lot, we invited Marina and her school pals to run wild in the old house once it had been emptied. They went crazy with markers, paints, silly string, shaving cream, covering walls, windows, ceilings, carpets. The party was the talk of the school.

She told me she had the coolest mom ever.

The week before Marina started seventh grade, her sister suffered a violent seizure at a remote campground. As I maneuvered her sister's body to clear her airway, she projectile vomited on Marina, me, and the floor. Eyes wide, Marina stared at the mess on her. The rancid smell permeated the camper. In the hour we waited for medical assistance, her sister's tiny body jerked and thrashed. Marina cried and shook with fear, and her father and I took turns holding her.

I accompanied her sister to the hospital in the main city. My husband drove Marina home to stay with a friend before joining me. Following her sister's medical crisis, Marina talked about restarting her sessions with the psychologist, but the therapist wasn't available and Marina had to deal with it on her own. After this, she hated her therapist and all therapists.

She stopped doing her chores. I nagged: clean your room, empty the dishwasher, scoop the kitty litter.

Her grades dropped. I nagged: turn in your homework, study for tests, complete your school projects.

Not cool mom.

I pressed her about the change in her behavior. She stayed in her room.

I resorted to using money. We paid for homework, test scores, and chores.

She excelled.

Cool mom.

During eighth grade, her sister's condition worsened. My energy spent, I couldn't monitor and pay her for schoolwork. I pared Marina's activities—except for harp lessons. She seemed at peace when she played her harp for her sister.

Marina refused to believe or blame her sister's situation for her anxiety. We pushed her into family counseling. The psychologist remarked on the change in our relationship from the prior year. Marina sneered at me and told the psychologist she hated me. With arms crossed, Marina refused to talk, so my husband and I talked. We attended four sessions. The psychologist saw no progress with Marina.

Not cool mom.

We bided our time, waiting for her sister's health to improve. It didn't. This time we considered splurging on Marina's Christmas wish list: cell phone, Uggs, cash. I consulted with the psychologist. She didn't recommend it.

Despite that, we purchased the forced pleasantness.

Cool mom. For a while.

In high school, Marina made new friends, joined the swim team, and participated in clubs. Her father and I had a simple rule: no socializing with juniors or seniors. She started a relationship with a senior. We put the kibosh on it. The combined moodiness of a teenager, a new school, and the relentless stress of her sister's condition—three failed surgeries and an experimental surgery scheduled in January—Marina's anxiety increased, with dizziness and chest pains.

Her father suggested Marina see her pediatrician, I suggested she play the harp for relaxation.

"You don't care about me," Marina yelled.

Not cool mom.

Test results from the cardiologist revealed no defect. The pediatrician suggested counseling. Marina refused.

I wanted to be the cool mom again.

So I bought that glitzy homecoming dress from Carsons, while her fifty-pound sister lay at home with 24-hour care, her useless legs down to scrawny toothpicks.

Before homecoming, I arranged for a caregiver so Marina and I could lunch after swim practice at Olive Garden, her favorite restaurant. Marina overslept. I yelled for her to hurry. I carried her sister to the car and put her on the reclined front seat. Marina sat in back, not talking.

"I'll pick you up at eleven," I said, when I dropped her off.

She got out and slammed the car door.

When my mom dropped by for a surprise visit, my Olive Garden plans changed. Marina was surprised to see her grandma when we picked her up.

"Grandma and I are going to Olive Garden," I said.

"All three of us?" Marina said.

"Just Grandma and me."

"Bitch," Marina muttered under her breath.

"Did you hear that?" I asked my mother.

Being diplomatic, she said, "I am sure you misunderstood her. Right, Marina?"

"She heard me," Marina said.

At Olive Garden, my stomach grumbled with the aroma of garlic. I rambled to my mother. I had hoped that my mother would be able to provide perspective—having raised nine teenagers herself. But she had no wisdom to share; I was the eighth of nine kids, and my mom was done with teenage attitude.

Marina's task for the day was to clean her room for the Homecoming sleepover I had naively offered to host. Since she hadn't played the harp for her sister in days, when she was finished, I asked for a harp concert. Just thirty minutes. I secretly set a timer. She resisted—but even when her long, elegant fingers plucked the wrong strings, it still sounded beautiful. I closed my eyes and stroked her sister's hair, letting the relaxing notes wash over me. After just two minutes, she stopped playing, breaking the spell. I opened my eyes. She left and came back.

After forty-five minutes and numerous intermissions, I checked the timer. She had played a total of only twelve minutes. Far short of the half-hour her teacher prescribed. I told her I was wasting my money on lessons, and that if she didn't like playing, she should quit.

In tears, Marina stomped out of the family room.

Not cool mom.

Later, I went upstairs to get Marina for an eyebrow waxing appointment I had promised her. I also had scheduled a hair appointment homecoming morning. The rose satin dress hung on the door with three-inch heels below it. "We'll leave in five minutes. Your room looks nice."

Cool mom.

Marina's phone vibrated on the dresser. I reached for it. She lunged and grabbed it. I held out my hand. "Give me the phone."

"It's nobody." She pulled away.

"Now!"

I glared at her with my palm open, jerking my hand. She gave me the phone. The screen read: "rubs your feet"—from the senior who played on the football team. I scrolled on, and gasped when I read the full text, describing his hands moving up her leg. I couldn't deal with a teen desperate for love coming home pregnant.

The phone weighed heavy in my hand, and I told her she was not going to Homecoming. I took the phone to show her father. He read the messages: lots of idle chit-chat, but also sexting that described long-distance petting, complaints against me yelling at her about swim practice, not taking her to Olive Garden. And the latest: her crazy mother timing her harp practice, heavily laden with the B-word.

Her father shook his head and reminded Marina of the rule that she wasn't to socialize, communicate, or hang out with seniors or juniors. "Number one, you're not going to homecoming. Number two and three will come when I calm down enough to think about it."

Marina cried. I canceled the eyebrow waxing and the updo. She cried some more. I emailed the parents my regrets about not hosting the after-party.

Not cool mom.

The next few days, Marina was repentant, sweet as cotton candy. "I'm sorry I wrote those things. I didn't mean them. Please let me go." Her father and I propped each other up when the other was close to caving. Even while I dreamed of her perfect evening, we answered with a resounding *No*.

Homecoming night she sat with us on the couch with popcorn and a new-release rented movie.

Marina continued to spiral out of control. Once during class, a classmate noticed blood seeping through her sleeve at her wrist and reported it to the teacher. Her school required a psych evaluation that night. In the commotion of the ER, under the stark fluorescent lights, with midnight approaching, she refused to speak to the doctors. They signed a waiver to readmit her to school only after my husband explained our other daughter's medical crisis. Doctor's diagnosis: non-suicidal panic attack, induced by anxiety.

As if in a broken taffy puller, my nerves clawed to stay together with each passing turn. We didn't know how to answer either Marina's or her sister's cry for help.

A few weeks later, Marina sat next to her sister, timing her seizures and logging about ten an hour in the notebook. Her younger sister's once-rare seizures had become uncontrolled and frequent since Marina started seventh grade. What had once freaked us out had become the norm.

Then, two days before Christmas, we faced the unexpected, the unimaginable. The hospital explained the dire prognosis for Marina's sister, and we made the grueling decision to forego life-saving measures. We relayed our reasons to Marina. Her sister died Christmas morning.

Before New Year's Marina developed gastric pains in the middle of the night. Our grief too raw, we wanted Marina to wait until morning to see the pediatrician. She accused me of not caring about her.

Not cool mom.

We went back to the same hospital where her sister died. The ER doctor found nothing. A slew of GI tests found nothing. The pediatrician again suggested counseling. Her father cajoled and prodded her to go to grief counseling. Lost in my own grief, my steely glare said get in the car now, and we left. She didn't relate to group sessions for children who had lost siblings and refused to go again. My husband reluctantly agreed.

We adapted to Marina's moods. In the morning, we didn't speak to her until she spoke first. Otherwise, she'd growl and snarl. Homework took a back seat. We asked her to attend weekly individual counseling. She refused.

That spring she requested to volunteer at an overnight summer camp for six weeks. We agreed with the caveat she attend weekly counseling.

We interviewed therapists. She rejected all of them, one for taking notes in her presence. Another for being too demonstrative—putting a compassionate hand on her shoulder. Eventually, we interviewed a counselor as a family. What Marina saw as too happy, we saw as upbeat. Marina said she looked like a hippie. We just saw a loose blouse. I made the decision to go with Loose Blouse, and Marina started counseling—and resented me for it.

Not cool mom.

I believed Marina and I had built a strong relationship when she was younger and hoped we could find it and rebuild it, stronger. First part of summer, she began volunteering at the Easter Seals camp. But she left after just three weeks, suffering from intense gastric pains. They cleared once she was home.

At the end of summer, we camped in our RV along the Lake Michigan coastline, Sheboygan to Mackinac Island. Nothing I did pleased Marina. At home, I could walk away from her nastiness, but in the RV, I was trapped.

While traveling, my cousin called and told me her mother was on a ventilator. My aunt chose to disconnect life support and she died. Marina was angry that my aunt would "choose death"—the way "you did for my sister."

That stopped me cold.

I told her I didn't choose for her sister to die. I explained that her sister had numerous complications and a ventilator would have added one more. We couldn't stop her suffering—we had to be strong and let her go. I couldn't tell if she accepted my explanation.

Sophomore year started, and Marina shared with me what happened her first day at school. I looked around. Was she talking to me? She continued seeing Loose Blouse. Her grief and depression hadn't disappeared; she stayed in her room and spoke to me only when she wanted something. But she began a job as a respite worker with two special needs boys. She took them to football games, the movies, and their special recreation activities. It gave her an outlet for her nurturing nature that I knew was still in there somewhere.

Senior year Marina studied Psychology and recognized what two years with Loose Blouse hadn't made clear: that she was depressed. Marina said she thought she needed medication, but a psychiatrist didn't agree. Instead, he told her she needed to deal with her grief.

Marina and I attended a lecture in early November: Surviving the Holidays after a Loss of a Child. Marina pointed to the presenter and said, "I want to see her." At her next session with Loose Blouse, she told her it was their last session. I scrambled to schedule an appointment with the presenter. Marina faithfully attended sessions with her new therapist and rescheduled when she had a conflict. She even related to me how the counselor was helping her.

It dawned on me that Marina's grief resembled the grief of losing a child. Over summer break, I invited her to meet with my monthly support group of parents who had lost special needs children.

Later that summer, her father and I came home early from a wedding. At the kitchen table, sitting with a girlfriend, Marina's eyes suddenly rolled back, her body stiffened. The girlfriend admitted Marina had smoked too much pot. "It was her first time," she said. I grabbed the phone and passed it to her.

"Call your mother to pick you up," I demanded. "Either you tell your mother what happened—or I will."

For the next several hours, we sat with Marina on the couch, soothing her paranoia and batting away her hallucinations. This was a punishment worse than grounding her. She vowed never to do it again. We had bought Marina a spunky used Honda CRV for high school graduation. Her father kept the car instead.

Almost cool mom.

●  ●  ●

We purchased a home in Florida and flew back to move Marina into her Wisconsin dorm the next week. College gave Marina her independence—and distance from me. When her poems were published in the university periodical, I flew three hours on a plane then drove two hours to hear her read for five minutes. We flew back for Family Weekend. I took her and her college friends to dinner on her birthday.

Cool mom.

Second semester, her grades dropped. She lied about heavy drinking and casual drug use. Evidence posted on Facebook.

We drew up a contract that stated she would use her savings from high school jobs to pay for sophomore year first semester, and we would reimburse her based on the grades she earned.

The partying continued. However, her grades improved.

She used up her savings.

Not cool mom.

We continued to pay.

Cool mom.

Junior year, she changed schools.

She changed majors.

She moved closer to us.

I wanted her to graduate more than she did. I changed the incentive, dangling a convertible Mustang for a 3.75 cumulative GPA upon graduation. First semester: 4.0. She told us her continued success wasn't about the car but the pride she felt on achieving her goal.

I held my breath.

She shared an apartment with piggy roommates and cleaned up after them instead of them cleaning up after her. She grocery shopped and prepared her own meals. She planned her social life around school, not the other way around. I reminded her about getting the flu shot. She already had.

An adultier adult was emerging.

Senior year she invited me to spend the weekend with her in her apartment in Miami.

We saw *Lion King*, the musical, and had dinner at KiKi on the River. We toured Wynwood to see the murals on the buildings. We danced at the drum circle on the beach under a full moon. She took me clubbing. I said I wanted to be home by midnight. The clubs opened at midnight. She brushed mascara on my lashes. She glossed red, red lipstick on my lips. She dressed me in her little white cocktail dress. She slipped five-inch heels on my feet. She introduced me to her friends. I smiled as I stomached the stench of cigarettes and hookah smoke. We danced until five.

She posted it on social media.

She shared her life with me.

Marina's face smashed into her pillow, body sprawled on the full-size bed—she had left me a sliver. My stomach grumbled at nine o'clock. I had rejected her idea to stop at Taco Bell at six in the morning. From the common fridge, I grabbed an orange. I sat on the resin chair on her ninth-floor balcony, facing east with a bare trace of the Atlantic visible. A smug smile crossed my face. I had spent the weekend with a decent, compassionate, independent human being.

Indispensable mom. Cool.

# The Presentation

by Karen Nicole Johnson

Sister Michelle, the principal of Saint Clare's High School, sat upright at her tidy desk, her brown hair tucked tightly inside the nun's white habit that framed her face. There was no fussing or fidgeting, no welcoming comments. Her eyes stared directly at my parents seated across from her.

"Do let us know where we can transfer her records," said Sister Michelle, both starting and ending the conversation in one sentence.

"I see," my dad replied. My mom shifted in her seat and cast me a look that told me I was in trouble.

I wasn't being forced out, but it was clear from this meeting that if I chose to return next fall, the principal might officially expel me. This wasn't news; my discontent had been brewing for months and now at the end of my sophomore year, my misery was clear to everyone.

I had told my parents from the beginning that an all-girls Catholic high school was not the right place for me, but my mom insisted that my sister had been happy there and had made many good girlfriends. Most importantly, she insisted, I was too young to make such a decision. I had pointed out that most of my friends in elementary school had been boys, not girls, that I thought an all-girls environment was a weird concept, and that I didn't want more religion classes, but none of my arguments prevented my enrollment.

Freshman year, the photo on my identification card depicted a fresh-faced 14-year-old, clean and innocent. A year later, my straight hair had been permed wildly, my eyes were made up with purple eyeshadow, and a deliberately chosen cocaine spoon hung on a necklace around my neck. The photo ID showed a teen in trouble, or certainly headed in that direction.

Many an afternoon I endured detentions for infractions like not wearing the uniform appropriately, chewing gum, wearing my name tag upside-down, or skipping the uniform shoes and wearing my sneakers instead. Time after time, I dragged down the sterile hallway and filed into detention. Detention was held in a classroom, the desks kept in a straight row just like the nuns wanted to keep all of us, in order, neat and tidy. One wall was all windows, though the windows were never opened—not even a crack—making the room bright but airless, a holding tank. An elder nun kept watch over the "bad" girls as we sat in misery for our sins.

One day, sitting in detention, bored beyond words, I thought about how vocal I had been about being unhappy, protesting in different ways, but here I was, still at St. Clare's. What if the path to the school change wasn't to fight more, but to refuse to fight at all? What if I became quiet, didn't engage, effectively withdrew?

It took a concerted effort for me to still myself. I didn't raise my hand, I didn't offer answers, I stopped asking questions. I disengaged. I deployed a similar approach at home. I caused enough concern to the adults in my world that my mom arranged therapy for me.

My therapist helped me explore why I was miserable and what I might change, or what changes I might seek to get to a better place. And although I had issues of my own to address, together we realized how much a change of environment would help. The issue my parents and teachers didn't see was how often I was surrounded by drugs. There were drugs in my neighborhood and drugs at my high school. I dabbled, but what I wanted most was an entirely different place, a fresh start, and to stay away from drugs. How could I convince my parents of such a change and yet not talk about the drugs or name names?

Over time, my grades suffered. On the outside, I became more defiant, yet achieved my rebellion by simply doing less. Teachers began contacting the principal and my parents. My situation became worrisome, leading to that day in late May when Sister Michelle called my parents and me to her office. The irony of my dad, an elementary school principal, being called into a principal's office didn't occur to me until long after the event.

On the short drive home from the meeting, my dad told me they would like a few words with me. My mom had been so angry she hadn't even been able to yell at me recently.

I sat at the kitchen table waiting.

"Okay, here's the plan," my dad began. Whenever he used that phrase, you knew whatever he said would not be repeated and that it would be wise to listen closely.

"Research and assemble facts. Figure out what you think will be the right place for you. Make sure it has a solid academic record, which will be no small task, as you'll be leaving one of the top institutions in all of Boston. You will stand when you present, not sit. If you can persuade us, the school you choose is where you will attend next fall. If you fail to find a suitable alternative, your mother and I will choose where you will attend and that will be it, decision done."

My mother glared at me. She got up from the table and started banging pots and pans as she made our evening's dinner, and I knew that this conversation was done.

As I thought about the plan my dad outlined, I realized the opportunity in the situation. My research involved phone calls and requests for brochures to be sent to the house. My focus shifted from being miserable to finding the right place and, in that mental shift, it gave me a chance to figure out what I wanted and what had been missing. I wanted to be in the city. I wanted more diversity, although back then that wasn't a word or a concept that was used. I wanted more freedom. No more uniforms; I wanted to choose my own clothes and shoes. I didn't want nuns or religious classes.

I found an international school that was preparatory, not a traditional institution. Differences included: no homerooms, no gym classes, no teams, no sports, and no proms. There were no grade levels; instead, there was a point system and when you accrued sufficient points, you graduated. I remember thinking: at last, I won't be treated like a child. The student population was diverse; in fact, many students were from out of the country, not just different neighborhoods of Boston. Newman Prep was in the Back Bay, which also meant it would require a bus ride, a trolley, and a walk to get there. I didn't care. I wanted this change even though it seemed nearly the opposite of what I had.

The night of the presentation, I stood on the yellow plaid linoleum floor of our 1970s-style kitchen. My parents sat at the round white table. I tried to look more at my dad, as I knew that I could use facts and logic to appeal to him. I made sure to make eye contact with my mother, too, knowing otherwise she would feel left out. My dad was known as the soft touch in the household, but I knew if Mom didn't approve of the plan, no matter how much support there was from my dad, nothing was going to happen.

I stood as had been asked. I placed brochures and papers on the kitchen table, and I began. "I need a change."

"You had a perfectly fine place to attend," Mom scoffed.

"Ruthie, let her talk," Dad said.

I worried Mom would be even grumpier with Dad telling her to be still.

"I've found the right school. It's called Newman Prep and it's located in the Back Bay. This is where I want to go."

"Ridiculous, it's a long and difficult commute," Mom replied. She fidgeted around, barely able to stay seated. When Mom was mad, she usually moved around the room, so her remaining seated seemed unnatural.

"Well, tell us how you would get there," Dad said.

"I'll walk to the bus stop on Washington Street, same as I already have been. I'll take the bus to Forest Hills and switch to the green line trolley down Huntington Ave, get off at the Copley Square stop, then walk the rest of the way, just a few blocks." I had prepared for this question.

"Do you have any idea how early you will have to get up to be there on time?" Mom asked.

"I do, and I don't care. I'll do the commute and never complain about it." I replied.

"Fine," my dad said, "now, tell us about the academic rating and why this is the right choice."

I could see what my dad was doing with this question. He was pulling both my mother and me out of arguing and back to the facts. I shared the acceptance, retention, and graduation rates, all information I had learned from my research. I shared the school rating and the solid academic footing, knowing this would appeal to both my parents. I remembered thinking I wanted to sound prepared, not like a smart aleck, so I did what I could to stick to the facts and leave out emotion. I avoided highlighting the obvious: there would be a mix of boys and girls, there would be no religion classes, and there would be no uniforms. Focus on what matters, I told myself, making sure not to put my hands on my hips or in my pockets.

"I believe I have found my dream school because of the environment Newman offers," I said.

"What about prom nights? What about senior year? You will give up these traditions if you attend a place like that," Mom said.

"I know, but I also know I don't want to be involved in those traditions. I don't want to go to a prom or buy a fancy dress. I want to be in the city. I've always wanted to be downtown." I knew this desire would resonate because, since I was twelve years old, I had told anyone who would listen that I wanted to be in the city. Our neighborhood, while technically in Boston, was at the very edge of the city line, and it felt more suburban than urban. I wanted to be in the center of the activity.

"This is a big choice, Karen. Are you sure?" Dad asked.

"I am. This is it."

I made my pitch. I have never forgotten how desperately I wanted to change schools and attend Newman Prep.

When I was done speaking, my parents said they needed time to talk together and that they would get back to me in a few days. I was the model child for several days while I waited.

Finally, after a few days, my parents told me over dinner one night. "We've reviewed the information you shared, made our own phone calls, and agree with the choice you've made. You may enroll in Newman Prep."

"Great!" I exclaimed. "Thank you, thank you. I promise to do well." I felt something switch inside myself after saying this, realizing that how the change turned out was up to me.

"Well, I guess we will all see," Mom said.

I couldn't help but notice her sense of questioning, wanting proof, but there was nothing I could do now but to go forward and make the change work.

Mom was agitated and we were still not talking much when my dad and I went to visit my new school. She refused to join the open house, instead muttering that I was leaving a perfectly good school and a perfectly good opportunity. She was furious about the impending change.

On the drive to visit Newman, I asked my dad what I might do to patch the situation with Mom.

"Follow through," he said. "Show us this was the right choice." He paused and glanced at me, "Once you're enrolled, your mother will be okay. If she sees you doing well, she'll be fine." He seemed confident and spoke calmly.

Transitioning into prep school was easy given the point system and the lack of focus on grade levels. Newman used the semester system, versus grade levels, which meant students were enrolling and graduating all the time. It was as though the school set a tone of "you do you and don't worry about what other people are doing." This was exactly the atmosphere I had longed for.

Shortly after starting, drugs were offered to me by several students, but with the experiences I'd already had, I found it simple to say, "it's just not my thing." That was the end of that. I was also given choices for non-required classes, which pushed me into thinking about what I enjoyed rather than what I was rebelling against.

Six months later, I was on the Dean's List. I'd found a part-time job after school, so I was able to stay downtown all day, commuting early in the morning and coming home late afternoon. One thing was clear: I was thriving. I hadn't been this happy in years and it showed.

One day when I came home, my mom told me she was happy about my grades and that she was proud of me. I thanked her, feeling relieved our relationship was no longer strained.

"Let me tell you this now and one day you might understand," she said, "a mother is only as happy as her unhappiest child. It was hard to watch you be so unhappy."

I hadn't realized my misery had been my mother's as well.

Months continued and then, one day, I came home and announced over dinner what the Dean had shared with me.

"I was told I can graduate early if I am willing to attend the summer semester. I want to do that."

"Wow, are you sure about this?" Dad asked.

"Yes, they say a letter will come in the mail and we'll need to decide about summer enrollment. Oh, and this coming semester, I will be on the Dean's List again for my grades."

"Unbelievable," Mom said. "But do you really want to forfeit a summer? Don't you want to do more summer things?"

"I'd just work full-time anyway to save money for college."

"Sounds like a plan," Dad said.

"Graduating a year early is quite an accomplishment," Mom said, looking happy.

Mom found me later that night in my bedroom. "You should start thinking beyond Newman Prep. Think about where you want to go to college. I bet you have a few ideas about that." I looked at her closely to see how she was she feeling and when I saw her broad smile, we laughed together.

Switching high schools had been one thing but learning about myself was the greater lesson—to know when I wasn't in the right place for myself and to resolve the problem, not just rebel. When I think back to the night of the presentation, I see the parenting direction my dad chose and how the freedom provided me the space to find my own direction. And while my mom might not have been too happy about the situation, she allowed me to find my way as well. Together they put me in position to solve the problem instead of having the situation solved for me. Being so involved in choosing my next school aligned me to making the change work which would have been less likely if I had no voice in the change. Now so many years later, I see what a brave parenting choice this must have been and how well the situation prepared me to investigate what the real issue(s) are in a situation and to work towards a positive outcome. My parents gave me a tremendous lesson that has lasted with me all these years later.

# That Moment at the Cow Pond

by C.D. Karabush

Jimmy is crying. Mommy's carrying him up the hill to our farmhouse. He's four and he can walk as good as me, but she's squeezing him tight anyway. Water sloshes from our bathing suits so we leave a muddy trail between the cow plops through the dusty pasture. It makes a blacker line across the hot macadam road.

She was in such a hurry to carry him she just left me behind. She told me in her mad voice, "Hold the baby's hand and help him walk across the pasture and the road safely." Is she mad at me or at Jimmy? I don't know why she's mad. So I tug my littlest brother along while he complains. I'm grouchy with him even though he's only two and I know he can't walk fast.

The wet path is muddy and squishy and nasty under my feet. Then the road is so hot I want to run fast. But the baby can't run fast, so our feet get burny. I hear Jimmy yelling for Mommy to put him down. I don't know what all the fuss is about: Jimmy wasn't even scared until Mommy grabbed him and ran out of the water. She wouldn't listen when I said he floated okay. I'm grouchy with all of them. It's Jimmy and our baby brother's fault that we left the cow pond and I never got to play in our new inner tube. They got to play with it, but I had to leave it behind. It just isn't fair.

Jimmy was perfectly content floating in the cow pond. He lay on his back in the water with his arms stretched out, floating the way Mommy does some-times, watching the fluffy clouds sailing across the hot July sky. They make pretty shapes and I like looking at them too. Jimmy watched them while he was floating and looking all relaxed. He wasn't scared, and he didn't cry "Help," or "Get me out." He didn't even seem to hear Mommy. She yelled from across the pond, "Jump in and save him!" Jimmy can't swim yet. None of us kids can. I'm only six, so I was scared to jump in the deep water to get him. How could I do that when I can't swim? Why did Mommy think he needed me to save him? He looked happy cooling off in the pond and watching the clouds. Mommy

329

was swimming fast as she could toward us as Jimmy drifted slowly toward her, staring up at the clouds. I watched the clouds too. The baby watched Mommy swim.

Mommy had told all three of us to stay out of the water and wait so we wouldn't drown while she practiced swimming. She said she'd come right back but it wasn't any fun waiting for her in the hot sun. Before she went swimming, my brothers had hogged the inner tube, bouncing and splashing in the shallow edge of the pond. They wouldn't give me a turn. That wasn't fun either. They always did stuff like that. I was still trying to get the inner tube when Mommy told us to get out of the water. They climbed up on the dock and ran out to the end to watch her. It was my chance, and I grabbed the inner tube they left behind.

I'm the biggest kid. I started school last fall. Every morning a big yellow bus stopped on the road in front of our farmhouse. Mommy gave me my Mickey Mouse lunch pail and I ran down our driveway and climbed on the bus. It took me to first grade with the other big kids. Jimmy isn't a big kid so he couldn't go on the bus with me, even though we were best friends. He wasn't happy he couldn't go with me. He had to stay home with our baby brother because they're both little kids.

All winter when I came home on the bus, they were playing together. I knew Jimmy'd rather play with me, so I told him we could play school together. I got to be the teacher. I let Jimmy use my lunch pail and my *Dick and Jane* book. He just threw them around. He would get in trouble if he did that at real school. I tried to teach him letters and numbers. He ran away and the baby chased him. Jimmy copied me, "Now class, let's read together," and "What is one plus one?" Then the baby laughed. He doesn't even know what numbers are, but Jimmy laughed with him anyway. They're just stupid little kids.

I stopped playing with them. I'm a big kid, and I shouldn't play with such little kids. When we watch *Superman*, they run back and forth and play cops and robbers. Mostly they hit each other, like Superman fighting the robbers. When we watch *The Lone Ranger*, they skip around and pretend they're cowboys and Indians on horses. Then they knock each other down. I'm too big to play like that. Besides, Mommy yells at me if I hit one of them back. I'm supposed to love them and help take care of them, even when they hit me or laugh at me.

So I play alone now. Sometimes I play Davy Crockett, King of the Wild Frontier. I climb trees and hunt the chickens in our yard. In the winter I make snow forts and I don't let them come in. Then Mommy yells at me and tells me I have to let them play. They tear down my forts. So I go inside and practice reading *Dick and Jane* instead. Dick and Jane's mommy never yells or spanks them. She never makes them wait in the hot sun while she swims around the cow pond.

I climbed up onto the dock with the captured innertube around my waist. While Mommy started swimming back, my brothers tried to take it away from me. But I held on tight. I was going to keep it. Jimmy said it was still their turn because they had to leave the water before they were done. He tried everything to make me give it to him. Nothing doing. I wasn't going to give it up until Mommy got back and I got my turn in the water with it.

*I'm keeping it no matter what. Go ahead, Jimmy, you can bump into me all you want. You can tug on the innertube. You can pull me with you toward the edge of the dock. I'm the big kid, and I have the innertube around me so you can't get it. Bump me all you want. All I have to do is bump you back. A little harder.*

# CREATIVE NONFICTION

## WHAT'S IN A LIFE?

# The Mushroom House

by Sandy Kubillus

Mom held a drawing she'd cut out from a magazine and eyed the peach-colored wall next to the kitchen table. She wore her painting clothes: a white sleeveless cotton blouse with splatters of various colors from previous projects. The stains contrasted with her auburn hair styled in a beehive hairdo from her weekly hairdresser appointment. Her oil paint jars and artist brushes sat on top of a newspaper covering the blue checkered tablecloth.

I grabbed a Coke from the refrigerator. When I looked back at Mom, she was holding a paintbrush in her right hand. She applied the first brushstrokes of brown paint to the five-by-ten-foot section of wall above the varnished chair-rail molding that separated the upper and lower sections of the wall. The half-inch dark brown streak contrasted against the peach wall like a newspaper headline.

Years ago, my dad, with the help of my mom, painted these walls—not one drop out of place. Dad never allowed me or my siblings to help, saying, "You're not good enough. You can learn when you get your own house."

My brow furrowed. "Wha...what are you doing?" I pushed my sandy blond bangs away from my eyes and moved closer. Even though I was a senior in high school, Dad would yell at me if I accidentally slammed a door or dropped the toilet seat lid, reminding me it was his house, and he allowed me the privilege to live there. "Did you ask Dad if you could paint on the kitchen wall?"

"It's my house too!" Mom's face flushed. "I don't care what your father thinks. This wall needs something, so I'm going to paint this picture." She thrust a drawing of three mushrooms at me.

My face contorted into a smirk. I imagined a yelling match with Mom's face turning red before she ran into the bathroom to hide her tears and turn on the fan to smother the honk of blowing her nose.

"Okay," I sighed. I grabbed my novel from the kitchen table and headed into the living room, waiting for the fight to begin.

335

An hour after Mom started painting, Dad walked up the basement steps and entered the kitchen. I eavesdropped from my rocking chair while I pretended to read.

Dad cleared his throat—then silence.

I tried not to look shocked as Dad walked into the living room shaking his head, his lips pursed on his clean-shaven face while he shuffled over to his black recliner and picked up the eleven-hundred-page *Atlas Shrugged*.

I could never get away with doing anything to Dad's precious walls. Curiosity got the better of me, so I closed my book and walked into the kitchen.

Mom scratched a pencil on the wall, outlining the shape of the mushrooms while her jaw moved habitually, chewing a stick of Juicy Fruit gum. She glanced at the drawing, seeming oblivious to her original brown brushstrokes.

She turned around and noticed me watching her. "Sandra, go grab that step-stool over there. I can't reach that high," she pointed toward the ceiling.

"Dad's okay with this?" I shook my head in surprise, admiring her courage to stand up to Dad. Maybe he thought it wasn't worth a fight.

"I don't think he's happy about it, but it's something I want to do." She smiled with a smug expression. "Besides, it's too late now."


Three years earlier, when Mom was shopping at Ford City Mall, on the southwest side of Chicago, she saw a sign saying "Grand Opening, Now Hiring" at The Cookie Factory. On a whim, she applied and was shocked when they hired her. She didn't need this part-time job. She worked full-time in a ware-house tagging prices on clothing, a mind-numbing and backbreaking task with a supervisor who demanded more speed.

At The Cookie Factory she learned how to ornament large cookies with dec-orative cursive, adding vibrant flowers, balloons, and other embellishments. Sometimes I'd stop by the store and she'd show me her latest creations, often smiley faces or simple cartoon characters.

Maybe Mom took the job to escape Dad's scrutiny after his machinist job ended when his employer went out of business the previous year. I was the only child left at home. My sister had graduated from college and my brother had married, both within a month of each other.

Although we lived in a mortgage-free, three-bedroom brick home, Dad always told us he couldn't afford the uniforms required for Girl Scouts, rental for band instruments, or family vacations. All of our clothes came from Mom's minimum-wage earnings. Both my parents had emigrated from Germany as young children and lived through the Great Depression, so the mentality of saving money was always a central issue in our household. I remember Dad telling Mom, "You owe me fifty-nine cents," for a bottle of oil he purchased for her decade-old car.

Dad spent most of his time reading *Forbes* magazine, books written by the capitalist philosopher Ayn Rand, watching the stock market returns, and concocting diets and exercises to help with his back pain and ulcerated stomach. Other than walking the dog and occasionally going to the hardware store, he led a reclusive life, criticizing his family and things he read or saw on television. His IQ of 136 was unmatched by my *National-Enquirer*-reading mom, or by me, even though I was in the top two percent of my class.

Shortly after Mom began working at The Cookie Factory, she started painting in her few spare hours each week using an easel in our unfinished basement. First, she tried paint-by-numbers. One painting, of the *Santa Maria* sailing over a blue wavy sea with the sails fully set, hung on my brother's former bedroom wall for decades.

She began buying blank canvases and painting freehand. At first, she copied pictures of Mickey and Minnie Mouse, then other animated characters, each drawing growing more complex. She painted a bowl of fruit with a wine bottle that wasn't quite symmetrical. She never attended art classes, saying that painting was just for fun. She learned from books borrowed from the library and a few she bought at Hobby Lobby.

Mom graduated to painting landscapes, most of which she had never viewed in person. Our only family vacation was a cross-country train ride to Seattle to visit my grandparents. Mom tried to put onto the canvas her interpretation of the mountains as she copied the details from pictures she cut out of magazines. She often went back to touch up her paintings, blending the colors to get the precise scenery. Over the course of a few years, Mom created more than a dozen paintings that hung on the basement walls or in the back bedrooms. When friends and relatives noticed them, they graciously responded with comments like, "Oh you did this, how nice." But I could see through their fake smiles.

A mural painted on the kitchen wall wasn't something Mom could hide if it didn't turn out well. Everyone who came to visit would see her painting when they sat at the table for a meal and a chat.

For the next few weeks, Mom carried her paint jars and brushes up from the basement, having to clean up an hour or so later, soaking her brushes in a jar of turpentine. She painted diligently, touching up the mushrooms, altering the colors. Her tentative initial strokes grew bolder. I watched her go back over sections trying to perfect them while climbing up and down the step stool to reach the areas near the ceiling. Often she would step around the table and grin at her work, then notice some imperfection and return to painting.

One day Mom stood back, smiled, and said to me, "I better leave well enough alone. I think it's done." The light peach-colored wall displayed one giant orange-brown mushroom tinged with white and yellow, flanked by two small brown mushrooms with white spots. Daisies and blades of grass sprouted between them. Her mural covered most of the wall, adding brightness and warmth to the plain kitchen.

Dad responded with a shrug, but always sat with his back to the painting.

Most visitors remarked on the size of the painting and smiled at her work, offering polite comments. Unlike Dad and my siblings, I felt proud of Mom's work—of her boldness to show everyone her artistry and her defiance of Dad's tidiness. She was claiming this house as hers, different from any other.

The mushrooms were Mom's final creation, although I never asked her why. Maybe she felt she wasn't good enough since others didn't appreciate it as much as she did. She never offered any of us siblings her paintings, even after we bought homes of our own and needed pictures to hang on the walls. I never thought of asking her—likely, my siblings didn't either.

As arthritis started troubling Mom's hands, she gave up other pastimes like sewing and crocheting. Then Dad developed cancer and needed her care. It wasn't until he weakened from the disease that he let her make more of the household decisions. If he didn't like some of her ideas, he'd say, "Wait till I'm dead, then you can change things." She did just that, installing central air conditioning, and buying a new living room carpet and furniture within a month of his death.

I wonder if Mom's mural gave me courage many years later to defy Dad when I moved in with my boyfriend. He refused to speak to me for his remaining years. I defied Dad once again with my career as an environmental consultant, which he thought was a man's job. Mom's boldness may even have spurred my ambition to become a published writer.

For over thirty-five years, Mom's painting of three large mushrooms dominated the kitchen while we sat at the table talking, eating a meal, or playing with the dogs. Everyone got used to it, including me. The mural appeared in the background of many photos and remained etched in the back of our minds. Both Mom and Dad died in that house, with Mom surviving Dad by over twenty years.

My sister and her adult children arrived from California for Mom's funeral. While they stayed at the house, she gathered Mom's paintings from the walls and the basement, coveting her long forgotten creations.

As we cleaned out the old house, it began to feel less and less like Mom's house, except for the mushroom painting, a permanent fixture shown to all potential home buyers, but likely to end up covered with a new coat of paint. I hated that thought. This was Mom's house with her permanent mark on the world.

The mushroom painting called to me as I walked through the house for the final time and turned out the lights. Now with all of the furniture gone, I could see the full effect of Mom's painting. I choked back tears while I snapped my last photos. I couldn't say goodbye to this last piece of Mom. I ran my fingers over the ridges of Mom's mushroom painting on the kitchen wall, staring at it, a lump filling my throat while I took it in one last time. With the stroke of a pen, the filing of papers, the house was sold to a woman who called it the Mushroom House. Gone was my childhood home, my parents' house for one week shy of fifty years.

As I examined it for the final time, something seemed missing—no signature. On all of her other paintings she signed *Inge* on the bottom right corner. Maybe she thought it was obvious since it was her and Dad's house. Or maybe she didn't want to fully claim it. I'll never know.

I walked down the stairs and out the door, turning the key in the lock on the old familiar door. I'm free, I told myself. Free of the demands of Mom, especially the past year when she broke her hip, then slipped into dementia before she passed away. Free of worry about whether I needed to hire another caregiver for the long evening hours after her full-time help left at five p.m. Free of calling her every night at six p.m. and then again at nine p.m. sharp before her pill alarm went off so I could walk her through her nighttime meds. Free of spending one twelve-hour day of every weekend with her, alternating with my brother and sister-in-law. Free of settling all her six bank accounts and various utilities.

But I didn't want to be free anymore. I'd rather have my mom back, sharing a meal while we sat at the kitchen table in front of her mushroom painting.

# Commitment

by Caryn Green

That April morning, he dragged his half-dressed, screaming mother out of the elevator, Robert knew something had to be done. And if not by him, then whom? Head of the family by attrition, he was 31. There was no one to share this overwhelming responsibility; advisers and sympathizers, certainly, but nobody close to help shoulder the load of his mother's mania, now so exacerbated since that very dreadful night almost a decade ago. The bitter anniversary approached.

Bob had managed to distance himself from that course of events, to view them through the wrong end of a telescope, to behave as though it all had happened to someone else, in another life.

His mother never could. In the ten years since Father's death she hadn't been right—or so was the general belief. Only family knew how far back her troubles really went. At Robert's exact age she'd endured a horrific six months when she'd lost her father, her grandmother, and second-born son—Bob's first little brother, the soulmate who never was—but she'd been able to rally as a younger woman, when she was fulfilling her destiny as a mother, homemaker and wife; reading them bedtime stories, scolding the domestics, chasing his father with a kitchen knife.

Even widowed, she might have maintained some semblance of balance when she'd returned from abroad with his youngest brother. Who took ill on shipboard. And never recovered.

That tragedy disrupted the family symmetry; three living, three deceased. Now the dead held the majority. There would be no more brothers beside him chasing Mother down this hallway; there was only hired help.

In the four years since his last brother passed, Mother suffered chronic pain, was often ill and melancholic. Having no permanent residence, she roamed, seeking cures with an attending nurse. She'd gone to Wisconsin first, to take the waters and get bilked by Spiritualists, then Canada, where she'd wandered unknown provinces for months, returning sick, to stay in Chicago as a virtual invalid, awaiting a journey to the Great Beyond some high priestess had prophesized would occur on September 6th.

On September 7th, she decided to winter in Florida instead.

There she enjoyed the privacy, the solitude, the citrus trees. Until March 12th. When she awoke convinced of Robert's imminent death. *Dearly beloved son*, she telegraphed, *rouse yourself! Live for my sake! All I have is yours from this hour.*

She seemed stunned when he met her at Great Central Station on March 16th.

"Bobbie darling, you are yet alive!"

"And in the prime of health." He kissed her upturned cheeks. "Mother, you're looking very well." And she did, to his great relief. He'd invited her to his Wabash Avenue home; she declined. His house triggered unpleasant memories, of a son who died and a city that burned and that frightful row with Bob's wife.

Who was currently out of town. Nevertheless. He brought her to Chicago's most exclusive hotel; they dined. She described Florida winter—the soft, dreamy rain—her lodgings—leased under an assumed name—her balcony overlooking the lilacs and roses, on which she'd caught severe cold.

"I was bedridden for weeks." Mother buttered a roll. "At the height of my fever, I told the nurse we must depart for home at once, and to pack a small valise."

Bob snorted, getting the joke. "Not a dozen trunks?" Only in delirium would she travel that light.

She enjoyed her lunch. She approved of the china pattern, the dining room décor; the waiter offered coffee and poured. She peered into the cup.

"Good show, there's no poison in this one."

Robert stopped stirring, keeping a poker face as his mother explained she'd been both poisoned and robbed coming home on the train. Tainted coffee had been served her in Jacksonville. She drank two cups. Then her pocketbook was stolen by a Wandering Jew, but he said he'd probably return it soon; one lump or two?

Robert booked an adjoining room.

The first night she slept, but not the next. She was frightened to be alone; could she sleep on his couch? He refused. Then might Bobbie sleep on hers?

He demurred. But eventually, waiting for the next knock like one waits for the other shoe to drop, he acquiesced.

As Good Friday approached, her symptoms intensified. She was nervous, excitable, unable to sleep. She frequented pharmacies; her shopping increased. She bought dozens of lace curtains that had no place to hang, armloads of soaps and perfumes, items of clothing, watches and jewels; little was paid for, nothing was used, everything would be returned—except those concoctions she consumed.

Robert engaged a woman to stay in her room, but that afforded little relief. Wakeful at night and fearful of the dark, she knocked constantly at his door. In her unhinged state, every wisp of chimney smoke was the city in flames, every passerby a threat, every creak in the floorboards the footsteps of Death.

Some nights neither of them slept.

She would pace, his heart would race, then the ghastly images replayed, of pillows stained with Father's brains, of his brothers gasping for breath, of soldiers limping off battlefields, the living dragging the dead. Then came warm tears, tickling his ears, and Robert would bolt upright like the soldier he was, straighten the bedclothes, steel himself.

Sometimes it took all his courage not to cave, to keep these visions from crippling him, and his head was nailed on straight. How these same scenes rehearsed in his mother's addled mind was horrifying to contemplate.

On April 1st, something snapped. Evading her burly attendant, Mother sprinted into the hallway, indecently dressed. The elevator had begun its descent when Robert rang it back, hearing the shaft resound with his mother's cries, the operator pleading for madam to settle down, clearly audible each time he opened the door. Might these be the voices she was talking about?

The car returned, bouncing as it leveled out. The doors opened on Mother raging in her nightgown, hair in disarray, bosom heaving, eyes darting like a cornered rat. Robert was a monster of mankind, she shrieked, his wife a scheming witch. His sainted father was turning in his grave, her other sons would never treat her like this.

"Mother please,"—employing the tone of firm but gentle authority that served in his own household. "We're in public view."

She didn't budge.

Pa would have yanked her out and scooped her up, oblivious as she screamed and kicked. But Bob was the son, not the husband, and not his father's size. So he gave a gentle tug and Hell let loose.

"You are going to murder me," her Satanic Majesty hissed, within earshot of hotel employees and guests. What chance now of keeping this incident from those hyenas in the press? The embarrassment would be acute.

But much more worrisome was what might happen next.

Eventually cajoled out of the corridor, Mother had dressed carelessly, wrapped her greying hair in a shawl and conversed with the Wandering Jew. For an hour. Through the wall.

"He plans to return my purse at 3." Her tone resounded of "I told you so."

And Robert's of sarcasm. "A singularly honorable thief."

She then scoured the hotel for a Mr. Shoemaker in 137, insisting he had called, ignoring the manager's assurance there was no guest registered by that name, nor any such room, and continued issuing strange reports throughout the afternoon. The windows boded ill. Voices were coming from the floors. Chicago's South Side was in flames.

As Spring progressed and the buds bloomed, so did Mother's eccentricities. She was mixing medications, dosing liberally; shopping daily, purchasing recklessly; carrying cash in large sums. She saw strangers lurking in hallways, molesters; she wanted the tallest waiter in the dining room sent to protect her; she was making a spectacle of herself. Again.

So Robert sought expert advice. And brought in some Pinkerton men.

▦ ◈ ▨

When he awoke on April 14th, Robert resolved not to keep checking his watch. He breakfasted at home, on dry toast and tea, read the news. Looked at the clock.

Ten years ago this moment their final family breakfast had begun. Father had come loping in, Mother's face brightened as she looked at him. *Dear husband, your cheerfulness startles me!*

Bob had slept in uniform.

Pa encouraged him to continue at Harvard Law, said one day they'd hang a shingle out; he'd chuckled over a humor piece, read some passages aloud,

344

then cleared his schedule until 11 o'clock to spend two hours with his eldest son.

It was the longest time they'd spent together since before the war. Robert blinked. The words blurred. Lips trembling behind his beard, he watched as one salty tear plopped on the page, making the ink run.

Mother's personal physician called in early May. They visited pleasantly. She described the climate and customs of the South, the scenery and food, the poison in her coffee, the Wandering Jew. The doctor pronounced her physically well but deranged.

Letters were exchanged. First with her eldest sister, who knew better than anyone what he was up against. But she was recuperating from surgery and unable to oversee "someone of unsound mind."

Mother's first cousin—his father's first law partner—opined. He agreed his cousin was insane, and control of her money should be taken away.

Neither of them thought she ought to be confined.

By then awash in worry and battling to manage his own mounting distress, Bob brought in a team of specialists.

The doctors—the top thinkers in mental health—believed her fear of fire posed a very real threat. Individuals with this phobia were known to defenestrate themselves.

The lawyers—all former colleagues of his father—cautioned of potential bankruptcy, the onslaught of more publicity. The threat to her safety.

And yet, he resisted the idea of restraint. In Illinois male relatives could not simply declare a woman insane and take over her affairs, a case had to be made; jurors empaneled, a conservator named. And all in the public glare. The thought wrenched his gut.

Robert consulted the Judge.

He'd been like a second father in the decade since that very dreadful night, as together they'd settled his father's estate, and afterward, for support and advice.

The Judge recommended she be institutionalized.

All the advisers met on May 16th. Her personal physician reported what he'd observed over the past year and a half.

"Your mother said Indians were pulling wires from her eyes..."

"She was describing her headaches," Robert snapped. "Mother has very figurative habits of speech."

"Of course." The doctor scanned the page, reluctant to proceed. "She said they removed her cheekbones, sometimes lifting her scalp like a flap—"

Robert's hands shot up. "Enough." The thought of his mother's soft, smooth skin being sliced brought forth a strangled sound, a cross between sob and cough.

The doctors and lawyers eyed each other, then their laps. The noon whistle blew. Robert drew a deep breath, composed himself. "That will do."

Then he detailed her behavior—not the worst offenses, just what sufficed to make the case, events witnesses could corroborate. The rampages through the hotel, the mixed medications and shopping sprees, her tenuous grasp on reality, and all the men agreed. The widow was insane.

Still, Robert equivocated. The guards always had her in sight, her purchases were being returned, she was enjoying robust health—was it essential she be confined?

Apparently, it was. On the 18th of May, Pinkerton reported strange men in Mother's room—sharpers, Bob presumed. She had amassed a thousand in cash and was talking about another trip—to Europe or California this time—with $56,000 in securities and bonds sewn into her petticoats. She'd always been a talented seamstress. Now, she was also a flight risk. A walking target for charlatans and flatterers, criminals and thugs. She'd be taken advantage of. Forcibly robbed. Or worse.

With that gruesome specter dangling over his head like Damocles' sword on a thread, the orders were filed.

The night before the trial, Robert gulped some bicarb, took off his collar and smoked a cigar in the gloaming. Listening to neighbor children play—his were still away— watching fragrant wisps disappear in the breeze, evoked hazy fragments of memories, of pretend sword fights, Mama calling from the window, "Gramercy brave knights!" He must have been five, his first brother was alive. Those were happy times. He could barely call them to mind, obscured as they were by more recent scenes: Mama brushing his middle brother's fevered forehead with her lips; the boy in his coffin, the click of the lid; then murmuring endearments in her dying husband's ear, stroking his bloodied hair; finally, grasping Bob's hand as his last brother pitched headlong from that damnable chair, facing death like the man he'd never live to be, only Robert was spared, why he?

He almost cried it aloud, but that would be tantamount to prayer, and Robert had always quietly questioned whether Anyone was there.

*What fates impose, that men must needs abide; it boots not to resist both wind and tide.* That's what Pa would say. The man had a Shakespeare quotation for every occasion.

Robert went inside.

But sleep would not come, the latch had been sprung, the visions emerged unbidden. The last time he saw his father standing upright. There were open seats in the box, would Bob like to see a comedy tonight?

Such a small request. With such enormous consequence.

Just back from the front, Robert had ridden all the previous day on muddy roads. So he declined.

Disappointment splashed across his father's craggy face; so unlike his. "That's fine," Pa said, "Forget I asked. The captain needs his rest!" Then he'd pulled on his gloves that never fit, flexed his fingers, made a fist. "I wish *I* didn't have to go."

But the commitment was made. His parents went to the play and met their fate, or more precisely, it snuck up on them from behind, while they were otherwise engaged, laughing, holding hands.

A decade later, Bob understood; that mention of his rank was the clue. Pa wanted to bask in paternal pride, to arrive at the theatre with his son at his side, in his officer's uniform. The band would have played, the crowd would have roared, and Bob would have been sitting next to the door. Where he could have changed history's course.

He imagined how it might unfold. During the second act his father would rise and draw on his coat; lately he was always cold. Act Three would commence: amusing dialogue, satiric wit; then a movement behind him, the draperies would shift; a form would emerge, a short struggle would ensue; Bob would get the gun, take the bullet from the chamber—there was only one— then he'd wave the impotent weapon aloft as Pa seized that sniveling piece of human waste by the scruff of his neck and his scrotum and hurled him onto the stage, deftly missing all the actors, but breaking *both* his legs.

On Wednesday afternoon, the 19th of May, Robert walked from his law office at Lake and Wabash to the Cook County Courthouse at LaSalle and Adams to see his mother arraigned. No, not arraigned; more precisely, committed. Declared legally insane.

Unbeknownst to her, she'd be brought before a jury. Evidence would be heard. Her assets would be removed from her skirts, Robert would be appointed conservator, and she would henceforth be supervised, getting rest, proper care, and exercise, in pleasant surroundings with a river view; he'd ordered the bars on the windows removed.

Robert's mother and his lawyer arrived at court, a step ahead of police escort.

It had taken an hour to coax, then coerce her into the carriage. Only the threat of handcuffs had finally reined her in, tears streaming as she vilified her captors and petitioned her saviors, spewing bitter invective upon her evil, ungrateful spawn, and still they sat together, the lawyers, son and mother, as the witnesses testified: the doctors, local merchants, the hotel employees, each revelation bringing the reporters to the edge of their seats; the mother's delusions, the son's anxiety, their shared, eternal grief.

Robert unfolded a handkerchief in the stifling heat, straightened in his chair, straightened his tie, tried to breathe. Soon he'd be called to do his manly duty, and he would discharge it with propriety. This was the commitment he had made, to protect his mother's safety, and honor his father's memory; this was the privilege and burden of being who he was, the guardian of his family's peculiar place in history.

Later the papers would describe his pallor, his despondency, the sorrow in his eyes, the fact that twice he broke down weeping as he testified; and yet, when he was called to the stand, the firstborn and last living son of Abraham Lincoln and Mary Todd raised his right hand and swore to tell the truth and nothing but, so help him God.

# The Not-So-Secret Admirer

by Irma Maria Olmedo

"You have a package in the mailroom," read the text on my phone as I entered my condo. When I returned to the lobby, I was surprised to find a large box labeled "Flowers from California." It wasn't Mother's Day nor my birthday. Donna, my daughter, had been sending passion fruit and guava from her garden since Bob died. And now flowers?

I needed a grocery cart to take the heavy box upstairs. How astonished I was to find ten beautiful bouquets, so many different types and a rainbow of colors: hot pink carnations, roses, lilies, and mums. I filled three large vases and their sweet fragrances perfumed my living room. There was no card nor return address. If they weren't from Donna's garden, they must have been quite expensive.

I pulled out my phone. "Donna, these are lovely flowers. Did you send them?"

"No, Mom, it wasn't me," she replied. "Maybe you have a secret admirer."

A secret admirer? My son, Daniel, who lived on the same block as I did, would bring me flowers rather than mail them. Bob, my husband of 50 years, and main admirer, had passed away two years previously and I was still mourning the loss. For a moment, I entertained a sweet but haunting thought that I was a recipient of flowers from beyond the grave.

But the thought of my husband reminded me of an email I had received two weeks earlier from my old college friend, Frankie, asking if I had received the flowers. I told him I had not, and he said he would follow up.

Perhaps these were the flowers Frankie was talking about. But he lives in Puerto Rico. And there were so many flowers, a fortune's worth, not what I would expect from an old friend from so long ago.

When I emailed Frankie asking if he had sent me flowers, he was pleased that I had finally received them. I texted him a photo of the three vases full of his extravagance.

349

He congratulated me on the publication of my book. He was sorry the flowers had not arrived by February 14, as he had intended.

February 14? Valentine's Day? I wondered about the date and my curiosity was piqued.

On her next phone call, Donna asked who had sent the flowers and I told her Frankie had sent them. She knew I had dated Frankie back in college, before meeting Bob, and we had exchanged emails after I sent out an announcement of my book, *Tales from the Barrio and Beyond.*

"But you sent your book announcement last April. Why flowers now, ten months later, and near Valentine's Day? Sounds suspicious to me."

"Yeah, that's funny." I shrugged off her subtle suggestion that Frankie might have another motive for his gift.

Frankie and I had not been in contact for many years before my book announcement. He had congratulated me and we wrote each other updates on our lives. I emailed him that I had a son, daughter, and granddaughter, and that my husband Bob had passed away two years ago of cancer. He emailed me he had two sons, a daughter and a grandson, and that his wife had been in a rehab home recovering from surgery. We exchanged long emails about our kids, grandkids, careers, health, world travels and related issues.

Frankie and I knew each other in the 1960s, as undergraduates at City College in New York. He was the comedian, always cracking jokes and laughing about things that happened in or out of class. He probably made up some of the stories just to be funny. He enjoyed making fun of professors of Spanish whose idiomatic expressions came directly from classical Spanish literature and made no sense to native New York Spanish speakers.

Back then, I was thrilled when Frankie invited me to dances at the Ecuadorian Club where his mother was an officer and where there often was live Latin music. He was a good dancer, as was I. The club was one of the few places where my very strict, old-fashioned father allowed me to go. Since I had few opportunities to date, Frankie was rather special and I developed a crush on him. But he was a flirt and many girls, especially non-Latinas, ran around with him. No way could I compete with their "Americano" ways, given my conservative upbringing. Still, he kept inviting me out. Maybe it was his mother's idea. She was Puerto Rican and probably wanted club members to see him with a nice Puerto Rican girl. I was the good girl all mothers loved.

After college in 1965, Frankie enlisted in a military program to avoid the war in Vietnam. We corresponded occasionally and I began entertaining the idea of something more coming of this friendship. We went out a few times when he was home, but I don't remember having any serious talks about the future.

In 1968, while Frankie was still away, I met Bob, a graduate student from Ohio who was pursuing a doctoral degree in philosophy at Columbia University. Falling in love was unexpected and wonderful. It was quite a surprise, meeting someone with whom I had so much in common and who shared a mutual attraction. Like me, Bob had an academic persona, enjoyed discussing books, politics, civil rights, war and peace, and controversies of the late 1960s.

Bob and I planned a December wedding since he had accepted a teaching position in Wisconsin. Frankie and his mother came to the wedding and he celebrated by catching the garter. I was ecstatic about my wedding and hoped that Frankie would also meet someone special.

We took our honeymoon in Puerto Rico, where Bob had never been. The island was bathed in sunshine and inviting beaches. We enjoyed a second celebration at my uncle's home, where Bob took a deep dive into my Puerto Rican culture with his introduction to all our holiday delicacies. He was quite a hit when he asked for seconds of pickled green bananas with gizzards and blood sausage—rather exotic for a gringo from the Midwest. Fortunately, he had lived in Ethiopia one summer and been exposed to many types of foods there. He was adventuresome and not put off by our *Boricua* specialties.

After a few years in Wisconsin, Bob accepted a college teaching position in Ohio and in 1975, we went to Puerto Rico with our two-year old daughter, Donna, to celebrate Christmas with my parents and sister who had moved back to the Island.

"I have a surprise," my sister, Eleni, said excitedly.

Who should it be but Frankie, his wife Nellie, and their two-year-old son, whom Eleni had invited to lunch. We spent that pleasant afternoon reminiscing about our college years and celebrating our new lives, happily married and with children.

Over the years, when I visited Puerto Rico, I occasionally ran into Frankie. Once when I was there for a conference, Frankie and Nellie invited me to join them for a dance. Nellie was charming and even encouraged Frankie to dance with me. I remembered how much I had enjoyed dancing with him in my early 20s. That seemed ages ago, a very different life than the one I was living now. The memories of those occasions were sweet and lovely.

Our next contact was in 2020 when I announced the publication of my book. It had been almost 50 years since I had married and two years since Bob had passed away. I was spending a lot of time on the telephone sharing my sorrow with other widowed friends.

In December 2020, I emailed Frankie a link to a beautiful YouTube program from the Chicago Lyric Opera with Ana Maria Martinez, a great Puerto Rican soprano. "You had told me that Nellie loves opera and I'm sure she'll enjoy it," I wrote.

"She'll have to listen to it with the angels," Frankie responded. "Nellie passed away last week, shortly after our 52nd wedding anniversary."

I was shocked by his news and expressed my deep condolences. I didn't ask a lot of questions, not wanting to pry at his time of grief. We continued to email, now having in common the loss of a long-time marital partner. I sent him some books on the grief process that affirmed the importance of acknowledging one's feelings of loss, disorientation, anger, even rage. There was no rushing towards what some referred to as "closure." The books helped me deal with comments such as "he's in a better place" or "one day you'll be together again."

Friends may have thought those were comforting words but they often had the opposite effect. It was difficult not to shout back, "Oh, shut your mouth! You have no idea what it's like to lose the love of your life."

I didn't ask Frankie whether he read the books or found them helpful. People have many different responses to grief and it's best to give others freedom to react as is appropriate for them.

In late April, 2021, I received a second large box of flowers. Frankie wished me a happy Mother's Day. I appreciated his thoughtfulness in sending flowers, beautiful lilies which opened up into a deep rich purple. What a joy looking at such gorgeous flowers every morning! I placed one of the vases on the windowsill looking out at the stunning views of Lake Michigan and texted Frankie a photo.

Yet, this joy was tempered as I remembered how excited Bob and I had been to buy this condo because of the views of Lake Michigan, with so many shades of blue when the sun shone that we both wished we had been painters to catch the hues with our palettes. I mourned that Bob enjoyed those views for less than a year before passing away. This sorrow was always with me whenever I experienced something wonderful that I wanted to share with him. Even the flowers that Frankie sent reminded me of how much I missed my Bob.

Frankie's flowers and attention helped me deal with the isolation of Covid and my grief. Covid had taken its toll on everyone and was especially hard for me, as it put a hold on my developing new friendships and getting out into the world to experience life without Bob. Even flying to California to be with my daughter and granddaughter was unwise given our fear of Covid. My son, who lived down the block, was reluctant to come over because of the risk of infecting me at my vulnerable age. I had to cope as best I could at home alone.

It was important to find an escape from my grief and mourning, to acknowledge that my life would go on. Frankie and I had each had a full life, had lost our lifetime loves, and were now alone. The emails between us became playful and flirtatious. It was fun to reminisce about our youth and to tease each other. I confessed that I'd had a crush on him when I was 21. He responded that he was aware of it but didn't want me to get conceited if he paid me too much attention. Frankie would ask what island in the Caribbean I would select for my birthday or Christmas holidays. I would respond that I preferred the Great Barrier Reef off the coast of Australia, one of my most exciting trips with Bob.

In May, I received a beautiful photography book from Frankie, *Wild Flowers of Puerto Rico*. I didn't know the island had so many gorgeous wildflowers and that someone appreciated them enough to publish a book about them. Though I love fresh flowers, these flowers in the book will not fade and die. In the long run, they may be more meaningful than the live flowers that die after one or two weeks.

In June, another surprise—a box with white roses, carnations, Peruvian lilies, blue delphinium, baby's breath and assorted greenery. No special occasion now, so why the flowers?

"Just to celebrate our friendship," was Frankie's email response.

Well, such a long-lasting friendship, longer than each of our marriages, is worth celebrating.

Late in June, I received the fourth box in four months, a delightful lavender bouquet with accents of pink. I asked Frankie why he kept sending me such gorgeous flowers.

"Just because," was Frankie's response.

One rather cold and rainy day in Chicago, I texted Frankie an updated photo of his flowers and added, "My living room is sunny with your flowers."

Frankie responded, *Tú eres el sol que le da vida con tu aura a esas flores.* "You are the sun that gives life to those flowers with your spirit."

"I knew you were an architect, Frankie, but I didn't know you were also a poet," I replied, smiling to myself. What a wonderful *piropo*. Other than smile to myself, I didn't know how else to respond. I had rather ambivalent feelings about this flirtation. This was such a new experience given that I had been happily married for 50 years. Of course, I enjoyed receiving beautiful flowers. What woman doesn't? And coming from someone I had a crush on when I was 21 was a special treat. Too bad I had not received those gorgeous flowers back then when they would have indicated some reciprocal romantic feelings on Frankie's part.

Donna was enjoying the flowers from afar almost as much as I was. She knew the grief process I was coping with was long-lasting and intense. Bob and I had had a wonderful marriage and I had difficulty accepting that he was no longer in my life.

"Mom, I'm happy with this little adventure in your life. But I'm ready to ask Frankie about his intentions," she wrote.

I shared Donna's comment with Frankie. As the jokester he had always been, he responded, "My intentions? Rather wicked!"

For my birthday in July, Frankie sent me a lovely arrangement of pink roses. In addition, another gift: a FaceTime call from Frankie, whom I had not seen in over 15 years. We had been in contact only via email and it was a treat to chat face to face. I could hear the *coquis*, Puerto Rican tree frogs, singing in the trees surrounding his house. He had not changed physically that much—a little less hair, a few more wrinkles, a little leaner. His personality was still the same; he still cracked jokes and chuckled. When I mentioned that a friend had invited me to visit her in Maui, he asked me to send him a photo on the beach wearing a thong; I quipped in a similar vein, "only when you send me one of yourself in a bikini on a beach in Puerto Rico." We both laughed.

We had both changed since our undergraduate years. I had obtained a doctoral degree and become a university professor. I had been shy and insecure as an undergraduate. Now in my 70s, I have strong views and am not reticent to defend them. As a professor, I have given talks internationally about my research, my self-confidence growing each time. In my twenties, I considered myself skinny and not very attractive. In my 70s, I'm proud of being slim and in relatively good shape. I'm even pleased with my gray hair, which Donna describes as "silver highlights."

During my marriage, my interests and tastes also changed. When I was single, I did not care for opera. Bob was an opera lover so we attended operas regularly, and I developed a love for the music, the drama, and the intensity of human emotions portrayed. I would tease Bob, saying that opera was a very Latino thing with its exploration of human emotions and passions: love, hate, jealousy, faithfulness, betrayal, grief, honor, longing, and loneliness.

Frankie also has changed. He has given talks about his architectural work in Europe, Latin America, and Asia. We share stories about our international travels, expressing our preferences for one country or another. It's fun reflecting on where we would like to live "when we grow up." He engages me in discussions about climate change and differential effects on infrastructure on places like Chicago and Puerto Rico, with sound advice on dangers of investing in beachfront real estate.

Today, Frankie works for a non-profit on the reconstruction of Puerto Rican infrastructure after the hurricanes. Even though he is of retirement age, he considers the work a personal mission. As an architect and planner, he has skills that few on the Island possess and are in great demand. He is so engaged he does not think he'll ever retire.

Neither Frankie nor I is very religious, but our sorrow at widowhood raises questions about our spiritual beliefs. What does it mean if over time one has recurring dreams about a deceased spouse, as I often do? At what point will we see that light at the end of the tunnel of grief, as Isabel Allende wrote about on the death of her daughter, Paula? What remains of a love that one has lived for over 50 years, two-thirds of one's lifetime, when one of you dies?

FaceTime is inadequate for Frankie and me to have such serious reflections about our grief over our deceased spouses. We need to engage in those conversations in person. Can we plan such a visit after Covid? I haven't been to Puerto

Rico in a long time, though Bob and I used to go every Christmas. Frankie hasn't been to Chicago in many years. But I wonder where such a visit would lead. Where is this adventure going? I have no idea and neither, I suspect, does Frankie. Dare I call it a budding romance? This relationship has been so gratifying but when I think of taking it further, I'm torn by memories of Bob and the life we built together.

I nevertheless daydream about possibilities for the future: a trip to Lisbon, one of Frankie's favorite cities, with its *fados*, tasty seafood, and sparkling wines; or a trip to Venice, one of Bob's favorites, with its intriguing architecture, delicious food, and the lure of a romantic evening on a gondola! We both celebrate what we still have, memories of loving and faithful spouses and a wonderful married life that we have both been blessed to live. For now, it may be enough just to have fun and enjoy the moment for what it is—unchartered, uncertain, and as Frankie volunteers, "All our clean living rewarded. Hahaha!"

# Trailing Blood

by Susan Cousins Breen

The last thing I remember was sitting on the toilet. And then I wasn't.

As I struggled to get up, the room blurred, and the floor tilted at an awkward angle. Bright crimson filled the toilet. Its dampness stained my nightgown, and then I knew why darkness had pulled me to the floor.

It was 1977, and about two weeks after Shawn's birth—hardly enough time to adapt to being a 25-year-old, first-time mother—when the hemorrhaging began, six years after the last episode. The new role took all my strength, and I assumed that being so tired and disoriented was part of having a baby. But it was the prolonged postpartum bleeding that drained my energy day by day—weakening me more than I knew.

I had moved through the first weeks of Shawn's life weak and light-headed, floating through the motions of caring for him. Looking in the mirror, my paleness startled me. How I managed to gently bathe Shawn in his little white tub and cradle him during feedings, I do not know.

I struggled to my feet and began the journey through our apartment, hanging onto the wall, the shower door, the door jam. In the hallway, I moved toward Shawn's room, fingers clinging to the wall, determined to reach the black rotary phone sitting on the table at the far end of the apartment. I careened from doorframe to piano bench to table. Passing Shawn's tiny blue-gingham room, I was relieved to see him sleeping quietly.

I dropped onto the sofa and called Kathy, my next-door neighbor. The seven numbers whirred slowly around the rotary dial. "Hello?" *Thank God, she's home.* "I keep fainting…there's so much blood… He's in his crib…," I mumbled into the phone.

Kathy came through the door with a neighbor, who had a car. Soon I was in Clara Maass Hospital. My obstetrician, Dr. B., barked stern, staccato orders about IV drips and blood type to the nurses hovering nearby.

357

My husband Gary arrived, thanks to his boss who had rushed him to the hospital. Shaken by my pallor and incoherence, Gary turned to Dr. B., "What the hell is going on? I thought the D&C [Dilation and Curettage] was going to fix this."

"I'm afraid I don't know," said my doctor, who had performed a D&C the week before, hoping to curtail the bleeding. "There must be an underlying hematological problem. I've called in a specialist, and we've started a platelet transfusion. It will take several pints of plasma to stabilize her."

Dr. P., the hematologist, arrived, spoke briefly with the obstetrician, then turned his attention to me, pulling down the lower rim of my left eye and then the right. "There's no red around the whites of your eyes, because you've lost so much blood," he explained.

The doctor cranked up the head of the bed; his features blurred, and his words became garbled. I struggled to remain conscious. The room began to pitch like a car on a roller coaster. "I'm sliding off the bed!" I cried out. Dr. P. quickly rolled the bed flat, and the room settled back into place.

"You don't have enough blood to remain conscious when your head is higher than your body," Dr. P. explained. "We'll do some tests and a clotting time to pinpoint the problem. You'll feel better after the transfusions."

While the doctors talked with Gary in the hall, a nurse who had been with me since the ER shook her head and said, "The way you looked when they brought you in, we didn't think you had a chance. You were fading fast!"

The tests showed a platelet defect. Dr. P said, "We know enough to make your blood clot for now and to get you home to your son. When you are feeling better, and Shawn is older," he advised, "make an appointment, and we'll isolate the details of the abnormality."

Shawn was five years old by the time I made the appointment.

There was an explanation—at last—for why a simple tonsillectomy when I was five had turned into a nightmarish emergency despite a typical recovery at St. Mary's Hospital. After two days at home, I began vomiting. As I clung to the toilet, the sea of red frightened me, as did the fear I heard in my mother's voice as she called out, "Bobby, it's not stopping." I remember hearing my father dial the phone and ask for an ambulance. In their panic my parents hurried my little sister, Allyson, and me into our black Buick, sitting at the curb, before the ambulance arrived.

Shortly after, Dad carried me back into St. Mary's, and a nun whisked my gurney down the hall to the emergency room. I do not know how the doctors stopped the flow but recall conversations about transfusions. These were the first of more than a dozen transfusions that would pour life back into me in the years to come.

For a week, I was the only patient in a three-bed room in the children's ward. Confined to bed and anchored to an IV pole, I spent long lonely days waiting for my parents to come. Oddly, I do not recall Mom's visits—she was home with three-and-a-half-year-old Allyson and did not drive—but she must have come. Except for the nurses checking on me and daily visits from Dr. M., I was alone for most of each day. How did I occupy myself? Did Mom bring toys from home? A coloring book and crayons? Picture books?

Around five o'clock, the clanging of staff yanking meal trays from metal carts signaled the arrival of dinner, and soon, my dad. As the minutes ticked by, I leaned as far as I could over the bedrail, straining for a glimpse of him in his business suit through the window next to my bed. When my legs tired, I peered into the large, round mirror, strategically placed at the end of the hall, providing the nurses with a view of each room, and me a glimpse of my dad's dark, wavy hair as soon as he turned onto the hallway.

⊠ ✿ ⊠

When I was 18, I was in the cardiac care unit of a New York City hospital after open-heart surgery to repair an atrial septal defect—a hole in my heart. Coming out of eight hours of anesthesia, it felt like someone was patting my chest where I imagined the incision to be. As the effects of the sedation eased, I saw that my feeling was correct: a blurry figure soaked up the crimson fluid as it seeped from the incision. The nurse laid the soiled cloth on a tray, picked up a clean one, and resumed lightly blotting the wound.

It is not possible to relay the trauma of heart surgery in 1971. My parents did not prepare me for all that would happen during and after the surgery. I woke to a 12-inch incision down the center of my chest, a broken sternum, wires crisscrossing the bed, and a breathing tube gagging me. And I heard a nurse ordering "More blood, stat." A bag of plasma arrived and a transfusion began. Within minutes, a tremendous coldness enveloped me, and I began shaking uncontrollably. Until then, no one knew I had received the wrong blood type. Through tears, I mouthed, "Get my parents!" But no sound came out.

I remember Dad holding my hand. Mom came in briefly during the first hour. I saw the shock in her eyes when she viewed the blood-soaked cloths covering my torso, and then, quickly left. Now, as a parent, I can understand her reaction, knowing that her daughter, fresh out of heart surgery, was hemorrhaging.

Two weeks later, still in the hospital, a nurse had to force me to look in the mirror at my incision. As an 18-year-old, I understood that hemorrhaging could have grave consequences. In my gut, I also knew I would never be the same after the trauma of doctors making a 12-inch slice between breasts to which I'd only recently become accustomed.

Married eight years, my husband and I had been thinking about having another child. But did I really want to get pregnant again after the experience following Shawn's birth? At the age of 30, I don't recall giving it much thought. It was Gary who was wary of trying again, afraid of losing me.

But first, I needed to complete the hematological testing begun five years prior. The follow-up appointment was long overdue. Until now there had not seemed to be any rush to get a diagnosis. It was clear: I had been in denial about the need to isolate the type of platelet defect that I had. This information could mean the difference between life and death with the next delivery or surgery.

Perched on a stool in the hematology lab of a Philadelphia hospital, I began the process of learning which defect caused the uncontrolled bleeding. The technician had already drawn tube after tube of my blood and was now setting out supplies for the clotting time test.

This was my second appointment of the day. I had met with Hematologist Dr. T., who would identify the disorder with the help of lab work and the clotting time test, which measures platelet function and how quickly the small vessels allow clotting.

The technician placed a small plastic device on my forearm and pressed down on a button in the middle. There was a clicking sound, and she removed the device to reveal four quarter-inch cuts on my skin. Partially inflating the blood pressure cuff on my arm, she set a timer for 15 minutes because, as she explained, "If you're still bleeding after 15 minutes there's no point in continuing the test. In an accident or during surgery, it is already an emergency if you haven't stopped by then."

Six-to-nine minutes was within the normal range.

As we waited, an uncomfortable silence permeated the lab, and the technician repeatedly blotted the cuts on the inside of my forearm. My heart beat just a bit quicker as nine minutes ticked by, and we moved out of the "normal range."

After six weeks of testing, Dr. T. explained the diagnosis, "Storage Pool Disease is a platelet defect in which your clotting ability is at best inconsistent and, at worst, doesn't have the factor needed to maintain a clot. We don't see this very often."

Not long after this, I received the first recommendation to get a medical alert bracelet. Other doctors gave the same advice, following prolonged bleeding episodes.

Doctors have described the disease as a "mild" bleeding disorder. But a bleeding disorder is only mild when you're not bleeding. Once the flow begins and the platelets fail to work, the situation becomes serious quickly. I bruise easily. There is prolonged oozing with superficial injuries. I have menstrual periods that are abnormally long. Intraoperative and post-operative bleeding often occurs. Unpredictability is a quirk of this congenital defect. For instance, doctors cannot predict when platelets might malfunction during surgery. According to my hematologist, few patients with Storage Pool Disease have enough surgeries to establish the disease's reaction rate for them. In my case, the disease's impact was easy to track. Uncontrolled bleeding had occurred with childbirth and several surgeries but did not accompany three other surgeries.

Dr. T. also pointed out, "Storage Pool Disease isn't likely to present during childbirth."

I was about to learn for the second time that this statistic did not apply to me.

A year-and-a-half later, it was a week before my due date. Gary had left for work; Shawn, now six, was on his way to school. It was an early Fall morning, and I was pulling on a pair of shorts when I began to bleed. My first call was to Gary, my second to Dr. K., the obstetrician.

At the hospital, there was a flurry of activity: an examination, an ultrasound, and then, a decision to deliver the baby. There were forms to sign and another speedy trip down a hospital hallway. Before the anesthesia took effect, Dr. E., our pediatrician, held my hand, assuring me that my baby would be fine.

When I awoke, my husband whispered, "It's all over hon, we have a little girl."

Two hours later in recovery, I heard moaning, unaware that the sound was coming from me. Dr. K. ordered lab work. Stat. Then I heard him say: "Her blood count has dropped significantly. We will have to go back in." Turning to the nurse, Dr. K. said, "Bring in Mrs. Breen's baby so she can hold her one last time."

Frantically, I grabbed Gary's hand when Dr. K. asked if there was anyone my husband wanted to call. "Call my parents," I remember saying. By the time I returned to the recovery room, they were there, escorted by a state trooper— the fastest they had ever made the 95-mile trip. Gary, Mom, and Dad looked drained and very relieved.

Again, platelet transfusions revived me.

In 1986, hoping to end three-week-long menstrual periods, I traveled to Detroit with Gary for a new procedure. Dr. G., a Sinai Hospital gynecologist who had developed endometrial laser ablation, used a laser to burn away the cells of the uterine lining. The next morning, we were back on a plane heading home. The ideal outcome would have been a complete cessation of menstruation. For two years, I was period–free until enough cells had regenerated and my periods returned. Four years later, a partial hysterectomy offered a permanent solution.

In 1989, I needed sinus surgery and my ears, nose, and throat doctor wanted a hematological workup beforehand. Dr. S., a world-renowned hematologist at the University of Pennsylvania Medical Center, offered hope. Brilliant and soft-spoken, Dr. S. was an expert on DDAVP (desmopressin acetate), a recently approved drug. DDAVP sounded like a miracle, and it has been when I have needed a procedure or surgery. Although a part of me still worries that I could hemorrhage, DDAVP has prevented prolonged bleeding in most instances since it became part of my pre-surgery regimen.

For decades, Storage Pool Disease has been part of my life's baggage. The diagnosis has made me more cautious, wary of the sharp edges on open cans and handling knives each time I prepare a meal. A cut can trigger a panicked thought: *Will the bleeding stop, or will this be the time that doctors cannot halt the hemorrhaging?*

Despite the fear of bleeding to death, I haven't been motivated to complete the application for a medical alert bracelet. It has laid on my desk for years, the edges of the application curling; the prices surely outdated by now.

With each episode, doctors remind me that I should have a medical alert bracelet. I always replied with a sigh, "I know," and resolve to order one. I have said it often, even written about it, and yet, I have not done so.

I reach out to Penny, my longtime therapist, who is familiar with the nuisances of my life. She asks two questions, "How would it feel to wear a medical alert bracelet? What would it mean to you?"

"The heaviness of the bracelet on my wrist would be a burden, representing the weight of the illness—physical and emotional reminders of why I wear it," I say, surprised at how easily an explanation comes to me.

"Knowing your perfectionism," Penny says, "I suspect you see the bracelet as acknowledgement that there's something wrong with you. By wearing the bracelet, the disorder will become a focal point, because up to now only family and close friends know about the Storage Pool Disease. You view the bracelet as a physical and emotional burden, but in truth it's a blessing, ensuring that you will get the help you need in an emergency."

It occurs to me that by not acknowledging the need for a medical alert bracelet for so many years, I have unwittingly increased the risk for a tragedy.

■ ● ■

As I retrace the trail of blood that has tainted the path of my life, I pause, quietly dig out the application for a medical alert bracelet, smooth the wrinkled pages, and begin filling in the information with a steady hand. I seal and stamp the envelope, rise from my desk, and head downstairs to enjoy the rest of the day.

# Of an Orange

by Nancy Chadwick

At the kitchen counter on a radiant winter morning, I scraped the shiny skin of an orange with a nifty zester. A waft of citrus exploded as the oily peel moved back and forth along the coarse bumps of the metal plate, raining orange sprinkles onto scone dough. When I breathed the scent, a connection from smell to taste ignited. My mouth watered, inviting me to take a bite from the fruit's flesh. At that moment, the delicacies of taste and touch and smell, of life, reawakened a memory. I settled my busy hands and recalled that day in July when sunlight and an orange were a ray of joy in otherwise dark days.

"You'll like the room," I said to you the day before. And when we arrived on that summer day, you nodded your head in satisfaction upon your first introduction to walls painted in dark green, a rectangular window with gold patterned curtains anchoring its sides, three nightstands, four chairs, and a heavy round pedestal table in dark wood. I, however, saw a dirty window you would later cite for neglect, dusty trails in the folds of the curtains, and misarranged furniture. Though the thin floor covering was a carpet in name only, it was sufficient for you to acknowledge that it elevated the room's status.

I promptly rearranged the room to make it more inviting: the third nightstand became an end table between two chairs, the pedestal table rounded a corner, and the remaining pair of chairs hugged a wall for multi-functional use.

"Do you like your new living space?" I asked.

*Who was I kidding? A "living" space?*

I glanced at the Kalanchoe flowering plant with its deep hunter green leaves and pink blooms sitting atop the table. I thought you could take care of each other. And then I thought how this green thing would live on when you would not.

I settled you into a hard-backed chair near your bed while I equipped the small bathroom where three towel bars on dirty-pink walls were lined up unevenly on your left side, a comfortable familiar as they were also on the left side in your bathroom at home. From a plastic Target bag, I took out Colgate

365

toothpaste in minty fresh green, Poligrip, the one with the green stripe along the tube, and laid them on a shiny steel shelf above the matching sink. I then set a bottle of antibacterial liquid soap with aloe next to the teeth-cleaning products before opening a fresh bar of Dove soap, in white for sensitive skin, from its box. I settled the last item in the bag, a black comb, in front of the line-up.

Reading from left to right, your hygiene products were little comforts from your life at home, but big in what had always been important to you—presentation of yourself to others. Your younger self had always dressed in scents and color as part of your attire—a spritz or two of Nina Ricci from neck to torso, painted nails in carnation pink, deep lily on your lips, and cotton candy on your cheeks. Perhaps you'd include a patterned scarf, in a pallet of Monet encircling your neck, to frame it all.

"I bought you new towels, in mint green, your favorite," I yelled from the bathroom doorway. I wasn't sure you heard me. I looked at you sitting stiff, your face dressed in fear while you scanned the unfamiliar setting. The never-used-by-anyone-else towels were more for my comfort than yours. The accents of green made me think of your love of plants and flowers and trees—of life. But then there was the white of the soap and the black of the comb. Pure living. Murky dying.

Two steps across from the bathroom, I slid open the closet door. You watched me hang your clothes on hangers, those padded ones you said don't stretch the shoulders. Because of your limited sight, I took care to group your favorite khakis with matching tops in red and pink, and cardigans of white and gray to help you dress. I then rested in an emotional heap.

You sighed and looked how I felt.

I groaned and must have looked how you felt.

The comfortableness of having your personal things near made me uncomfortable. In this unfamiliar room, the chair, the bed, the paintings on the wall—none of these were yours. And what was familiar—your clothes, your address book, your magnifying glass—was out of its place. Your connections to home had been misplaced, your possessions misguided and never to return.

*Were you comfortable? Will you be all right, here?*

Weeks later when I sat with you, I saw that your lunch tray was highlighted in bright summer sun, allowing you to see well the items placed before you on a table that hovered over your lap. You didn't need my help to spot the quartered orange nestled in a small plastic bowl—bypassing an egg salad sandwich cut on the diagonal, a clear cup of yellow Jell-O, and a bowl of chicken noodle soup.

How you once revered food! You showed your love for it by the hours you spent in the kitchen preparing three meals each day for Tim and me when we were kids. I watched you follow with precision each new dinner recipe from the *Good Housekeeping Cookbook*, noting the dish's success with a dogeared page. Now, in your golden years, your complete satisfaction in having iceberg lettuce with your thousand island dressing, a bit of water cracker with a slab of Brie cheese, and a double chardonnay in a single chardonnay wine glass, not necessarily in that order, has now become only a memory.

You grabbed each quarter's end and freed the citrus from their orange wrappers, biting into the dripping pulp. You swallowed hard and fast and welcomed more.

"Mmm, it's good, so cold," you told me, licking your lips.

I was overcome with relief to see your appetite return and to see a spark of enjoyment as you treaded through your darkening world. My mourning of you because you were no longer desiring food eased.

I popped from my chair sitting opposite you to search for a tissue in a bedside table drawer behind you. I pulled it open to see a small square box with a clear plastic cover, uncluttered among an emery board you once used to maintain a coifed image inclusive of tidy and filed nails, a Sharpie pen to write in thick black letters the names of your nurses, and an address book to stay connected to friends in the outside world. Inside the box was a rosary, the one of mother-of-pearl beads, that I had given to you many years ago from a trip to Rome and the Vatican. You thought the rosary, in the purest of holy white, would give you a front-row seat to be with God upon your death. You rolled each bead through your fingers, feeling the cross in your palm and couldn't feel a connection with God until the strand was in your hand.

Soon after I had settled you in your room, you realized you didn't have the "white one," as you called it, different from the other five rosaries you harbored in your apartment. You directed me back to your place to search for it. I wasn't surprised to find it where you said it would be. Your memory of its location told me of your connection to your faith. I had grabbed your magnifying glass and a wheel of hearing aid batteries, too, just in case.

But that was back then.

You stacked the spent orange quarters into the dish, and I wiped a trail of juice from your wrist.

And then we settled into our seats. Silence.

Your moments of joy ended.

"How could God do all these awful things in this world?" you asked, citing the suffering and deaths from a pandemic as a primary bad. You cried, "Why is God doing this to me?" You pleaded for answers I didn't have, then dropped your head into your open hands. I saw your anger at God was running in tandem with your impending death.

I realized a cruel reality: life as you had known it was ceasing. This contradicted my own view of Nature as a cyclical wonder of unending life. I thought of how hard you fought during your last weeks, of the pills to keep you alive, of an orange to keep you happy, of an Ensure to keep you healthy.

"Can I get you anything?" I asked. "I just want to make sure you are comfortable. Are you comfortable Mom?"

"Comfortable?"

You chuckled at the irony.

I cried inside because of the absurdity of my question. You could never be comfortable. Only death could promise that to you.

My tears welled. That you could forget your body harbored a cancerous growth that had choked the desire for food and enjoyment of every bite, a body that had lost its senses and its ability to breathe fully, to walk, to function.

Because of an orange.

And I could be reminded of the good of life.


The summer months of an umbrella of blue overhead and a full-button sun bled into the days of early fall that begged one to be outside in the middle of it all. Before leaving your room to enjoy the relaxing warmth you desired, you plunked your straw hat on your head, slipped on your Jackie-O sunglasses, and tucked a couple of tissues inside your shirtsleeve. It was a routine you counted on, a dressing up to go outside just as you had always done.

Pushing you in a wheelchair down the hall and onto the elevator felt as if we were running from the bonds of mortality in anticipation of freedom in an immortal world in full color and high definition. Many greeted you and told you how much they liked your hat. You smiled and waved to your admirers with your slender hand and bony fingers. How the wearing of a hat made you feel more of yourself, adorning you out of the person you had become—with thin fuzzy hair peeking from your temples—and into the person you once were—with tight chocolate curls tucked around your head.

Upon the swinging open of an automatic door, you caught a hot breeze, then tipped your head back to take in as much air as your inhale would allow, then exhaled in bliss. We found relief from the direct noon sun in the shade of overgrown dogwoods on the large circular patio dotted with a few weathered wood tables and chairs. I pulled up a chair, rested, then breathed the fresh air, letting out all the impurities of mind and spirit, as if to purge my body of what we had escaped. You sank lower in your seat.

And then we didn't speak but allowed our surveys of unruly tree limbs, parched earth, and a few pink roses withering on neglected bushes to direct our attention. Behind your black tinted sunglasses, your eyes absorbed the moments, spotting bird feeders that hosted fluttering sparrows and an occasional cardinal. You delighted in a scampering squirrel and how near it was to you. I saw how badly the trees needed pruning, dead bushes required extrication, a flower patch needed weeding, as a desperate call for a fresh landscape in color.

Though you and I were viewing the same scenery, you were realizing the good in the world, and I, nothing but the wrongness.

I didn't want to disturb the conversation you were having with yourself as I wondered what you were thinking. Were you wondering when you would die? Were you praying to die in your sleep? But it wasn't for me to ask. I respected your privacy.

I noted every deliberate breath you took, at first thinking it an alarm that you were in distress, but then recognizing it as confirmation that you were living in your moment.

"Being out here makes everything right with the world," you said, nodding your head.

Brimming tears slipped from under my sunglasses. I cried because I saw the softness in your face and calming of your words that told me you were making peace with yourself, the world, and maybe with your God.

Because of an orange to your tongue, a symphony of birds' songs in your ears, and a breeze to the face, that you could find joy, life, in a cold pulpy citrus, and a rightness with the world before your death the following month.

# Keep It to Your Shelf

by Sarah Ray Schwarcz

*Any book worth banning is a book worth reading.*
—Isaac Asimov

I welcomed a warm flood of hope as I turned a corner of a Vernon Hills bookstore aisle last month. A large kiosk filled with books recently banned in many locales blocked my path. Standing proud. Persistent. Available. The display took my breath away. I circled the table, nodding and smiling at the neatly stacked copies of *To Kill a Mockingbird, One Flew Over the Cuckoo's Nest, The Book Thief, Maus, The Handmaid's Tale, Heather Has Two Mommies,* and *Looking for Alaska.* Seeing these books comforted me. I had to squelch my desire to reach out and touch each one, to give it a special blessing and a thanks for all it taught me. Still somewhat shy in my eighth decade, I try to avoid odd glances from other shoppers. Plus—you know—Covid protocols.

An overwhelming emptiness engulfed me for a moment as I tried to imagine their absence in my life. Like trusted friends, those that I'd read had wakened my mind, engaged my interest, and taught me about life in myriad ways I could never directly experience. Forgetting about Covid for a split second, I reached out to touch the displayed stacks of books. Breathing a sigh of relief, I smiled and whispered, "They are still here...still here."

My thoughts wandered back to a typical weekend in the late 1940s. I was nine years old. I woke early each sunny Saturday, finished my chores quickly, and asked permission to go downtown to the library. I gathered my library books, packing them into the largest cloth sack I could find. After quietly closing the front porch screen door, I headed up the slight hill for a couple blocks, shifting my book load frequently. I passed several magnificent old brick houses. These mini mansions with their expansive lawns were sprinkled among more modest homes like mine. Nevada Street to Third, Third to Hill, then on to the remaining streets. I could have walked my route blindfolded. By 1947, post-World War II cookie-cutter bungalows had started to sprout on the western edge of the city, but not in my older, established area of town in 1947, which retains much of its historical character to this day.

The delicious smells of breakfast eggs and sizzling bacon along the walk made my adventure a delight. After walking four more blocks—taking care to avoid any cracks, to save my mom's back—I emerged on an old oak-lined street high on the Iowa bluff and approached the top of the cable car ride.

I plunked my nickel on the counter at the turnstile to ride the Fenelon Place Elevator, a 296-foot-long cable car to downtown Dubuque, which drops almost straight down the hillside.

This ride was always a quiet thrill, never rollercoaster speed, back when time stood close to still most days. Though the cable car tilted steeply on the hillside, I felt safely tethered as I listened to the creak of the cable car's hefty pulleys and ropes, the smell of their greasy lubricant mixing with the fresh-cut grass on either side of the tracks. All was right in my world. From the moment my Buster Brown shoes stepped into the tiny, slanted car and I tucked up tightly to the wooden seat back, I imagined the world opening to me as I embarked on my exciting adventure. There were eight seats, four on each side, all facing the middle. It was a relief to rest my heavy book bag on the seat below me when the ride was not busy. I always chose the highest empty seat, so if we crashed, I would have the protection of the bottom seats.

I treasured traveling my town safely at age nine without a parent. Each year formed a notch on my imaginary independence bracelet, and I loved my Saturday trips to the Dubuque Carnegie Stout Library to renew my stash of books and to travel the whole world, cover to cover, one page at a time. All for that one nickel on that tiny, sheer-drop ride. A few allowance coins jingled in my pocket, ready for the usual overdue charges, because I always checked out way more books than I could read in a week. I needed to save a nickel for the home trip. When she was in a good mood, my mom joked that surely by now we must *own* the library, having paid for it with my overdue fines most weeks.

Each time I approached the tall, pillared building and climbed the steps, I played a mind game that the building was a train loaded with passengers seeking new adventures, just like me. I didn't plan my selections ahead of time. Serendipity always played a large role throughout my book and life choices. The titles on the shelves called out to me, like early Instagrams.

Once inside, I headed to the check-in desk, glad to empty my heavy load so I could negotiate the stacks quickly. The children's section held favorite treasures of fantasy, mystery, and horses. Gigantic, black-maned horses didn't fit in small-town apartments, but they could always be counted on to gallop proudly through the pages of a novel with perfect ease.

I lost track of time as I choo-choo'd up and down the aisles, selecting new books for the coming week, stopping frequently to flip to a page to sample the writing. A book had to catch my interest quickly or I rejected it. Such easy decisions at age nine. Learning how to find writing that immediately drew me into a book back then has served me well as a late-life writer. I picture my author role as a friendly conductor shouting *All aboard* to my readers, young and old.

As I made the rounds of the children's sections I came upon one particular sign frequently. Each visit I'd try to avoid it as much as possible, swinging wide, or turning back to curve up another aisle. That sign represented so many limits in my life, and at age nine, a fine bounty of "No's" accompany your days. I accepted most of them, but honed a lifelong questioning attitude, which I am sure my parents labeled *obstinacy*.

When that library sign pops into my mind today, I see it attached to the front of an eye-high wooden podium, blocking entry to the grownup stacks ahead. *Adult Section. You must be 12 years old to check out these books.*

Full stop. My book train derailed. Warning...debris on tracks ahead. I was shy, but I remember working up courage every few months to approach the librarian and strike up a conversation, practicing my sweetest smile and best manners in a quiet aisle beforehand. I explained how much I loved books and told her I was rapidly approaching the day I would have read all the children's section books that interested me. I'd ask her if the age rule had changed yet, and maybe the librarians had forgotten to remove the sign? The answer was "No" for so many years.

I remember consoling myself with a silly thought each time I received a "No." *One day I will write a book myself, and no one can ever tell me I am not old enough to read it!*

In December of 1950, I came of Adult Library age. I believe I expected to receive my driver's license as well on that day, for I was certain I was now a grownup, and all knowledge and entertainment would be available to me. Only one drawback. I realized for the first time that day—as I walked through those glorious, new, humungous stacks—I would probably never again be able to experience the feeling of having read almost every book in any library section. I missed the book routes behind me, but I thrilled to the possibilities of all the books on the tracks ahead of me.

I wish I could remember the titles of those first adult books I checked out at age twelve. And regarding the age restrictions affecting me as a child? They pale in comparison to what children face today—the complete banning of so many books…at any age level.

If I am ever placed in charge of podium signs in libraries and bookstores, my signs will always say *Access to All Books, Welcome Aboard.*

# Author and Poet Biographies

## Kelly Q. Anderson

Kelly Q. Anderson specializes in short-form writing. Her work has been published in *The New York Times, Atticus Review, The Citron Review, Litro,* and *Five Minute Lit.* Her poems have appeared in *Lucky Jefferson* and *NO RULES* at Cornell. Learn more at KellyQAnderson.com or on social media: @KellyQAnderson

## Rita Angelini

Rita Angelini is a retired Certified Public Accountant pursuing her passion for writing. She has published two short stories and written a memoir about life with her special needs daughter, KiKi, that was a finalist for the Royal Palm Literary Award. Rita has served as Treasurer for OCWW since 2014.

## Paco Aramburu

Paco Aramburu is an adoptive son of Chicago, arriving from Argentina after he, his wife, and two children escaped the military dictatorship. In 2019, he became President of the Off Campus Writers' Workshop. He has written two novels, is finishing his third, and has published numerous short stories.

## Allison Baxter

Allison Baxter has published short stories and articles. Her most recent short story, "On Ice," will be published in *Mystery Magazine.* She is a columnist for *First Draft,* the newsletter for the online chapter of Sisters in Crime. She teaches high school ESL and lives with her family in Illinois.

## Susan Bearman

Susan Bearman is a writer, editor, web designer, and writing coach. A long-time OCWW member, she serves on the *About Write* editorial committee and as a developmental editor for *Meaningful Conflicts.* She has published a picture book and ghostwrote an interview guide published by McGraw Hill. More at bearman.us.

## Ronit Bezalel

Ronit Bezalel is an award-winning filmmaker, writer and photographer, based in Chicago and Jerusalem. Her films include *70 Acres in Chicago: Cabrini Green,* which screened worldwide as a catalyst to discuss affordable housing issues. Her work can be found at ronitfilms.com.

## Elizabeth Bower

Elizabeth Bower is a writer, teacher, and lifelong learner, with degrees from Connecticut College and Harvard Graduate School of Education. She has written for the *Harvard Educational Review,* worked at Loyola University Chicago and Northwestern, and is a Lake Forest College MLS candidate. "Mosaic" is her first published poem.

## Susan Cousins Breen

Susan Cousins Breen, a Garden State transplant, writes creative nonfiction and memoir. She is a feature writer for regional and alumni magazines. Before taking on freelance projects, she was one of the *Swarthmore College Bulletin* editors and publications editor at Rowan University in New Jersey.

## Anna Carvlin

Anna Carvlin is a public health advocate, yoga instructor, writer, and aspiring fiddler. She has a certificate in creative writing and is working on an MA in English. Carvlin has published two books, and her essays have appeared in several publications. Her memoir *Urgent Conditions* is forthcoming.

## Nancy Chadwick

Nancy Chadwick's debut memoir, *Under the Birch Tree* (2018), and upcoming novel, *The Wisdom Of The Willow* (2024), are from She Writes Press. Her essays have appeared in *The Magic of Memoir, Adelaide Literary Magazine,* and the Chicago Writers Association Write City and Brevity blogs. Find more at nancychadwickauthor.com.

## Cathy Chester

Cathy Chester returned to her love of writing after ending a 42 year career in her valued profession: teaching. Poetry and Short Story Fiction are her current genres, but she hopes to branch out. Her work flows from an ageless one-ness she shares with nature, which is often her guiding spirit.

## Barbara Chiprin

Barbara Chiprin is a romantic and an aspiring author in the process of editing her first novel. She worked in technology for over thirty years turning bits and bytes on and off. She is a triathlete enthusiast and an amateur photographer.

## Belinda Copeland

Belinda Copeland is a lover of words and rhymes, a published writer, an artist, and a singer. She can be seen around Chicago drumming for causes with Clamor & Lace Noise Brigade, shimmying with Perilous, hanging art, singing songs, acting out the words of others, and changing the world.

## Anna da Silva

Anna da Silva is a writer and a sociology professor at Lehman College, CUNY. She co-founded *The Salty Quill* writing retreat and is currently working on her first novel. One of her short stories was recently published in *Juked* and another one is forthcoming in *Liminal Spaces*.

## Elizabeth DeSchryver

Elizabeth DeSchryver is a published poet, playwright and short story author. She earned her PhD in English from Northwestern University, so logically she spent the next 24 years working for a technology consulting firm. Now retired, she divides her time between writing, thinking about writing, and volunteer work.

## Toni Louise Diol

Toni Louise Diol published her first poetry book several years ago and is working on a second. She has published several short stories in *Chicken Soup for the Soul*. Married for 57 years, she is the proud grandmother of eleven wonderful little and big people.

## Michelle Dybal

Michelle Dybal has been a writer since she knocked on the door of a smoky teachers' lounge in fifth grade, and asked to start a school paper. Since then, she has been involved in corporate communications, journalism, and marketing/development for nonprofits. Fiction is her latest writing frontier to explore.

## Sheila Elliott

Sheila Elliott writes both poetry and prose. Her work has appeared in *Distilled Lives*, *Literary Yard*, *Quill and Parchment*, and elsewhere. A chapbook, *Sand and Salt*, was published in 2021. Elliott co-facilitates an Oak Park based writers group, is on Poets and Patrons' board, and active in other organizations.

## Fred Fitzsimmons

Fred Fitzsimmons is an aspiring poet and writer with stories, poems, a novel, and a play in process. He is a transplant from Boston to the Midwest, married for 57 years, a retired business executive of 59 years, and President Emeritus of Off Campus Writers' Workshop.

## Nancy Hepner Goodman

Nancy Hepner Goodman is a retired Registered Nurse who worked in pharmaceutical clinical research. She writes creative nonfiction and poetry. Her work has been published in *Storied-Stuff.com*, *East on Central*, and *Highland Park Poetry*. In her spare time, she quilts and attends numerous OCWW events.

## Caryn Green

Caryn Green is a local media veteran, award-winning author, citizen journalist and publisher at indie imprint Manitou & Cedar Press. Freelancing as a designer, editor or reporter when opportunity strikes, the OCWW board member is revising her second book, a genre-bending blend of fiction and fact, while touring in a live-work minivan.

## Polly Hansen

Polly Hansen is a professional flutist, writer, and producer of two nationally syndicated radio programs. Her unpublished memoir, *Nasty Girl*, won *Memoir Magazine's* 2022 Memoir Prize for Books in the Coming-of-Age category. Her work is published in *45th Parallel*, *Quibble Journal* and other magazines. You can find her at pollyhansen.com and @9ofPentacles.

## Mary Hickey

Mary Hickey is obsessed with the art of fiction writing. She holds degrees in English, History, and Reading. While an English teacher, she championed the power of stories. Into her second act, she is active in Sisters in Crime and working on her first mystery with armchair traveler descriptions and an amateur sleuth.

## Peter Hoppock

Peter Hoppock took up fiction writing after a successful career as an advertising creative. He published his first short story in 2012 and has since published numerous short stories and novellas in a variety of literary magazines. *Mr. Pegg To You* was a finalist in the 2013 Press 53 Novella Contest.

## Renee James

Renee James is a failed English major, a retired magazine editor, and the author of a half-dozen novels and several short stories. *Monet World* is her first published poem.

## Laura Joyce-Hubbard

Laura Joyce-Hubbard, *TriQuarterly* fiction editor, has published work in *Creative Nonfiction, Sewanee Review, Chicago Tribune, the Rumpus, Boulevard, Ninth Letter*, and elsewhere. Her awards include *Southeast Review's* 2021 Nonfiction Prize and the 2020 William Faulkner Essay Prize. As a USAF C-130 pilot, she flew NATO peacekeeping missions into Bosnia-Herzegovina.

## Sherry Kromer-Shapiro

Sherry Kromer-Shapiro is an exhibiting and published photographer, combining black-and-white images with text. After becoming allergic to darkroom chemicals, she received an MFA in Writing from The School of the Art Institute of Chicago. No matter the form her creativity takes, she is committed to exploring women's issues.

## Karen Nicole Johnson

Karen Nicole Johnson has published numerous nonfiction articles and a chapter in the book *Beautiful Testing*. After a long career in software testing, she is focused on writing and is working on a full-length memoir. See her website at: KarenNicoleJohnson.com.

## C.D. Karabush

C.D. Karabush has been an avid reader since early childhood. She started writing at nine and progressed to (mostly bad) teenage poetry. Over the course of several careers, she wrote technical manuals, marketing copy, and professional articles. Inspired by her children, she writes about her own childhood of the 1950s-60s.

## Tracy Koppel

Llewella Forgie (one of Tracy Koppel's two nom de plumes) writes both contemporary romantic suspense and historical romances that are either fantasy or speculative fiction. She knows more about murder and duels than one might expect from someone who can't kill a fly. She lives in Chicago with her husband, two college-aged daughters and an overworked internet router.

## Sandy Kubillus

Sandy Kubillus claims to have no imagination, therefore she writes from experience. Currently she is searching for an agent for her memoir featuring several dogs. She often rides her bike to work or pushes her old, blind cocker spaniel in a hot pink stroller.

## Kirk Landers

Kirk Landers is a former magazine editor and capitalist job creator who has published a number of novels under various bylines. *Into the Beast* is part of a short story collection based on his experiences during the Vietnam war.

## Jason Lavicky

Jason Lavicky is a professional video editor/animator/illustrator by day and a novice writer by night. He has self-published a children's book, *Ivory*, and a set of pop-up coloring books. He is OCWW's Director of Production and Graphics.

## Della Leavitt

Della Leavitt was born into a family of Chicago storytellers and found her writing voice after careers in tech, teaching, and educational research. She is currently marketing a historical novel, *Beyond Maxwell Street (1923-1956)*. Della serves as Board Secretary for Off Campus Writers' Workshop.

## Beth Lewis

Beth Lewis has a love/hate relationship with Chicago's north suburbs, where she is a lifelong resident. She writes and manages website content, and her first short story was published in the 2021 OCWW anthology, *Turning Points*.

## Roberta Albom Liebler

Roberta Albom Liebler writes about the subtle changes that shape lives. In her debut novel, she explores the intersection of individual choices, public health, and the environment. Having taught and developed curriculum in diverse disciplines, she continues to expand her perspective as a loyal member of OCWW.

## Tara Maher

Tara Maher is an accomplished aviation insider turned writer. Before her pen met the page, she trained future cabin crews in emergency management and served as a line flight attendant. She is a lover of coffee and dark chocolate, has two completed novels, and carries a *no grit, no pearl* outlook.

## Kitty Malik

Kitty Malik is a freelance pharmaceutical copywriter honing her creative writing skills through OCWW. Kitty writes creative nonfiction, middle-grade fiction, and picture books. She cherishes kindness, compassion, and a sense of humor. This is her first published work.

## Sarah Malone

Sarah Malone is a semi-retired educator and organizational change and leadership consultant. She has taught at Northwestern and Benedictine Universities. She is a poet and memoirist who gives voice to what is visible yet not seen, to what is felt yet not understood—to what was, what is, and what is hoped for.

## Margot McMahon

Margot McMahon is an environmental artist, and writer, with an environmental journalism degree. She is publishing her fourth book with *Aquarius Press* for release at UIMA this December: *RESIST! A Visual History of Protest*. Her three children live on three coasts, and one is nearby. She and her husband live in Oak Park.

## Kathy Mirkin

Kathy Mirkin writes fiction and poetry for adults and children. Her published short stories are in literary magazines. She has received writing scholarship awards from the Highlights Foundation and The Society of Children's Book Writers and Illustrators. She is working on a novel, short stories, poetry, and picture books.

## Nora Naughton

Nora Naughton divides her time between writing and working to obtain a garden design certificate from the Chicago Botanic Garden. She is currently revising her first novel with themes of urban isolation and the redemptive power of nature.

## Mary Nelligan

Mary Nelligan is a writer, writing coach and anger enthusiast. Her debut short story was nominated for a PEN/Robert J. Dau Short Story Prize, and her essays have appeared on *Scary Mommy* and *YeahWrite* websites, among others. She is currently working on a novel.

## Irma M. Olmedo

Irma M. Olmedo, a retired University of Illinois-Chicago professor, has started a second career as a fiction writer. She has published extensively on bilingualism, education, and immigration in academic research journals and now uses her research background to write short stories focused on the diaspora experiences of Puerto Ricans.

## Carol Orange

Carol Orange's recent art heist novel, *A Discerning* Eye, won the Global Book Award for mystery/suspense. She has worked in the art world for 20 years as an editor of art books and as an art dealer. Her short stories have appeared in *The Atherton Review* and *Warren Adler's Anthology.*

## Nora Orschel

Nora Orschel majored in English, and after college was a Recreation Specialist for the Department of the Army in Germany. Back home, she worked as a teacher and as a senior editor at McGraw Hill designing writing programs online. Now she is trying to be a writer.

## David Pelzer

David Pelzer has published several short stories, including one that appeared in OCWW's *Turning Points* anthology, and was a finalist in the 2019 Hemingway Shorts competition. He is currently at work on a literary novel, *The Blue Guitar.* David resides in Highland Park with his lovely bride Trudy and their poodle Alexander.

## Marcia Pradzinski

Marcia Pradzinski is a poet, memoir writer, and nascent short story writer. Journals and anthologies, both print and online, have featured her poetry and flash memoir. She has published two books of poetry and is currently working on a memoir about raising a child with disabilities.

## Laurel Ross

Laurel Ross lives in Chicago where she is a writer, birder, prairie restoration volunteer, chorister (alto), storyteller, and Zen Buddhist practitioner. A retired conservation ecologist, she is currently working on a memoir that celebrates her youthful excesses.

## Meg Salzman

Meg Salzman has been writing essays, short stories, and working on a *novel in the drawer* for as long as she can remember. Finding Off Campus Writers' Workshop just prior to the pandemic was a glorious gift. Meg is a retired translator, editorial assistant, and most recently, AP high-school French teacher.

## Hugh Schulze

Hugh Schulze is a writer and filmmaker living in Chicago. His feature films, *CASS* and *Dreaming Grand Avenue*, are available on iTunes.

## Sarah Ray Schwarcz

Sarah Ray Schwarcz is a retired teacher/principal, writes poetry (*Leaping Leopards on Firefly Wings*), memoir (*Pearls and Knots*), and children's magical realism (*Game Over, ShrinkWithers!*). Proving it is never too late to create, she welcomed her writing muse at age 73. She serves on the OCWW *About Write* editorial board.

## Stanford Searl

Stanford Searl is a poet and Quaker writer who lives in Culver City, California. In 2019, he published two poetry chapbooks, including *Songs for Diana* and *Mary Dyer's Hymn and other Quaker Poems*. He is working on a memoir about his spiritual journey.

## Alan Souter

Alan Souter graduated from the School of the Chicago Art Institute and the University of Chicago. His career spans the fine arts: international photojournalist, magazine illustrator, published poet, author of 50+ traditionally published books, award-winning film documentarian, video and stage producer. He wrote nonfiction under his first name, Gerry Souter.

*Alan (Gerry) passed in October, 2022.*

## Moira Sullivan

Moira Sullivan is a retired translator and a voracious reader of all the genres. She enjoys writing short stories and poetry that explore the strangeness, pain, and horror of everyday life. She has published three of her stories.

## Thomas Sundell

Thomas Sundell is the author of *A Bloodline of Kings* (Crow Woods Publishing and, as *Philip of Macedon*, by Minoas SA in Greek), and twenty-three additional novels, posting these and other fictions each Wednesday at sundellwritings.wordpress.com. *Trouble* was inspired by the song of the same name by Moon Taxi.

## Lisa Sukenic

Lisa Sukenic is an author, poet, and educator. She has been teaching for 36 years, currently at The University of Chicago Laboratory Schools. Her debut historical novel in verse, *Miles from Motown*, was published in 2021. She has poetry and short stories in several anthologies.

## Michelle L. Thoma-Culver

Michelle L. Thoma-Culver realized she was a fiction writer when she was three years old. She has been answering—albeit sometimes in a mumble—the call of her vocation ever since. Originally from Bellwood, Illinois (known for its astronauts), she now lives with her husband in Chicago.

## Thomas Dawe Tepper

Thomas Dawe Tepper lives in Northbrook. At Wharton, he studied economics, accounting, and investing. As a single parent, he successfully raised four children. His hobbies include stock market trading, pickle ball, racquetball, chess, origami, art, and more. He has written nonfiction, is revising three short stories and writing a novel.

## Joyce Burns Zeiss

Joyce Burns Zeiss is a retired teacher, wife, mother, grandmother, and a sheepherder's daughter. Her debut novel, *Out of the Dragon's Mouth*, (Flux, 2015) is the story of a young Vietnamese girl's flight to freedom. *American Mai,* its sequel, is currently looking for a publisher. Zeiss, a Northwestern Wildcat fan, lives in Evanston, Illinois.

# *Meaningful Conflicts*
# Leadership Team

While most anthologies consist of works selected by an editor, *Meaningful Conflicts* was a developmental project in which authors and poets were challenged to constantly revise their works to achieve an optimal end result. Our poets worked directly with our poetry editor, while our prose authors participated in a six-month process of feedback from critique groups, developmental editors and final editors. These are the people who filled leadership roles in poetry, prose, and graphic design and production.

## Kelly Q. Anderson, Developmental Editor

…assumed the role of literary surgeon for *Meaningful Conflicts*, helping writers trim, edit, and cut with assurance. A former newspaper columnist, Anderson has familiarity with meeting word count, choosing vivid details, and "getting to the damn point already." This is her first editorial role in book creation.

### SHARED WISDOM

*Nearly all editorial feedback goes over well if you do it with warmth.*
*An editor is saving you from bad online reviews,*
*they are giving you little hints on how to be amazing.*
*Also, sleep on it. Most editorial feedback sounds better*
*after you've had a full night's rest.*

## Susan Bearman, Developmental Editor

…worked with two *Meaningful Conflicts* critique groups, mentoring eleven of the contributing prose writers to help shape and polish their stories. She also participated in the editors critique group and was a critique group leader for the 2021 anthology, *Turning Points*.

### SHARED WISDOM

*Working with our anthology contributors has been an immersive writing*
*experience, allowing me to dwell in the revision space and experience it from many*
*different points of view. Like a great extended workshop, critiquing and editing can*
*reignite creativity while simultaneously granting a sense of*
*objectivity that is hard to access when you focus solely on your own writing.*

## Christopher Chambers, Poetry Editor

…read 100 or so poetry submissions, selected the finalists, and worked with the writers to revise these poems for publication. Chambers has worked as an editor for thirty years and is co-editor of the anthology, *Ice Fishing for Alligators*. He is the author of *Inter/views,* a book of poems, and two books of fiction, *Delta 88* and *Kind of Blue*. He is currently editor of *Wisconsin People & Ideas* magazine.

### SHARED WISDOM

*Poetry can be intimidating and does not always kiss on the first date,
requiring a certain amount of desire, time, and effort on the part of its readers (and
writers). It was a pleasure to read the poems submitted for this anthology, and a
privilege to work with these intrepid writers. Anything worth reading is worth reading
more than once, and these poems will indeed reward re-reading.*

## Elizabeth DeSchryver, Group Leader

…managed and led a critique group of five other authors for *Meaningful Conflicts*. Her stories have been published in two previous OCWW projects, *A Reason to be Here* and *Turning Points*. While she is mainly a playwright, her poetry and stories have appeared in other anthologies.

### SHARED WISDOM

*Enjoy the process, not just the result.
Write because you love creating new worlds, new stories, beautiful language.
Recognize that the act of creation is a success in its own right.*

## Caryn Green, Group Leader

…facilitated a creative nonfiction discussion group, basing her technique on years of both on-the-job journalism experience and workshop participation. A veteran of the local media scene and award-winning indie publisher, she recently redesigned the OCWW website and edits the monthly newsletter.

### SHARED WISDOM

*Integrating the principles of compelling fiction writing into real-life narratives
can be a challenge for writers who have dedicated their careers
to the objective reporting of fact, especially when those facts
are disturbing, controversial, or deeply personal.
This collaboration encouraged us to push beyond our boundaries
to produce truly original work at heights
we would never have attained flying solo.*

## Peter Hoppock, Editor

...signed on as co-editor of *Meaningful Conflicts*, reprising his role as co-editor of OCWW's previous anthology, *Turning Points*. Along with management responsibilities, he provided both developmental editing and final editing on manuscripts. He concedes that he had no idea how rewarding working with so many writers, at various stages in their writing arc, could be.

### SHARED WISDOM

*The developmental editing process gives you exposure to a wide variety of styles and content, and invaluable insights into craft elements that might otherwise take years in an MFA program to acquire.*
*It's work—and it can be hard work—but it's also honest work.*

## Renee James, Editor

...planned and organized *Meaningful Conflicts* and, with Peter Hoppock, performed final editing on the prose stories. James has a long background as a magazine editor and publisher. She was instrumental in launching Off Campus Writers' Workshop's collaborative novel project (*A Reason to Be Here*) in 2018, and in planning the 2021 anthology, *Turning Points*.

### SHARED WISDOM

*Writing is a solitary vocation, but Off Campus Writers' Workshop shows that the writing process—which is a learning process—can also be a social experience. Our anthologies embody that approach: we learn from each other, none more than those of us who work as editors as well as authors.*

## Tracy Koppel, Developmental Editor

...loves working with writers to make their stories the best they can be, which is why she was a developmental editor for *Turning Points*, and agreed to reprise her role for *Meaningful Conflicts*. For the same reason, she has also taught classes at SavvyAuthors. She has taken classes with OCWW, Savvy Authors, Outreach International Romance Writers of America, the Writers' Police Academy, Sisters in Crime among others— good classes are her kryptonite. After deciding to quit taking more classes so she can make the final revisions to her WIP, she signed up for five more.

### SHARED WISDOM

*Everyone sees something different in a piece of writing. As long as the writer has a clear vision of their work, feedback from many thoughtful readers can help the writer bring their true vision into reality.*

## Sandy Kubillus, Group Leader

...organized a critique group of memoirists. As an adjunct instructor at a local community college, Sandy had access and experience with Zoom and time-management skills. She has been a member of OCWW since 2015 and published her first short story in *Turning Points*.

#### SHARED WISDOM

*Be persistent about finding a time to meet and keep everyone on track.*
*None of our group members had met before and our critique group*
*allowed us to interact on a much more personal level.*

## Jason Lavicky, Director of Production and Design

...designed the cover and interior pages for *Meaningful Conflicts*. Over the years he has designed a variety of children's books, pop-up books, and book covers. He drew on this experience to create a look and feel for *Meaningful Conflicts* that embraces the many distinct voices and diverse stories that makes it so special. He is OCWW's Director of Production and Design.

#### SHARED WISDOM

*I love telling stories, whether it's through pictures or words.*
*While the execution may be different, the sentiment is always the same.*
*I hope the reader (or viewer) enjoys consuming these stories*
*as much as I enjoy creating them.*

## Della Leavitt, Group Leader

...stepped in when her critique group suffered organizational disarray. Drawing upon years of management experience for a wireless data network and coordination of a national education research grant, Della created a flexible schedule aimed to avoid dropouts and maximize group participation. She also brought prior critique group experiences including participation in the previous OCWW anthology, *Turning Points*. The result: each group member participated actively, from peer critiques to submission of revised, varied stories.

#### SHARED WISDOM:

*I appreciate the range of voices and experiences of OCWW's writers.*
*I believe multiple, diverse perspectives serve to strengthen our writing.*

## Tara Maher, Developmental Editor

…helped authors refine their stories' plot, conflict development, and character arc. She drew on manuscript critique skills developed over many years of critique group participation and studying with Professor Fred Shafer. Prior to taking up fiction writing, she was a classroom instructor in the aviation industry and completed a B.A. in Communication at the University of Colorado, Boulder.

### SHARED WISDOM

*If you want to fly, give someone else a lift. I've learned more about writing*
*from reading others' excellent prose than muddling through my manuscripts.*
*The many voices I've had the privilege to explore through reading and editing*
*is a gift that continually gives. I believe the more you read and study the craft of*
*writing—such as attending OCWW craft sessions and partaking*
*in their critique groups—the stronger you will become as a writer.*

## David Pelzer, Group Leader

…led a prose (literary fiction and memoir) content development group, keeping our six-member group of contributors "on track" regarding content, length and deadlines.

### SHARED WISDOM

*We've heard it said that writing is 10 percent inspiration and 90 percent perspiration.*
*Our group not only provided mutual support and encouragement, but also challenged*
*each other to "go deeper" in our writing, often by extending scenes, or even thoughts.*
*Revising forced us not only to edit our "rough stuff," but also to re-imagine it,*
*allowing us to uncover the fullness of stories that had begun as vague visions.*

## Sarah Ray Schwarcz, Group Leader

…is honored to collaborate with dedicated writers to draft and refine our initial submissions for *Meaningful Conflicts*. Sarah has published in OCWW's three anthologies: *Overcoming* (2013), *Turning Points* (2021), and *Meaningful Conflicts* (2023).

### SHARED WISDOM

*The inspiration that springs from critiquing our stories with other writers improves our*
*craft and transforms our work from solitary to shared, in our quest for great content.*
*Read a lot. Read aloud. Search for critique partners who are serious about this journey,*
*laugh along the way, and carry chocolate in their backpacks!*

## Gerry (Alan) Souter, Group Leader

...provided critique group leadership through example and experience. He drew on many years of experience as a journalist, handling local, national, and international assignments from monthly and weekly publications. He also brought extensive experience as a book author to the project, including more than 50 nonfiction works and a novel. Of special value to this assignment was his past work as a *Chicago Magazine* contributing editor and a *Chicago Sun Times* social critic, plus his current work as a Windy City Reviews book reviewer.

### SHARED WISDOM

*My colleagues' creativity is a discovered joy. Learning never stops, it only enriches.*

## Thomas Sundell, Group Leader

...coordinated the sharing of stories and the mutual critique process for a group of five, keeping the group focused on constructively assisting one another to improve each author's story and accomplish the writer's intent.

### SHARED WISDOM

*The drafting of a story is the task of an individual.*
*The re-write benefits from the multiple viewpoints of a group,*
*providing useful understandings and reactions,*
*which the author may consider and apply in revising the piece.*

## Joyce Burns Zeiss, Group Leader

...lead a group of five fiction writers to read and critique each other's manuscript. She was a contributor to *Turning Points*, OCWW'S 2021 anthology, has written two novels, and has extensive critique group experience.

### SHARED WISDOM

*Receiving different perspectives on your manuscript is why you need a critique group.*
*But remember to be discerning.*
*Constructive criticism from other writers is like walking through a buffet line.*
*Consider all the offerings, choose what you like, and leave the rest on the table.*

# Acknowledgments

In addition to our network of volunteers within Off Campus Writers' Workshop, the authors, poets, and editors of *Meaningful Conflicts* are deeply grateful for the expertise and guidance of the following people and companies:

**Ruth Beach**, a manuscript editor held in high regard in the book
publishing industry, made time for our anthology
and delivered a copy-edit marked by brilliance and verve.

**Dawn McGarrahan Wiebe** and the team at **Windy City Publishers**
brought so much professionalism and care to the production
of this work. We have been fortunate to have their service and
wisdom for our two previous anthologies, too.

**Jay Rehak** is an extraordinary educator who showed us
how to create a team process for developing and honing
fiction and creative nonfiction.

**The Book Stall**, an independent bookseller in Winnetka, Illinois,
has generously supported our anthology projects by stocking
our books and filling orders over the counter and by mail.

Made in the USA
Monee, IL
13 April 2023

31612223R00236